THE ALTERNATIVE
HOLIDAY CATALOGUE

Other travel books available in Pan

Arthur Eperon
Travellers' France
Travellers' Italy

John Slater
Just Off the Motorway
Just Off for the Weekend

Ken Welsh
Hitch-hikers' Guide to Europe

THE ALTERNATIVE

HOLIDAY CATALOGUE

Edited by Harriet Peacock

Pan Original

Pan Books London and Sydney

The great source of pleasure is variety
Samuel Johnson

Dedicated to the few hundred who bring pleasure in variety to
millions – the specialist holiday professionals.

First published 1981 by Pan Books Ltd,
Cavaye Place, London SW10 9PG
© Cobblestone Press Ltd 1981
ISBN 0 330 26454 0
Printed and bound in Great Britain by
Richard Clay (The Chaucer Press) Ltd, Bungay, Suffolk

CONTENTS

ACKNOWLEDGEMENTS

Overall Editor: Harriet Peacock
Project Editor: Léonie Glen
Copy Editor: Bob Snedden
Writers: Patricia Lyons, Paul Strathern
Senior Researcher and Writer:
 Hilary Whyte
Researchers: Frances Robinson,
 Philip Fairclough, Jillian Miller,
 Hilary Latham, Barbara Jackson
Project Co-ordinator: Wendy Verstappen
Project Consultant: Roberta Kedzierski
Production Consultant: Penny Mills
Typing: Stevenson Secretarial Services

Editorial Director: Peter Verstappen

We wish to express a special vote of thanks to the following organizations who have been unfailingly helpful and professional in their assistance:

Bord Failte
The British Tourist Authority
The English Tourist Board
The Isle of Man Tourist Board
The Northern Ireland Tourist Board
The Scottish Tourist Board
The States of Guernsey Tourist
 Committee
The States of Jersey Tourist Committee
The Wales Tourist Board

Permission has been kindly granted by Army & Navy Stores Ltd to reprint catalogue pictures used in this book.

Original woodcut illustrations are by Hilary Paynter, cartoons are by Nigel Paige.

INTRODUCTION

'Them which is of different naturs thinks different,' said Dickens' Martin Chuzzlewit. The *Alternative Holiday Catalogue* is an apt celebration of how various our natures and our corresponding interests are. The pages which follow profile over one hundred and fifty different subjects and contain over five hundred and fifty special interest holidays for you to choose from.

And what a wealth of choice you have. Antique collectors and archaeologists, cineastes and crochet enthusiasts, the fox hunting set and fishing fanatics will all find their specialities outlined here. So will golfers and those who always pined to pan for gold, brass rubbers and gardeners, historic home lovers, musicians, naturists, potters and tennis buffs to name but a few of our wealth of categories.

Thus in combination, as its title implies, the *Alternative Holiday Catalogue* sets out to present you with a kaleidoscopic choice of appealing options. G. B. Shaw wrote that 'the secret of being miserable is to have leisure to bother about whether you are happy or not'. Across our land we don't bother about our leisure, instead we passionately pursue our private obsessions. Some, such as fishing, cookery and gardening, are well known and widely popular to the point of supporting their own associations, clubs, magazines and a raft of books. Others such as beekeeping, real tennis and stone polishing are far more specialized in their appeal.

A similar contrast exists between holidays designed for the activity-oriented (not to say the hyperactive) such as our large multi-activity category and those which celebrate more contemplative ways. Religious retreats is perhaps the ultimate example here but there are many others including calligraphy, genealogy, needlework and last, but by no means least, Zen.

Putting the book together has been a massive, seemingly never-ending labour of love. At the outset we hoped, if we were awfully lucky, to cover one hundred different special interests. In the event we have half again as many and every post seems to bring further intriguing categories ranging from bell ringing and crossword puzzle mastery to public speaking and life planning.

This exceptional variety is both a credit to the remarkable range of talents we pursue and to the exceptional investment in both time and money individuals are prepared to make to pass their special skills and interests on to a wider audience.

In an age where prophets decry increasing conformity and depersonalization, there could be no more affirmative testament to the wealth we possess in our diversity. Thank God for that.

Peter Verstappen
Richmond, Surrey

HOW TO USE THIS BOOK

At the outset a few brief pointers may assist the reader in obtaining maximum enjoyment from the *Alternative Holiday Catalogue*. These are as follows:

● All holidays are arranged alphabetically by subject area, then by county and town in the county. Eire, Northern Ireland and Wales are considered part of the county name. Thus, under any given subject, listings in these areas will fall under E, N and W respectively.

● Prices quoted are followed by either the designation (1981) which indicates that the establishment involved has confirmed a 1981 price or by the designation (est) which indicates an estimate of the 1981 price by the proprietor or by Cobblestone Press Limited. These estimated prices are necessary in the absence of a finalized price as we went to press. One of these designations appears the first time price is mentioned. Subsequent prices are on the same basis unless otherwise specified.

● We have attempted to give our readers as much useful information as possible. Nonetheless all particulars – and notably pricing details – are subject to change which is beyond our control. Therefore we cannot accept responsibility for subsequent alterations or changes.

● We strongly urge all readers to write for the relevant literature and then enter into phone or written correspondence before booking.

● Confirmation of course details is particularly vital where college of further education courses are involved. In these difficult times these establishments are notably vulnerable to the vagaries of funding (or lack thereof) and of available staff.

● Where courses are residential we have attempted to outline the available choice in terms of rooms. Where this is not the case we have attempted to list nearby suitable accommodation.

● Where several recommended courses are held at the same location we have specified which listing contains full details of available accommodation. We have further cross-referenced subject areas for which the establishment or organization has listings.

● Where the holiday-maker is best advised to bring specialized equipment, clothing, etc, we have attempted so to specify. Again it's best to check with proprietors before you go.

● At the back of the book you will find a cross-reference by course/geography to assist you in selecting the areas of your special interest in the regions that appeal.

This is the first edition of what's planned to be an annual publication. We recognize that you work and save all year for your holidays. Lack of clarity, misinformation and poor recommendations are thus particularly unfortunate. We'd welcome your comments and suggestions on the good and the bad. These should be addressed to:

Harriet Peacock
Cobblestone Press Limited
22a Red Lion Street
Richmond
Surrey TW9 1RW

ANTIQUES

DEVON, Torquay

Art and Antiques Weekend
Imperial Hotel

If you're an Arthur Negus fan, here's the holiday for you. This art and antiques weekend gets off to a rousing start with a reception to meet Mr Negus and his colleagues, followed by dinner and dancing. Saturday is devoted to illustrated lectures and visits, with evening cocktails before you sit down to one of the Imperial's justly famous gastronomic feasts. If you'd like any personal treasures professionally assessed, bring them along to the Sunday afternoon discussion. The session ends on a festive note with a sherry party, dinner and dance.

Imperial Hotel, Torquay, Devon. Telephone: (0803) 24301. Organizer: Swan Hellenic, 237/8 Tottenham Court Road, London W1P 0AL. Telephone: (01) 636 8070. Reservations: Ron Bignell. Duration: Friday p.m. to Monday a.m.; February, April and October. Price: £117–£165 per person, suites £147 (1981); October prices on application. Includes room, private bath, all meals, lectures, excursions. Includes service but not VAT.

See also GARDENING, GOURMET, MUSIC.

DEVON, Torquay

Antiques
Overmead Hotel

At the Overmead Hotel, built originally for a Russian princess, you'll find old-fashioned service and style combined with welcome modernities such as an outdoor swimming pool. Highlights of your week's holiday include a visit to Plymouth's Tuesday antiques market and a morning browse through the antiques shops of Totnes. Take afternoon tea at Saltram House after a tour of its 18th century treasures. Lunch at Dartington Hall another day, and visit Tiverton and Bickleigh Castle, where four lecturers on porcelain and general antiques host your tour of the outstanding collection of furnishings.

Galleon World Travel Association Ltd, Galleon House, King Street, Maidstone, Kent ME14 1EG. Telephone: (0622) 63411. Duration: 19–26 September. Price: £142 (est) per person. Includes lectures, visits, transport, room, breakfast, dinner, VAT.

See also CRUISING, GARDENS, HISTORY, PONY TREKKING, SURFING.

LOTHIAN, Dalkeith

Collecting Antiques
Newbattle Abbey College

This course will open up the fascinating world of antiques collecting – from silver salt spoons to large furniture. A panel of specialists will give illustrated lectures and you'll visit a specially selected country house to see its rich collection of furnishings and *objets d'art*. You can make good use of your free time, exploring Edinburgh's excellent antiques shops.

16th century Newbattle Abbey, former home of the Marquesses of Lothian, stands in 125 acres of landscaped gardens and woodlands on the banks of the Esk, seven miles from Edinburgh. The magnificent interior includes fine examples of 17th century woodwork, moulded plaster ceilings and a lavishly appointed drawing room. It also incorporates remnants of the 13th century Cistercian Abbey which once stood on the site. As Scotland's only adult residential college, it now offers a wide range of short vacation courses. Up to seventy-five students stay in study bedrooms in a new wing (built in 1968, there are sixty-five singles and five doubles).

Newbattle Abbey College, Dalkeith, Lothian EH22 2LL. Telephone: (031) 663 1921/2. Duration: 1 week, August. Price: £104 (1981) per person. Includes tuition, excursions and full board. No VAT.

See also CASTLES AND HISTORIC HOUSES, FESTIVALS, MUSIC, PAINTING.

NORTH YORKSHIRE, Harrogate

Go Antiques
Hotel St George

This frequently recommended hotel is set in its own gardens in the heart of Harrogate, famous as a centre for antiques and host to the Northern Antique Dealers' Fair each September. It can take 138 guests so you won't have any problem booking one of their 'Go Antiques' breaks. The package includes an introduction to local antique dealers, all you need to know about local and country auctions and a helpful periodical to browse through while you're enjoying your free half-bottle of champagne.

There are many small antique shops tucked away in the town as well as in nearby Ripon and Knaresborough. There are also bustling antique and flea markets most weekends. From the hotel you can get a complete list of antiques shops, both large and small, plus information on local auctions. The St George is near five golf courses. See GOLF for details.

Hotel St George, Ripon Road, Harrogate, North Yorkshire HG1 2SY. Telephone: (0423) 61431 or Best Western (01) 940 9766. Manager: John Abel. Price: 3 nights £60.50 per person (1981). Includes bed, breakfast, dinner and VAT. No single room supplement.

SUSSEX, Chichester

Antiques
1 Restoration of Antique Furniture
2 Antique Collectors' Workshop
The Earnley Concourse

The Earnley Trust is a non-profit making charity that offers up to three hundred short-term adult courses annually at its comfortable, purpose-built centre seven miles outside Chichester. The fully carpeted double and single bedrooms are centrally heated and some have private baths. There's a self-service dining room, and guests have the use of squash and tennis courts and an indoor heated swimming pool.

The first course deals with techniques to eradicate woodworm, remove heat, ink and spirit marks, and will show you how to make your own polishes. You'll also have a chance to restore your own pieces of furniture. In the Antique Collectors' Workshop, Bernard Price, an expert who has featured on radio and television, gives a valuable introduction to post-1840 items that are attracting ever-growing attention from collectors – art nouveau, art deco, William Morris etc.

Other courses are available; send for a brochure.

The Earnley Concourse, Nr Chichester, Sussex PO20 7JL. Telephone: (0243) 670392. Duration: 1 23–27 February, 27–29 March. 2 27–29 March. Price: 2 days £36.10 per person (1981), 4 days £68.70. Includes tuition, double room with private bath and all meals. VAT extra. Supplement of £7 per person for Course 2. Minibus from Chichester Station 90p each way.

See also CREATIVE WRITING, FLOWER ARRANGING, FOLK AND JAZZ, LANGUAGES, MUSIC, PUPPETRY, SURVIVAL TRAINING, WINE TASTING.

ARCHAEOLOGY

COUNTY DURHAM, Stanley

Roman Archaeological Sites
Beamish Hall

This study holiday combines a series of lectures on the arrival of the Romans and their northern settlements with guided field trips. You'll visit selected sites along Hadrian's Wall and visits to relevant local collections such as the South Shields Roman Museum. Your tutor, Mrs Susan Hazelgrove, will send you a suggested reading list upon admission to the course.

For details of accomodation see MUSIC.

Beamish Hall, Adult Education College, Stanley, County Durham DH9 0RG. Telephone: (0207) 33147. Duration: 1 week or weekends; August. Price: week, £60 (est); £45 (est) in county residents; weekends, £19.55, £12.15 in county residents, per person (1981). Includes tuition, accommodation (single study bedrooms) and all meals. Excursions by coach extra. No VAT.

See also ASTRONOMY, GARDENING, JEWELLERY, MUSIC.

ENGLAND

Roman Britain Coach Tour
Swan Hellenic

Swan Hellenic, specialists in arch-

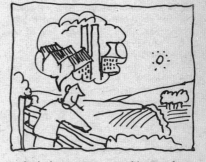

aeological tours, operate this one from London. Travelling in a deluxe Pullman coach, you'll visit such sites as Verulanium (St Albans) the fortress of the 9th Legion at York, Hadrian's Wall, Caerleon Fortress, Cirencester, Maiden Castle and Fishbourne. This is a marvellous introduction to most of Britain's major antiquities.

All guides are highly qualified and include such experts as the former Professor of Roman/British history at Durham University.

Swan Hellenic, 237/8 Tottenham Court Road, London W1P 0AL. Telephone: (01) 636 8070. Duration: 12 days, June, July, August. Price: £629 (1981). Includes accommodation in 3 or 4 star hotels, private bath, all meals, transport, entrance fees and gratuities. Single room supplement £6 per night. Includes VAT.

See also ARCHITECTURE, CRUISING: COASTAL

NORTHUMBERLAND, Wooler

Archaeology
1 *Excavations on Black Law*
2 *Hadrian's Wall and Beyond*
3 *Northern Frontier of Rome*
Cheviot Field Centre

The Field Centre offers different types of field studies, all led by specialist staff. It was founded by the Northumberland Archaeological Group to establish an archaeological museum and has expanded quickly. Still in charge is Colin Burgess who headed the 1979 dig which uncovered Black Law, one of the century's most important Bronze Age settlement discoveries. Total beginners and experienced diggers alike can learn how to uncover stone and timber houses dating from 2000 to 1000 BC.

Examination of the major sites on Hadrian's Wall is less taxing but equally fascinating. Mark Savage will take you by coach or on foot to all the most revealing Roman encampments. Evenings are devoted to a series of illustrated lectures on the most recent excavations and research on the Northern Frontier.

The region has many lesser known Roman frontier lines that are just as important as Hadrian's well-known Wall. Adam Welfare conducts a straightforward introduction to the frontier area, with field visits to sites on the Antonine Wall and other installations, such as the practice siege-works at Woden Law.

The Summer School is in the residential centre of the quiet market town of Wooler, in the scenic Cheviot Hills. You normally share a room. Applications for the course's thirty places must be in by 21 March for May courses, and 11 April for July and August courses. Non-returnable registration fee £20.

Cheviot Field Centre, Summer School, Padgepool Place, Wooler, Northumberland NE71 6BL. Telephone: (066 82) 711. Warden: Kevin Danforth. Duration: 1 week each. 1 July to August. 2 May. 3 August. Price: 1 £49 per person (est). 2 and 3 £88 per person (est). Includes tuition, transport in field, single room and all meals. VAT extra. Bring soap, towels, waterproof clothing, strong footwear and a thermos flask.

See also BATTLEFIELDS, CASTLES AND HISTORIC HOUSES, WALKING.

SHROPSHIRE, Shrewsbury

Antiquities and History Break
Hawkstone Park Hotel

This sprawling country house hotel is a popular conference and leisure centre which offers you a chance to explore 300 acres of superb Shropshire countryside, guided by a local who really knows his stuff. There are breathtaking scenic walks, cliffs honeycombed with passages and caves, and a 13th century castle. The hotel makes an ideal holiday centre. Amenities include unlimited use of two 18 hole golf courses, outdoor heated pool, games room and a two-mile-long lake stocked with perch, roach, dace, bream and pike.

Hawkstone Park Hotel, Weston under Redcastle, Shrewsbury, Shropshire SY4 5UY. Telephone: (093 924) 611. Manager: John Freeman. Duration: weekends, January to 29 March. Price: £56 per person, £64.40 (est) after April 1981. Includes full board, guided tours and sporting facilities.

SHROPSHIRE, Wroxeter

Hen Domen Training Excavation
University of Birmingham

Excavations on this timber castle started in 1960, and revealed a complicated set of structures in the bailey gate. The first three days of your time at the excavation are treated as training; you're taught techniques of recording, photography, surveying and pottery processing. In addition to at least ten seminars, there are field trips to study settlement patterns around the castle. Preference is given to students with prior field experience so mention any you've had.

University of Birmingham, Department of Extramural Studies, PO Box 363, Birmingham B15 2TT. Telephone: (021) 472 1301. Administration: Margaret Jones. Duration: 2 weeks, early June. Price: £65 per person (est). Includes tuition and all meals. Campsite available, bring own tents.

STAFFORDSHIRE, Keele

**Archaeological Excavation
Training School**
Keele University

Whether you're an absolute novice or an old archaeological hand, you'll get valuable training in excavation at this site, a moated medieval building quite close to the University itself. With previous experience you'll probably get a chance to take part in the more advanced work. Evening sessions complement the work on the site. The main aspects of training cover excavation techniques, various types of site records (written, drawn, photographic), survey and post-excavation work, especially how to treat the treasures you may find. You'll be sent a reading list and details of required clothing and equipment upon acceptance.

University of Keele, Department of Adult Education, Keele, Staffordshire ST5 5BE. Telephone: (0782) 625116. Director: Brian Threlfall. Duration: 2 weeks, July/August. Price: £65.25 weekly per person (1981). Includes single study room, full board, tuition. £40 non-residential. £10 deposit payable on enrolment, non-returnable. Closing date for applications, end of third week in May. No VAT.

WILTSHIRE, Marlborough

Prehistoric Wiltshire
Marlborough College Summer School

Strictly speaking this is not a course on archaeology but you'll no doubt find it fascinating if you're interested in the field. Some of Europe's most impressive prehistoric monuments lie within twenty miles of Marlborough which makes it an ideal starting point. Your guide, the curator of Avebury Museum, will lead you to ceremonial sites both famous and forgotten (including, of course, Stonehenge and the White Horse) and will inform you of the most up-to-date theories about their construction and purposes.

You'll stay in one of England's historic and most attractive public schools, set in extensive grounds. Accommodation is quite civilized – there are single, double and family rooms, as well as dormitories and if you're bringing children they can sleep separately in single sex, age-related dormitories. Good news for anyone with dismal memories of public school meals: the catering is of a very high standard.

There's plenty to do in the evenings too – the choice of entertainment includes concerts, films, dances and a weekly sherry party.

Marlborough College Summer School, Marlborough, Wiltshire SN8 1PA. Telephone: (0672) 53888. Secretary: Mrs Glynis Lewis. Duration: 1 week, August. Price: £150 per person (1981). Includes course, full board, holiday insurance, evening entertainment, service and VAT. Reductions for children under 14.

See also CHINA, FISHING: GAME, FURNITURE RESTORATION, MUSIC, SCULPTURE.

ARCHITECTURE

BERKSHIRE, Eton

Local Architecture
Eton College

Eton College dates back to 1440. What better way to start such a course than with a tour of the ancient school itself, where you can admire buildings that date from its foundation – while staying in single study bedrooms in the school's modern residential section. You'll also examine the history of the architecture of small English towns and villages through slides, lectures and visits further afield. Every evening there are concerts, films and lectures, all included in the course fee. If you wish, you can combine your architectural studies with sports instruction or another half-day course at no extra charge.

The school's excellent facilities include tennis and squash courts, a 9 hole golf course, an outdoor swimming pool and a boat club on the Thames beneath Windsor Castle.

Eton College, Eton, Berkshire. Enquiries: Independent Summer Schools, Southfield, Bath Road, Marlborough, Wiltshire SN8 1PA. Telephone: (0672) 54222. Organizer: Brian Ashley. Duration: 5 days, August. Price: £160 per person (1981). Includes course, lectures and other evening entertainment, full board in a single study bedroom, insurance, service and VAT.

See also DRAMA, LITERATURE.

COUNTY DURHAM

English Romanesque Architecture
Durham University

The English Romanesque course is a survey of County Durham's pre-Gothic architecture, especially the magnificent Norman cathedral and parts of Durham Castle (now the University). Excursions are made to the fine Saxon churches of Escomb, Jarrow and Monkwearmouth, and to some of the county's outstanding Norman churches. On the return to London there'll be a stop at Southwell to explore the great Norman minster. Course Director Christie Arno is a lecturer in London University's Extramural Department. Accommodation is in single rooms at Hatfield College, Durham University.

Association for Cultural Exchange, 9 Emmanuel Road, Cambridge CB1 1TW. Telephone. (0223) 65030. Duration: 5 days, April. Price: £75 per person (est). Includes tuition, 4 nights accommodation, dinner, bed, breakfast, visits, coach travel from and to London. A wide variety of other cultural courses available. Send for brochure. No VAT.

See also CHURCHES AND CATHEDRALS, THEATRE GOING.

GLASGOW to LONDON

Study Tour of British New Towns
Countrywide

Book early for this annual tour – in 1981 it's the fourteenth. It's widely publicized abroad and there are only eighty places.

One of the big draws is the opportunity to discuss planning and architecture with other tour members, including international experts. You leave from Glasgow, where the city sends you off in style with a civic reception, and finish in London.

You'll stop on the way at the new towns of East Kilbride, Irvine, Livingstone, Washington, Warrington, Milton Keynes, Stevenage and Welwyn Garden City. Initial background talks on British planning and new towns systems will be given by the director of the Town and Country Planning Association, David Hall, with discussions at each town on its plans, architecture, social and economic problems plus meetings with on-site experts. Your accommodation is in first-class hotels with private bathrooms.

Town and Country Planning Association, 17 Carlton Terrace, London SW1Y 5AS. Telephone: (01) 930 8903. Director: David Hall. Duration: 12 days, July. Price: £644 per person (est). Includes guide, transport, full board, booklets and literature.

HEREFORD AND WORCESTER, Pershore

English Gothic
Association for Cultural Exchange

This five-day study course on English Gothic concentrates on the magnificent examples found in Gloucester, Worcester, Great Malvern and Tewkesbury. Other buildings studied are the Saxon church at Deerhurst and some fine parish churches, notably those at Bredon, Evesham, Chipping Campden and Pershore. Course Director Christie Arno, a London University lecturer, will also lead a visit to some small villages. Cost of the course includes coach travel. Accommodation is in single rooms at the Pershore College of Horticulture.

Association for Cultural Exchange, 9 Emmanuel Road, Cambridge CB1 1JW. Telephone: (0223) 65030. Duration: 7–11 September. Price: £80 per person (est). Includes tuition, visits, 4 nights accommodation, breakfast and dinner, return travel from London.

SCOTLAND

Scottish Castles, Houses and Gardens
Swan Hellenic

Swan Hellenic specialize in tours of archaeological interest, including six eleven-day tours of the 'Great Houses and Gardens of Britain'.

This one starts in Edinburgh, where you board a deluxe Pullman coach to take you through the Borderlands and such ancient towns as Perth, Haddington and Kelso. A highly qualified guide will capture your imagination with details of the history of the ancient castles, magnificent stately homes and gardens visited during your tour.

Swan Hellenic, 237/8 Tottenham Court Road, London W1P 0AL. Telephone: (01) 636 8070. Duration: 9 days, June, July, August, September. Price: £484 per person (1981). Includes accommodation in 3 and 4 star hotels, all meals, entrance fees and gratuities. Single room supplement £6.50 per night. Includes VAT.

See also ARCHAEOLOGY, CRUISING: COASTAL.

SOMERSET, Taunton

Restoring and Draughtsmanship
The Leonard Wills Field Centre

Eminent architect John Brandon-Jones leads this course, intended to help local historians (professional and amateur) increase their knowledge of drawing, and architects and draughtsmen to broaden their experience of ·historic buildings. He'll demonstrate and you'll practise simple methods of recording buildings through the drawing of elevations, plans and perspectives. Students will study local buildings of various periods and styles including Cleeve Abbey and, naturally, Nettlecombe Court itself.

The Leonard Wills Field Centre, Nettlecombe Court, Williton, Taunton, Somerset TA4 4HT. Telephone: (09844) 320. Warden: John Crothers. Duration: 29

July–5 August. Price: £84 per person per week (1981). Includes tuition, full board. No VAT.

SURREY, Dorking

Farmhouses and Cottages in Surrey
Juniper Hall Field Centre

Get to know the lie of the land – study local architecture at the Juniper Hall Field Centre in Dorking where they run week-long courses on Surrey Farmhouses and Cottages. Joan Harding and Victoria Houghton will help you to appreciate the finer points of old buildings in the Surrey countryside by means of lectures and by taking you on trips to particular sites of interest (all transport included in fees).

Courses at Juniper Hall are aimed at people who are interested in a subject for its own sake, rather than for the purpose of sitting an examination – though they provide excellent background knowledge for students as well. Residential accommodation for these popular courses is often limited, but it's possible to pay a 'non-residential fee' and arrange your own accommodation at a nearby hotel or bed and breakfast establishment. Dinner and packed lunches can also be arranged for an extra fee.

Juniper Hall Field Centre, Dorking, Surrey 5H5 6DA. Telephone: (0306)

883849. Warden: John Bebbington. Duration: 14–21 August. Price: £84 per person per week (1981). Includes tuition, full board. No VAT.

SURREY, Strawberry Hill

Thameside Villas
Association for Cultural Exchange

The Association for Cultural Exchange is a non-profit making educational organization offering study tours for small groups of between twenty and thirty-eight people. On this course there is the opportunity to explore some of the fine late-17th and 18th century arcadian villas along the banks of the Thames. You'll be based at Strawberry Hill, Horace Walpole's famous 'gothick' villa at Twickenham, and will study other houses including Burlington's villa Chiswick House, Marble Hill House, Orleans House and Ham House. There are also lectures on Walpole himself, Alexander Pope, the villas of Palladio and the Palladian movement in England. They're popular courses so book early.

Association for Cultural Exchange, 9 Emmanuel Road, Cambridge CB1 1JW. Telephone: (0223) 65030. Duration: 3–5 July. Price: £38 per person (est). Includes tuition, visits, 2 nights accommodation, breakfast and dinner and 1 lunch.

ART APPRECIATION

CUMBRIA, Bassenthwaite Lake

French Painting Before the Impressionists
Higham Hall

Higham Hall is a large castellated manor situated in high parkland with magnificent views of Bassenthwaite Lake. It's centrally heated with amenities such as hard tennis court and putting green outdoors, and table tennis, a fully-licensed bar and lounge/library with colour TV and good food (with waitress service) indoors.

This course is presented in conjunction with the University of Newcastle. You'll follow the development of French art from the 17th century landscape painting of Nicholas Poussin and Claude Lorraine,

through the Rococo and Neo-classical romanticism of later painters, up to the *plein air* of the naturalistic landscapes of the Barbizon school.

Higham Hall, Bassenthwaite Lake, Cockermouth, Cumbria CA13 85H. Telephone: (059 681) 276. Warden: Peter Hadkins. Duration: 3 days, 27 February–1 March. Price: £24 per person (1981); £22 for Cumbria residents. Includes tuition, and full board, single or shared rooms.

See also DRESSMAKING, MUSIC, WAR GAMES.

WEST SUSSEX, West Dean

The Isms of Modern Art
West Dean College

This comfortable residential college, housed in a splendid castellated country mansion, offers a wide range of craft courses year-round. Facilities include the Oak Hall with bar and library and conference, music and games rooms; tennis courts, a croquet lawn and extensive workshops, as well as several smaller studios. Full board and accommodation in comfortable study bedrooms is available but some students are accepted on a non-residential basis.

The Art Appreciation course will be taken by Laurence Bradbury of the Tate Gallery. He traces the development of 20th century movements in painting from the Impressionists to the present day with a special emphasis on Surrealism. During the course Len Bickerton, Art Advisor to the Edward James Foundation (West Dean College) gives a lecture on the Surrealist paintings in the Edward James collection – some of which you'll be able to see.

West Dean College, West Dean, Chichester, West Sussex PO18 0QZ. Telephone: (024363) 301. Duration: 13–15 February. Price: £39.50 per person (1981). Includes tuition, full board and V.A.T. Single room supplement £3.

See also CALLIGRAPHY, CANEWORK, COLLECTING, THEATRE GOING, UPHOLSTERY.

ASTROLOGY

DORSET, Bournemouth

Bed, Breakfast and Your Birth Chart
Bryador Guest House

Michael Bryan runs a guest house with a difference. For the price of your bed and breakfast, you also get a birth chart and a brief character analysis. Mr Bryan has studied astrology up to the Certificate Level of the Faculty of Astrological Studies and has a small library on the subject in which you're free to browse. You'll stay in a modern two-storey house of red brick, close to the railway station.

Bryador Guest House, 9 Francis Road, Bournemouth, Dorset BN1 3RY. Telephone: (0202) 25936. Manager: Michael Bryan. Duration: all year. Price: £36.50–£45 per week (1981). Includes bed, breakfast and birth chart. Daily rate £5.50–£7.50. Children up to 5 years half-price; 5–16 years, three-quarters price.

ASTRONOMY

CHESHIRE, Burton

Astronomy Now
Burton Manor College

Noted astronomer and author Colin A. Ronan led a 1980 course which examined the most up-to-date astronomical discoveries. There was a report on spacecraft observations of Saturn and a look at the latest views on the origin of the solar system. Cosmology and an investigation of planetary surfaces and atmospheres were also featured plus talks on measuring distances in space, and the history of astronomy. For details of the 1981 course, send SAE for brochure.

For details of Burton Manor see CINEMA AND VIDEO.

Burton Manor College, Burton, Wirral, Cheshire L64 5SJ. Telephone: (051 336) 2262. Principal: Allan Kingsbury. Duration: weekends. Price: £15 per person per day (until April 1981). Includes tuition, full board twin room and VAT.

See also DANCE, ECOLOGY, FURNITURE RESTORATION, GARDENING, LANGUAGES, CINEMA AND VIDEO.

COUNTY DURHAM, Stanley

Mapping the Sky
Beamish Hall

These residential weekend courses, geared for beginners, are led by F. R. Stephenson, University Research Fellow in the University of Liverpool's Department of Geophysics. You'll study the complexities of the solar system, stars and galaxies, with practical work in observation using a small telescope and visit Close House Observatory at Wylam and the South Shields Planetarium. The college also has a theatre, library, music room, and workshops for pottery, painting, photography and metal work.

Beamish Hall Adult Education College, Stanley, County Durham DH9 0RG. Telephone: (0207) 33147. Duration: weekends, April. Price: £19.55 per person (1981). Includes tuition, accommodation (single study bedrooms) and all meals from Friday dinner to Sunday lunch and VAT. Bring powerful binoculars.

See also ARCHAEOLOGY, GARDENING, JEWELLERY, MUSIC.

BATIK

NORFOLK, Near Norwich

Batik

This is an unusual week-long holiday idea from the Association of British Craftsmen. It combines learning a craft under the individual instruction of a professional with a delightful stay in a country village.

Mary Taylor, a batik artist specializing in landscape pictures, lives with her TV executive husband in a large thatched farmhouse in a village near Norwich. They have two attractive centrally-heated guest rooms in which you'll stay, each with separate washing facilities, and you also have the use of the well-equipped studio where Mrs Taylor produces her own boldly designed items including dress fabrics and counterpanes. Even beginners will be astonished at how quickly, with a minimum of four hours instruction each day, you'll master the techniques of the craft.

After you've booked the course with ABC you'll be sent the Taylors' address and travel directions. Your hosts will meet you at the station then you'll live with them as family for the week.

Avocations (Bristol Crafts) Ltd, 37 Coombe Bridge Avenue, Bristol, Avon BS9 2LT. Telephone: (0272) 686417. Contact: Gerald Richardson. Duration: 1 week, all year. Price: £117 per person per week (1981). Includes tuition, use of equipment, full board (twin room). Single room supplement 15% extra. No VAT.

See also DRESSMAKING, ENAMELLING, NEEDLEWORK, STAINED GLASS, TAPESTRY, WOODWORKING.

BATTLEFIELDS

KENT, Chilham

Tournament of Knights
Jousting Association of Great Britain

Journey back into history – watch the thrills and the spills of a Jousting Tournament re-enacted in authentic detail by expert stuntmen in the grounds of historic Chilham Castle, parts of which are over 900 years old. Jousting is one of our oldest and noblest sports dating back to medieval times when knights were bold and maidens fair – or unfair if you happened to be the loser. Great pains (with the minimum of injury) are taken to stage these tournaments in lifelike detail with all the correct medieval trappings. Max Diamond, Principal of the Jousting Association of Great Britain, offers you five hours of colourful entertainment, including a visit to a Jousting Dungeon Armoury and the notorious 'drag' (a horse pulling a man on a rope) then winds it all up with a medieval banquet served by buxom wenches. Cost varies according to performance, size of group and entertainment required. Send for brochure for details.

British Jousting Centre, Chilham Castle, near Canterbury, Kent. Telephone: (022 776) 704. Principal: Knight of the Black Gauntlet. Duration: 1 day, April, May, August. Accommodation: 3 miles from Chilham at Howfield Manor, Howfield Lane, Chartham Hatch, Kent. Telephone: (022 773) 294. Director: Jack Pardoe. Price: doubles with bath £30 plus VAT per couple (1981 est). Includes continental breakfast. English breakfast £2.50 including VAT.

NORTHUMBERLAND, Wooler

Battlefields and Strongholds
Cheviot Field Centre

As with many frontiers the Anglo-Scottish border boasts a bloody history. The region you'll explore has witnessed some fierce and famous battles – Flodden, Homildon and Sedgeley Moor for example – and was plagued for centuries with minor skirmishes that climaxed in the reiver raids of the 16th century. Roger Miket will take your group to the sites of many such frays and to strongholds from prehistoric hill forts and towers like Smailholm to great castles such as Alnwick and Warkworth. History will leap to life during indoor 'war-games' where your leader divides the group into opposing factions, describes original battle scenarios and lets you have a go.

For details of accommodation see ARCHAEOLOGY.

Cheviot Field Centre, Summer School, Padgepool Place, Wooler, Northumberland NE71 6BL. Telephone: (066 82) 711. Warden: Kevin Danforth. Duration: 1 week, August. Price: £85 per person (1981). Includes tuition, accommodation, all meals and transport in the field and VAT. Bring soap, towels, waterproof clothing, strong footwear and a thermos flask.

See also ARCHÆOLOGY, CASTLES AND HISTORIC HOUSES, WALKING.

BEEKEEPING

HERTFORDSHIRE, Welwyn

Beekeeping
E. H. Taylor Ltd

E. H. Taylor have been manufacturing and exporting bee hives, wax foundation and all relevant appliances for a century. Taylor's special offer to customers who buy their 'Beginner's Outfit' is a free two-day course that combines theory with practice. On the first day you'll examine life in a bee colony, hives and equipment, do spring work, and learn how to transfer a nucleus of bees and handle them with minimum damage to all concerned. The second day you'll cover honey flow, swarming, harvest time, honey and wax extracting and preparing for winter. It's non-residential; you're expected to arrange for your own accommodation.

E. H. Taylor Ltd, Beehive Works,

Welwyn, Hertfordshire AL6 OA2. Telephone: (043871) 4401. Duration: 2 days, end April to early May. Price: free. Accommodation in Welwyn (approx. 2 miles) or Stevenage (approx. 5 miles). Apply for details.

BEER

COUNTRYWIDE

Beer Festivals

These beery booze-ups take place anywhere from tents to university colleges. Here you can relish regional Real Ale from Ruddles to Robinsons, taste tankards of Theakston's Old Peculier, and get addled on everything from Adnams to Ansells. Best bets are the Cornish Real Beer Festival in the City Hall, Truro (one day, early August); the East London 'knees-up' at Leyton Marshes, run (amazingly) by the Inland Waterways Association (three days, mid August), and the Bedford Beer Festival (four days, early October). These lively events often feature jazz bands and (often impromptu) other entertainment. Opening hours are usually from around 10.30 a.m. till midnight.

There may be a small admission charge but the beer prices are always reasonable. Sometimes there's a reduction if you bring along your CAMRA (Campaign for Real Ale) membership card. For details of all beer festivals (mainly May to October) see the latest copy of 'What's Brewing'.

These festivals don't provide accommodation so book at a local hotel or inn well beforehand, or bring along your own tent and sleeping bag. Snacks of various kinds are available at the festivals themselves, together with the usual T-shirts, beer mugs, plaques, etc.

DORSET, Shaftesbury

Real Ale Bargain Breaks
Royal Chase Hotel

Traditional beer needs to be brewed well, stored properly and served with care. If you're a real ale lover and have nine or more friends who share your pleasure in a pint of the real thing, here's a chance to get two nights accommodation with full English breakfast, five free pints from a range of traditional cask-conditioned ales all brewed by local concerns and a bottle of Thomas Hardy's Ale to take home – reputedly the strongest beer brewed – in a numbered bottle it's a collector's item. Also included are £4 worth of vouchers towards hotel restaurant meals or 'pub grub'. Special hotel hours mean the bar stays open till midnight and opens early on Sunday. Local guide books to CAMRA (Campaign for Real Ale) pubs, T-shirts, special tankards and interesting brewery pints are on sale at reasonable prices. Book well in advance: this is a popular offer. The standard two-night package can be extended pro-rata, and if you want to include Sunday as a third night you're given a great deal.

Royal Chase Hotel, Shaftesbury, Dorset SP7 8OB. Telephone: (0747) 3355. Duration: 2 nights November–April. Price: £24–£28 per person (1981). Includes 5 pints of real ale, 2 nights accommodation and breakfast, £4 worth meal vouchers, service and VAT.

BIBLE STUDY

DEVON, Lynton

Bible Study House Parties
Lee Abbey

Lee Abbey is a large, turreted country house set in its own 260 acre estate on the magnificent North Devon coast. It offers Christians of all persuasions year-round holidays which combine usual holiday pursuits such as swimming and surfing (on a private beach), walking, tennis, putting or just relaxing, with opportunities to attend daily morning sessions on all aspects of Christian life. The evening programme usually consists of a group activity such as a sing-along followed by an informal discussion of the Gospel. There's room for 130 in single, double, family or shared rooms, all with central heating and hot and cold water. Amenities include lounges, library, chapel, laundry and children's playroom. Two cottages and a beach chalet are also available. Food includes milk and vegetables from the Lee Abbey farm and gardens.

Lee Abbey Fellowship, Lynton, Devon EX35 6JJ. Telephone: (059 185) 2303. Warden: Rev. John Perry. Duration: all year, Saturday–Friday. Price: from £48 per person (full board) (1981). VAT extra.

LONDON

Conferences and Retreats
The Royal Foundation of
Saint Katharine

St Katharine's has a long history. It was founded in 1148 by Queen Matilda as a centre for prayer and hospitality. This tradition continues today. Last year a thousand people attended weekend conferences and retreats here. They cover a wide range of topics; the 1980 courses included a Jewish–Christian weekend, a conference on East London, Liturgical Dance and the Poetry of R. S. Thomas. Some are for groups with particular concerns, others for those seeking to develop a Christian approach to modern living. There are nine annual retreats, some traditional with sermons and general silence, some with the emphasis on silence and conducted meditation and others with opportunities for encounter and discussion. There's accommodation for twenty-nine guests in nineteen singles and five doubles and the beautiful garden is open to guests.

The Receptionist, The Royal Foundation of St Katharine, 2 Butcher Row, London E14 8DS. Telephone: (01) 790 3540/1003. Duration: weekends, all year. Dates on application. Price: participation fee £12.50 per person. Includes conference and full board.

BOTANY

ISLE OF ARRAN, Glen Sannox

Herbal Lore and
The Art of Home Brewing
Isle of Arran Field Studies

This holiday is based on the special passion of guide John Williams – what he calls 'botanical archaeology', which is digging into the origins of common and scientific names of plants in an effort to uncover their past and present uses and associations. For one day's outing plus lecture he's assisted by a trained herbalist. To round the holiday off, you'll spend an enjoyable evening with a home-brewing expert learning (with plenty of sampling) the do's and don'ts of this thirst-quenching pastime.

For details of Isle of Arran Field Studies and accommodation see WILDLIFE.

Isle of Arran Field Studies, Woodside Cottage, Glen Sannox, Isle of Arran, Strathclyde, Scotland KA27 8JD. Telephone: (0770 81) 207/282. Chief Naturalist: John Williams. Duration: 1 week. Price: from £15 per person per day (1981). Includes tuition, full board and VAT. Bring binoculars and pocket lens.

ISLE OF ARRAN, Glen Sannox

Mushroom Moulds and Miracles
Isle of Arran Field Studies

Fungi have been called 'the Third Kingdom' after plants and animals. On this fascinating course, naturalist John Williams will tell you why they're so vital to the ecological balance. First you'll learn just what fungi are and how they operate, how to discover as many types as you can, sorting the edible from the inedible, the revolting from the delicious. Of course, as you prowl through the fascinating Arran countryside, you're sure to come across all sorts of other things not specifically on the agenda.

For details of this organization and accommodation, see WILDLIFE.

Isle of Arran Field Studies, Woodside Cottage, Glen Sannox, Isle of Arran, Strathclyde, Scotland, KA27 8JD. Telephone (0770 81) 207/282. Chief Naturalist: John Williams. Duration: 1 week. Price: from £15 per person per day (1981). Includes tuition, full board and VAT. Bring binoculars and pocket lens.

See also WILDLIFE.

TAYSIDE, Enochdhu

Botany Courses
1 Trees and Forests
2 Wild Flowers
3 Mountain Flowers
4 Field Botany
Kindrogan Field Centre

Study botany in bonnie Scotland, where Ailsa Lee runs a field botany course for beginners with emphasis on identification and the ecology of flowering plants and ferns. Expeditions are made into the surrounding countryside, with its coniferous and deciduous woodlands, where there are several mountains over 3000 feet. There are numerous lochs, the River Ardle, and dry and wet moorland – all ideal ground for specimen collecting.

Accommodation at the Kindrogan Field Centre includes all meals (packed lunches) and is of hostel, rather than hotel, standard – that is, guests may be asked to help serve meals. You'll spend some time in the centre's laboratories and classrooms as well as in the field. The courses on trees and forests are run by John Hendry, and courses on wild flowers, with emphasis on flowering plants and ferns, are run by the Extra-Mural Department of the University of Dundee. All these courses are ideal for those wishing to start serious studies at a higher level, as well as for enthusiasts.

The Scottish Field Studies Association, Kindrogan Field Centre, Enochdhu, Blairgowrie, Tayside PH10 7PG. Telephone: (025 081) 286. Warden: Brian Brookes. Duration: 1 10–17 June; 2 12–14 June; 3 8–15 July; 4 29 July–5 August, 19–26 August. Price: £84 per person per week (1981). Includes tuition, full board. No VAT.

See also GEOLOGY, WILDLIFE.

BOWLS

NORFOLK, Cromer

Beginners' Bowls
Linkside

You'll spend the week with twenty-three other beginners, learning the basics of this popular and relaxing pastime. The first game is organized on Sunday, with daily playing sessions at 10.00 a.m. and 4.00 p.m. in North Lodge Park.

Linkside is a large, comfortable red brick house that can accommodate up to seventy guests. As its name indicates, it's near a golf course and also has its own croquet and clock golf facilities plus a children's play area.

For details of Holiday Fellowship see WALKING, *Loch Awe.*

Holiday Fellowship, 142/144 Great North Way, London NW4 1EG. Telephone: (01) 203 3381. Leader: Mr W. Hodson. Duration: 1 week, June. Price: £72.77 per person (1981). Includes equipment, accommodation and all meals. VAT and transport to Cromer extra. Bring flat-soled shoes.

See also BRASS RUBBING, CREATIVE WRITING, ECOLOGY, FOLK MUSIC, GENEALOGY, JEWELLERY, ORIENTEERING, THEATRE GOING, WALKING, YOGA.

Brass Rubbing

AVON, Ammerdown

Brass Rubbing
Holiday Fellowship

You'll learn all about brass rubbing in a converted stable block built of Cotswold stone and donated by Lord Hytton. It's part of the estate and stands next to his private residence set in extensive grounds (to which guests have access) overlooking the wooded Mendip Hills. There are more single than double rooms here and two have been specially adapted for people in wheelchairs.

There are twenty places available, and materials are on sale at the centre. You'll learn about reversing, retouching and mounting, using facsimiles for practice, and you'll make visits to some of the fine brasses in nearby churches. There's also a brass rubbing course for the disabled.

For details of Holiday Fellowship see WALKING, *Loch Awe.*

Holiday Fellowship, 142–144 Great North Way, Hendon, London NW4 1EG. Telephone: (01) 203 3381. Duration: 1 week July. Price: £80 per person (1981). Includes tuition, and full board. VAT extra. Membership £10.

See also BOWLS, CREATIVE WRITING, ECOLOGY, FOLK MUSIC, GENEALOGY, JEWELLERY, ORIENTEERING, THEATRE GOING, WALKING, YOGA.

GLOUCESTERSHIRE, Cirencester

Brass Rubbing
King's Head Hotel

The King's Head is an historic 14th century coaching inn in the market square of Cirencester in the heart of the Cotswolds. Like all the best old buildings it has a secret passage that connects it with Cirencester Abbey across the market place. Legend has it that monks doing penance eased their burden with furtive visits to the inn. The hotel combines old world charm with modern comforts: colour TV in every room, radio, telephone, a lift and, in sixty-six of the seventy-three rooms, a private bath. The ancient vaults have been turned into the 'Monk's Retreat', where you can play skittles. Your holiday includes three hours of brass rubbing in Cirencester's beautiful old parish church and you'll be given a comprehensive list of brasses at seven outstanding churches in the area with directions to get you there. Paper, crayons, dinner, bed and breakfast are all included in the cost.

King's Head Hotel, Market Place, Cirencester, Gloucestershire GL7 2NR. Telephone: (0285) 3322. Manager: Michael Gannon. Duration: 3 days, all year. Price: £62 per person (spring 1981), £68 (summer 1981 est), £62 (autumn/winter 1981 est). Includes 3 hours rubbing, all equipment, list of local brasses, bed, breakfast, dinner and VAT.

BRIDGE

CUMBRIA, Loughrigg Brow

Bridge
Loughrigg Brow

If you're an experienced bridge player here's a chance to get together with players of equal ability in a wonderfully situated Victorian country house on the slopes of Loughrigg overlooking Lake Windermere. You don't receive formal instruction. Instead, competitions are arranged and you play every evening under the watchful eye of a knowledgeable tutor who's available for consultation.

During the day, walks are arranged in the surrounding Lake District National Park. These are geared to both energetic hikers and more casual ramblers. There's accommodation for sixty-one guests in single and twin bedded rooms, some in an annexe to the main building; all bedrooms have central heating. The intensive bridge course is ideal if you're interested in perfecting the Acol bidding system. Sessions under the guidance of a National Master of the Bridge Union include end plays, choice of lead and signalling conventions.

Loughrigg Brow, Ambleside, Cumbria LA22 9SA. Telephone: (096 63) 2229. Under auspices of: Country Wide Holidays, Birch Heys, Cromwell Range, Manchester M14 6HU. Telephone: (061) 224 2887. Duration: 5 days, February, March, November. Price: from £22.45 per person (1980); Intensive Acol System tuition fee £4; equipment supplement £3.50. 1981 prices and dates not final at press time, write for details.

DERBYSHIRE, Buxton

Duplicate Bridge Weekends
St Ann's Hotel

St Ann's is an elegant one-hundred bedroom Georgian hotel built in 1776 for the

Duke of Devonshire and now a Grade I historical building. Mary, Queen of Scots was among the notables who flocked to Buxton to sample the famous spa water. Now card lovers flock to St Ann's for their popular bridge weekends including a New Year's gala that runs from 28 December to 1 January. These are licensed by the English Bridge Union (EBU) and Master Points are awarded. You play two sessions; one in the afternoon, one in the evening. Amenities include two bars, a fine restaurant, a grill room and three large drawing rooms. A swimming pool filled with spa water is a two-minute walk away and two 18 hole golf courses are also within easy walking distance.

St Ann's Hotel, The Crescent, Buxton, Derbyshire. Telephone: (0298) 2788. Proprietor: Joyce Critchlow. Duration: 22–25 February, 8–11 May, 5–8 June, 14–17 August. Also weekends in September, October and November. Price: £50 per person (1981). Includes bridge fees, full board and VAT.

DERBYSHIRE, Hope

Bridge
1 Bridge for Beginners
2 Advanced Duplicate Bridge
3 Improve Your Bridge
Moor Gate

These three courses cater for beginners, players of reasonable standard and those with only a basic knowledge. In the second course, your tutors set up duplicate competitions for pairs of teams of four. Hands that are especially interesting will be displayed and analysed next morning, followed by optional practice play.

You'll stay in a rambling country house in the heart of the Peak District National Park. Sights such as Chatsworth and the famous limestone caverns at Castleton are within easy reach. Accommodation is for sixty-one guests; all rooms are heated.

Moor Gate, Hope, Sheffield S30 2RF. Telephone: (0433) 20348. Under auspices of: Country Wide Holidays, Birch Heys, Cromwell Range, Manchester M14 6HU. Telephone: (061) 224 2887. Duration: 4 days, end of October (for beginners), 4 days, end of November (advanced duplicate), 4 days, mid-March (basic knowledge). Price: £30 per person (est) including VAT. Equipment supplement £3.50.

DEVON, Bovey Tracey

Bridge Weekends
1 Competition Bridge
2 Bridge for Beginners
Coombe Cross Hotel

The hotel is licensed by the English Bridge Union for duplicate bridge. Each evening competition winners are awarded master points and prizes, and you can also arrange informal afternoon sessions. All competitors must be paid-up members of the EBU. Lundie Rees, who organizes these weekends, tutors on Thursday evening and Friday morning before the weekends of 31 October (1980) and 6 March (1981); the extra day costs £15 per person (including VAT).

If you'd like to take up this fascinating game, Mrs Jackie Waters will give five two-hour beginners' sessions (13–16 March).

Coombe Cross Hotel, Bovey Tracey, Newton Abbot, Devon TQ13 9EY. Telephone: (0626) 832476. Proprietors: Misses Anne and Elizabeth Hebditch. Duration: 1 27 February–2 March, 6–9 March also October and November; 2 13–16 March. Price: £52 per person (1981). Includes full board (from dinner on arrival to breakfast on departure), bridge equipment, service and VAT.

See also CASTLES AND HISTORIC HOUSES, ECOLOGY, GARDENS, ORNITHOLOGY.

HAMPSHIRE, Barton on Sea

Advanced Duplicate Bridge
Barton Chase

The advanced course is designed for players of a reasonable standard who want to broaden their experience. Every evening your tutors arrange duplicate competitions for pairs of teams of four; hands that are particularly interesting will be displayed and analysed next morning, followed by optional practice play.

Barton Chase is a large sea-front building ten miles from Bournemouth with accommodation for eighty-three. Stonehenge and the great cathedral cities of Winchester and Salisbury are within easy reach. Heating in all rooms is by coin meter.

Barton Chase, Barton-on-Sea, New Milton, Hampshire BH25 7EF. Telephone: New Milton (0425) 610171. Under auspices of: Country Wide Holidays, Birch Heys, Cromwell Range, Manchester M14 6HU. Telephone: (061) 224 2887. Duration: 1 week, mid-October. Price: £60 (est) + £3.50 supplement (advanced duplicate). Senior Citizens £27 (est). Prices include VAT.

LONDON

Bridge
1 Seven week course
2 Beginners
3 Intermediate
The London School of Bridge

Bridge is the most popular indoor game in the world. If you want to join Great Britain's four million players the beginners' classes are designed to start you off gently. All instructors are of international standing. Staff members have won national competitions and represented England internationally. Each lesson combines theory and practice and is introduced by a lecture that highlights various aspects of bidding or play. Then there's a question and answer session and a game using pre-dealt hands to illustrate points explained in the lecture.

If you're already familiar with the basics, the intermediate course pairs you with players of your own standard in closely supervised games. As a prospective student, by arrangement you can have a single lesson to determine your class level.

A course consists of seven sessions lasting just over two hours each. Afternoon and evening lessons always fall on the same week day. Afternoon sessions run from 2.30 to 4.30, evening from 8.30 to 10.30. A licensed club at the school is open daily from 2.30 to 11.30 p.m., and is an ideal place to practise with others you've met on the course.

The London School of Bridge, 38 Kings Road, London SW3. Telephone: (01) 589 7201/3. Director: Nico Gardener. Duration: 1 September and October, seven weeks (1 session per week); 2 and 3 all year. Price: £35 (est) for 7 sessions (approx. 16 hours), £5.00 (est) for a single visit. VAT included. Accommodation at The Wilbraham Hotel, Wilbraham Place, London SW1, 2 minutes walk from the school. Telephone: (01) 730 8296/7/8. Daily rates start at £15 per person for a single room, £17 bed and breakfast (1981). VAT included.

STAFFORDSHIRE, Rugeley

Summer Courses in Calligraphy
Spode Centre, Hawksyard Priory

Here is an opportunity to examine the nature and principles of calligraphy, and to develop or refine your individual calligraphic skills on one of these six-day courses put together by Stanley Knight and some of his fellow members of the Society of Scribes and Illuminators. Beginners are welcome, while more advanced students can take advantage of expert advice on complicated technical problems.

Your week will include a visit to Lichfield Cathedral Library to see the celebrated manuscript of 'St Chad's Gospel', among others and a visit to the Gladstone Memorial Pottery Museum. Pupils should bring as much of their own equipment as possible (see brochure for details). Some materials such as drawing boards are on sale. Book early – only fifteen students accepted.

For accommodation see RELIGIOUS RETREATS.

The Spode Centre, Hawksyard Priory, Rugeley, Staffordshire WS15 1PT. Telephone: (0543) 490112. Duration: March (Friday to Sunday), July (Saturday to Friday), September (Friday to Sunday). Price: course fees on application; accommodation £7.50 per night (est) for twin rooms, £10.00 for single rooms. Includes all meals. VAT extra.

See also MUSIC, RELIGIOUS RETREATS.

SUSSEX, West Dean

1 Calligraphy for those with some experience
2 Calligraphy for beginners
West Dean College

Calligraphy weekends for beginners and for more advanced students are run by David Williams and John Shyvers. They'll teach you different styles of beautiful lettering so that you can make your own posters or Christmas and birthday cards at home. All tools are provided and courses are open to everyone past school-leaving age. More advanced courses include calligraphic gilding and colour.

For details of West Dean College see ART APPRECIATION.

West Dean College, West Dean, Chichester, West Sussex PO18 0QZ. Telephone: (024 363) 301. Principal: Peter Sarginson. Duration: 1 13–15 February, 15–20 March; 2 20–22 February. Also weekends May, July and September. Price: £39.50 per person per weekend; £93 per person per 5 days (1981). Includes tuition, full board, twin room. Single room supplement £1.50 per night.

See also ART APPRECIATION, CANEWORK, COLLECTING, THEATRE GOING, UPHOLSTERY.

WALES, DYFED, Llanwrda

Calligraphy
Gwaith Llaw y Werin

At the finish of this short course you should be able to practise your calligraphy unsupervised. A maximum of six pupils per tutor ply their pens every morning from 9.30 a.m. to 12.30 p.m., before partaking of a free farmhouse lunch and then either practising in the workshop or just enjoying the glorious scenery. It's a flexible course which includes discussions on the history of letter forms, relationship of letter form to the tools and materials used, and the psychology of lettering. You'll receive demonstrations and practice in 'one stroke' brushwork, constructed brush letters and the use of various nibs. Emphasis is on the pen but brushwork can be included if you want. There are talks and practical work every day.

Gwaith Llaw y Werin, Cottage Industries Crafts School, Wernfeudwy, Ffarmers, Llanwrda, Dyfed, Wales SA19 8PJ. Telephone: (05585) 434. Proprietor: Judith Hoad. Duration: Monday to Friday, April to October. Price: £39 per person per week (est). Includes tuition, equipment, materials and lunch. Accommodation list on request (e.g. £52 per person per week (est). Includes room, breakfast and dinner). Minimum unaccompanied age 16 years.

See also QUILTING AND PATCHWORK.

CANEWORK

WEST SUSSEX, West Dean

Caning
West Dean College

This is one of the most popular courses on offer at the college. Great demand for Margery Brown's original courses has brought in Joy Viall as an additional tutor. She's Secretary of the Basketmakers' Association. Her two-day course supplements Margery's five-day one on cane seating and willow basketry.

For details of West Dean College, see ART APPRECIATION.

West Dean College, West Dean, Chichester, West Sussex PO18 0QZ. Telephone: (024363) 301. Duration: 1 20–22 February; 2 22–27 March. Price: 1 £39.50 per person (1981); 2 £93 per person (1981). Includes tuition, full board and VAT. Single room supplement £3 per weekend, £7.50 per 5 days.

See also ART APPRECIATION, CALLIGRAPHY, COLLECTING, THEATRE GOING, UPHOLSTERY.

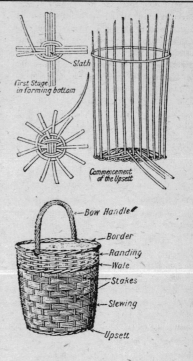

Slath
First Stage in forming bottom
Commencement of the Upsett

Bow Handle
Border
Randing
Wale
Stakes
Slewing
Upsett

CANOEING

EIRE, COUNTY WICKLOW, Ashford

Canoeing
Tiglin Adventure Centre

Canoeing is one of the fastest-growing adventure sports in Britain, and these courses, ideal for novice or expert enthusiast, are usually run as a series of weekends all year round. Each weekend is also complete in itself; you can join in at the level appropriate to your experience. Beginners start off on a small lake and progress through easy river descents to a sea trip and then on to more demanding descents. You'll get a chance to use fibreglass, general purpose and slalom-type kayaks, supplemented on some courses by open double Canadians, sea-kayaks and KI LD racers.

Experienced canoeists flock here in winter and early spring to have a go on Wicklow's white water rivers, the best in Ireland for this exhilarating sport.

The increasing popularity of family canoeing has led to a special weekend course in May designed to teach the basics of safe canoeing to parents and children.

You must bring your own craft; specify

in your application which type you intend to bring.

The main centre in lovely Devil's Glen Forest is a fine old stone building that is part of a former complex once owned by the family of playwright J. M. Synge. The dormitory annexe sleeps thirty-six in four, six and eight bedrooms and you have the use of showers, a drying room, lecture/common room, games area and stores.

Tiglin Adventure Centre, Ashford, County Wicklow, Eire. Telephone: Wicklow 4169. Dial through operator. Secretary: Yvonne Christian. Duration: all year. Price: £14 per weekend (1980). Includes meals (but help is expected with domestic chores), specialized clothing, equipment and in-course transport. £70 for 1 week (1980). White water paddling is strenuous and demanding, so the Tiglin Director reserves the right to refuse admission to applicants whose ability he considers not up to standard.

See also ORIENTEERING, WALKING.

HIGHLAND, Fort William

Great Glen Canoe Expeditions
Insh Hall

This adventurous holiday takes you by double kayak from the foot of Ben Nevis through Loch Ness to Inverness. You'll camp in a three-man tent and cook on a primus supplied by the centre. You don't have to be super-fit or an expert canoeist but you should be confident on the water.

The course starts at Insh Hall on Saturday. Arrive in time for 6.30 p.m. dinner and a briefing by the instructor in charge. On Sunday morning there's an introductory canoeing session on Loch Insh, including capsize drill and in the afternoon you'll be driven to the Caledonian Canal at Corpach where the expedition begins. At its end, you'll be collected at Inverness and taken back to Loch Insh to celebrate and swap tales over a barbeque with other guests who took the sailing course or canoed on the River Spey.

Insh Hall, Kincraig, Fort William, High-

land PH21 1NO. Telephone: (05404) 272. Proprietors: Clive and Sally Freshwater. Duration: 1 week, July and August. Price: £103 per person (1981). Includes all meals, equipment and tents. Minimum age 16. Must be able to swim 50 yards in light clothing.

See also MULTI-ACTIVITY, SAILING, SKIING.

WALES, GWYNEDD, Capel Curig

Canoeing
Plas y Brenin

The centre boasts a recently updated canoe fleet including a wide range of general purpose slalom kayaks and a good selection of specialist sea boats as well as a range of specialist spring, slalom and surf boats. Specialist Canadian canoes are also available. All canoeists may be issued with wetsuit, buoyancy aid, spray deck, paddle, anorak and helmet but bring your own gear if you prefer. You'll use a heated pool outdoors for rescue and Eskimo roll training.

It's an introductory course for complete novices or those with limited experience. You'll receive instruction in all the basic strokes and kayak handling skills on local lakes, white water rivers and in the sea – plus instruction in surfing techniques and expert advice on canoe maintenance and repair, clothing and equipment and how to plan canoe journeys. If the weather permits, the course winds up with a two-day camp. Those who wish will be able to take the British Canoeing Union Star Tests.

For details of the centre, see ROCK CLIMB-ING.

Booking Department, Plas y Brenin, Capel Curig, Betws-y-Coed, Gwynedd, Wales LL24 0ET. Telephone: (06904) 214. Administrator: Roger Osgill. Duration: weekly, April to October. Price: £99 per person per week (1981). Includes tuition, full board and VAT. Equipment issued free. Must be able to swim. Minimum age 16. Special weeks for 14–16 year olds. Duration: 1 week, August and October. Price: £89 per person per week (1981).

See also CLIMBING, MOUNTAIN SKILLS.

CAR MAINTENANCE

LEICESTERSHIRE, Loughborough

1 Car Maintenance I
2 Car Maintenance II
Loughborough University

The mechanically-minded can choose from two courses led by John Baggaley. If you don't know a spanner from a sparking plug, Car Maintenance I will give you a good grasp of the basics – how an engine works, how to identify engine parts, and you'll gain some experience of regular inspection, servicing, tuning and wheel changing. You are encouraged to work on your own car as well as on demonstration vehicles.

The more advanced course involves dismantling and rebuilding an engine to familiarize yourself with its components and associated systems. You'll become acquainted with methods of inspecting major parts such as clutch and gearbox, and with decarbonizing, valve and ignition tuning, lapping in valves and fault diagnosis. Complete service procedure is also taught: electronic tuning, carburettor adjustment using a CO meter, checking tyres, wheel balancing, track and brake adjustment. Both courses will be held in the well-equipped workshops and garages of the Loughborough Technical College where all tools and equipment are provided.

For details of accommodation see SCULPTURE.

Centre for Extension Studies (BR), University of Technology, Loughborough, Leicestershire LE11 3TU. Telephone: (0509) 63171 extension 249/213. Duration: 1 26 July–1 August; 2 2–8 August. Price: £118 per person per week (est). Includes tuition, use of tools and equipment, full board and evening entertainment. No VAT.

See also CREATIVE WRITING, NEEDLEWORK, SCULPTURE.

CASTLES AND
HISTORIC HOUSES

CHESHIRE, Stockport

Chatsworth House
Alma Lodge Hotel

Michael Tebbutt, Curator and Manager of Weston Park in Shropshire, arranges and leads some weekends. Art historian Hugh Belsey takes others.

This weekend is an in-depth study of magnificent Chatsworth House, the work of three great builders. Local historian Roy Christian will guide your investigation of Chatsworth, its magnificent park and its village, Edensor.

Leisure Learning Weekends, Embassy Hotels Ltd, Station Street, Burton-upon-Trent, Staffordshire DE14 1BZ. Telephone: (0283) 66587. Leaders: Michael Tebbutt, Hugh Belsey. Duration: 20–22 March. Price: £52 per person (1981). Includes room (with private bath), all meals from Friday dinner to Sunday lunch, all excursions, entrance fees, service and VAT.

See also CHURCHES AND CATHEDRALS, LITERATURE, PHOTOGRAPHY, POTTERY.

DEVON, Bovey Tracey

Devon Heritage
Coombe Cross Hotel

Mrs J. Bundle, the guide, has been an avid history buff since her Oxford University days and she's only too happy to share her deep knowledge and love of West Country art and architecture. She'll lead your exploration of the area's outstanding country homes and historic towns, some of which are open only to Coombe Cross visitors. There are two visits each day for which transportation is provided. During the week two evenings are set aside for illustrated talks on topics ranging from glass, china and antiques to the intriguing subject of 'The Englishman at Home'.

Coombe Cross Hotel, Bovey Tracey, Newton Abbot, Devon TQ13 9EY. Telephone: (0626) 832476. Proprietors: Misses Ann and Elizabeth Hebditch. Duration: 1 week 23–30 April, 9–16 July, 3–10 September. Price: £150 per person (est). Includes double room, full board (packed lunches), entrance fees, transport, VAT and service. Single room supplement £12.50.

See also BRIDGE, GARDENS, ECOLOGY, ORNITHOLOGY.

EIRE, COUNTY MAYO, Ballina

A Castle To Stay In
Beleek Castle

Five hundred years ago, Beleek Castle was built on the banks of the River Moy. It's still furnished in the grand manner with four-poster beds, great oak tables, huge chandeliers, antiques, suits of armour and open turf fires. Set in wooded parkland, it's close to the sea and sandy swimming beaches. The good life here includes salmon, trout and sea trout fishing on the River Moy, the Owenmore System and Easkey River; sport fishing in the Atlantic; and riding from the castle's own stables or from local ones. The castle also has an arrangement with the local golf club.

Beleek Castle, Ballina, County Mayo, Eire. Telephone: (096) 22061/21878. Dial through operator. Duration: April–December. Price: daily rate £13.50 per person (est), bed, breakfast, private bath. Half-board £120 a week, full board £144.50 a week. For children under 12 years sharing parents' room, 50% discount on the daily room rate or 15% discount on the weekly rate.

EIRE, COUNTY MAYO, Cong

A Castle to Stay In
Ashford Castle

You can live like a lord at Ashford, a fantasy which mixes the remains of a 13th century castle, an ancient French chateau and the thirty-year architectural efforts of Lord Ardiluan in the 19th century. Ashford is one of Europe's most spectacular castle hotels in a magnificent setting on the shores of Lough Corrib, Ireland's second largest lake. The castle's opulent interior is furnished with period pieces, *objets d'art* and fine original paintings. You have free use of the hotel's 9 hole golf course and tennis courts and are ideally situated for hunting, fishing and shooting, which they will arrange. Ashford is also a handy base for touring the west of Ireland by car. It's within easy reach of scenic highlights such as Galway Bay, Connemara and the Aran Islands.

Ashford Castle, Cong, County Mayo, Eire. Telephone: (094) 22644 or (Cong 3). Manager: Rory Murphy. Seasons and prices: April, October to December 31, £240.70 per person per week (1981). May, June, October £302.70; July, August, September £311.10. Includes double room, breakfast, dinner, service and VAT.

HIGHLAND, Freswick

A Castle to Accommodate You
Freswick Castle

Freswick, with its elegant drawing room and period décor, was built in the 17th century on ancient foundations. Two of the original dungeons remain and one is now a welcoming restaurant and bar. The castle is surrounded by water on three sides and at high tide the sea all but laps the east wall. Hundreds of teal can be seen in the bay daily, and salmon and sea trout run up the Freswick river which empties into the sea just below the castle windows. Fishing in the river and nearby lochs is good, and so are the golf, shooting (by arrangement) and bathing on the castle's sandy beach. Baron Newell, your friendly host, personally sees that his guests enjoy the best of local produce. Trout, lobster, crab and prime Scotch beef are all on the menu.

Freswick Castle, Freswick, Caithness, Highland, Scotland. Telephone: (095 581) 354. Proprietor: Gerald Newell of Staffa, Baron of Freswick. Duration: Closed December to Easter. Price: £19.50 per person per day (1980). Includes bed, breakfast, service and VAT. Dinner £8.62 (1980) set meal or à la carte, includes VAT. Special tariffs for children and family bookings.

HIGHLAND, Inverness

Historic Home
Culloden House

What better way to soak up the atmosphere of history than to stay in an historic house. Choose Culloden House and you'll be cared for in grand style. This magnificent Adam residence was built in 1772, twenty-six years after the bloody battle of the same name. Bonnie Prince Charlie slept on this site on the eve of the battle in a castle whose vaults lie beneath the present structure.

Comfort and elegance are keynotes. The period furniture (replica) and Adamesque decoration are completed by modern comforts such as central heating and TV. Bedrooms are spacious, carpeted and bathrooms opulently fitted. Culloden House's outstanding Scottish cuisine makes good use of native game and fish. You may contribute to the menu: there's fishing for salmon and trout and deerstalking. You're within half an hour's drive of Inverness, with its famous castle and 18 hole golf course, and also close to Aviemore ski centre and Loch Ness.

Culloden House, Inverness, Highland, Scotland. Telephone: (046 372) 461. Proprietor: Kenneth McLennan. Duration: all year. Price £55 per night (est) double suite; £40–£45 double rooms; £32 single rooms. Includes room, breakfast, service, VAT and limousine transport to and from Inverness.

LOTHIAN, Bonnyrigg

A Castle to Accommodate You
Dalhousie Castle

In its 800 year history, Dalhousie Castle has played host to the famous and the infamous including Edward I, Henry IV, Oliver Cromwell and Queen Victoria. But you'll be treated even more royally than they were thanks to modern comforts such as central heating, colour TV in every room, wall-to-wall carpeting and twenty-four-hour room service, not to mention private baths and showers.

Traditional Scottish dishes and flambé cuisine are served in the candle-lit dungeon restaurant. You also have the run of seven acres of woodland grounds. The management is glad to advise on golf, riding, fishing and skiing, all available nearby, and will arrange shooting on neighbouring estates. Edinburgh's just eight miles away so you're ideally situated for shopping, theatre, sporting events and the Edinburgh Festival.

Dalhousie is a marvellous combination of ancient splendour, traditional service and modern comforts.

Dalhousie Castle, Bonnyrigg, Nr. Edinburgh, Lothian. Telephone: (0875) 20153. Proprietor: Keith McLennan. Duration: all year. Price: £55 per night (1981) double suite; £40–£45 double room; singles £32. Includes breakfast; service and VAT extra.

LOTHIAN, Dalkeith

Houses and Castles of Lowland Scotland
Newbattle Abbey College

Lowland Scotland boasts a surprising number of fine, historic buildings in gorgeous country settings for the visitor to admire. During the week, your guide will show you houses of historic interest, chosen as apt examples of Scottish building styles – from medieval tower houses and modest town houses to Edwardian mansions. You'll listen to an illustrated lecture before each visit and some free time is allowed for general sightseeing and shopping. Transport and entrance fees are included in the cost of the course.

For details of accommodation, see AN-TIQUES.

Newbattle Abbey College, Dalkeith, Lothian EH22 2LL. Telephone: (031 663) 1921/2. Duration: 1 week, 27 June–4 July. Price: £112 per person (est). Includes tuition, excursions and full board. No VAT.

See also ANTIQUES, FESTIVALS, MUSIC, PAINTING.

NORFOLK, Norwich

Norfolk
Lansdowne Hotel

A May weekend in Norfolk will take you to Blickling Hall (birthplace of Anne Boleyn), Mannington Hall, Holkham and Felbrigg. Your guide is Michael Tebbutt.

On the August weekend, you'll visit two charming, smaller houses, one of which is not normally open to the public, and two much grander ones. Beeston Hall, one of the former, is Gothic with a fine Georgian interior. Turreted, moated Oxburgh Hall was described by Pugin as 'one of the noblest specimens of domestic architecture'.

Leisure Learning Weekends, Embassy Hotels Ltd, Station Street, Burton-upon-Trent, Staffordshire DE14 1BZ. Telephone: (0283) 66587. Leader: Michael Tebbutt. Duration: 15–17 May, 28–30 August. Price: £52 per person per weekend (1981). Includes room (with bath), all meals from Friday dinner to Sunday lunch, all excursions, entrance fees, service and VAT.

See also CHURCHES AND CATHEDRALS, LITERATURE, PHOTOGRAPHY, POTTERY.

NORTHUMBERLAND, Wooler

Abbeys, Castles and Country Houses
Cheviot Field Centre

Adam Welfare, a tutor in Roman Archaeology at Newcastle University, is an authority on the medieval history of the Anglo-Scottish border country and this is a perfect place from which to study it. The vast list of major medieval sites and structures in the Border country includes Alnwick, Bamburgh, Abbotsford, Wallington and Cragside. This course combines visits to some of these impressive buildings with illustrated background lectures on the history and archaeology of the region.

For details of accommodation see ARCHAEOLOGY.

Cheviot Field Centre, Summer School, Padgepool Place, Wooler, Northumberland. Telephone: (066 82) 711. Warden:

Kevin Danforth. Duration: 1 week 22–29 August. Price: £85 per person (est). Includes tuition, accommodation, all meals and transport in the field. VAT extra. Bring soap, towels, waterproof clothing, strong footwear and a thermos flask.

See also ARCHAEOLOGY, BATTLEFIELDS, WALKING.

SUSSEX, Fittleworth

Discover Country Houses and Gardens
The Old Rectory

England's heritage springs vividly to life during this summer week. A knowledgeable tutor leads you through changing fashions in architecture, landscaping, furniture and portraiture as found in the great country houses of the south east, Parnham, Chilworth Manor, Clandon Park, Goodwood and Coates Manor among them. One of the most unusual gardens for instance is created out of a chalk pit at Highdown. The fee includes transport and guide but not entrance fees.

For further details of accommodation see SENIOR CITIZENS, CRAFTS.

The Old Rectory, Fittleworth, Pulborough, Sussex RH20 1HU. Telephone: (079 882) 306. Proprietors: Brenda and Graham Salmon. Duration: 1 week, 17–24 July. Price: £87 per person for double room, £100 per person for single room (1981). Includes tuition and full board. VAT extra.

See also CLOCKS, GENEALOGY, MUSIC, ORNITHOLOGY, QUILTING AND PATCHWORK, SENIOR CITIZENS.

WALES, SOUTH GLAMORGAN,
Cardiff

Historic Houses of South Wales
Royal Hotel

Tredegar House is a superb Restoration house, generally considered the best of its kind in Wales. It contrasts vividly with Fonmon and the skilfully restored Penhow Castles, both medieval and both claiming to be the oldest inhabited castle in Wales. You'll visit these as well as William Burges' fairy tale reconstruction, for the Marquess of Bute, of Castel Coch. Its towers, turrets and drawbridge epitomize the Victorian vision of a medieval castle. Hugh Belsey will lead the tour, assisted by experts on the properties.

Leisure Learning Weekends, Embassy Hotels Ltd, Station Street, Burton-upon-Trent, Staffordshire DE14 1BZ. Telephone: (0283) 66587. Leader: Hugh Belsey. Duration: 3–5 July. Price: £52 per person (1981). Includes room (with private bath), all meals from Friday dinner to Sunday lunch, all excursions, entrance fees, service and VAT.

See also CHURCHES AND CATHEDRALS, LITERATURE, PHOTOGRAPHY, POTTERY.

WEST MIDLANDS, Wolverhampton

Shropshire I and II
Mount Hotel

There are two different courses available. Weekend I focuses on Weston Park, built in 1671 as the seat of the Earls of Bradford. You couldn't have a more interested or informed guide than Michael Tebbutt, the curator and manager of the house, who'll also escort you to and guide you through Attingham Park, Benthall Hall and Mawley Hall.

On the second weekend, he'll introduce you to two smaller houses – Longnor Hall and Aeton Round, both privately owned. The Welsh border castles of Chirk and Erdigg, 14th century home of the Yorkes, round out this weekend.

Leisure Learning Weekends, Embassy Hotels Ltd, Station Street, Burton-upon-Trent, Staffordshire DE14 1BZ. Telephone: (0283) 66587. Leader: Michael Tebbutt. Duration: 10–12 April, 18–20 September. Price: £52 per person per weekend (1981). Includes room (with private bath), all meals from Friday dinner to Sunday lunch, all excursions, entrance fees, service and VAT.

CAVING AND POTHOLING

CUMBRIA, Sedbergh

Caving and Potholing Courses
Whernside Cave and Fell Centre

Whernside Cave and Fell Centre has an international reputation as a potholer's paradise, offering expert tuition in the study and exploration of caves and potholes, as well as fellcraft and field studies. It has all the facilities of a first rate outdoor centre and the location couldn't be better – in the Cumbria section of the Yorkshire Dales National Park, part of Britain's most important limestone country. Superb scenery is all around and

there are hundreds of caves within a twenty-five-kilometre radius.

Whernside is a converted Georgian house with dormitory accommodation for thirty-two, and a camp site within its seven-acre grounds. If you prefer farmhouse, inn or guest house accommodation the warden will be pleased to suggest addresses in the area.

The weekend caving and potholing courses offer novices a practical introduction to different kinds of underground terrain. Evening sessions cover such topics as how caves are formed, where to find them in Britain, proper clothing and equipment, and safety precautions.

The week-long courses, designed for keen novices and those with limited experience, give an introduction to caving as a pursuit, and go on to provide a thorough grounding in techniques. You can, if you wish, be introduced to an appropriate caving club later. Programmes begin at 5.00 p.m. on Sunday and finish after breakfast the following Saturday.

Yorkshire Dales National Park, Whernside Cave and Fell Centre, Dent, Sedbergh, Cumbria LA10 5RE. Telephone: (05875)
213. Warden: M. K. Lyon. Duration: weekends, 20–22 March, 22–24 March, 4–6 September, 2–4 October, 30 October–1 November; weeks, 19–25 April, 26 July–1 August, 11–17 October. Price: weekend £30 per person (1981); week £78 per person. Includes tuition, use of equipment, full board (dormitory) and VAT. Transport from Oxenholme Station £2.50 each way (requires 7 day's notice). Minimum age 15 years.

See also ECOLOGY, WALKING, WILDLIFE.

CERAMICS

SHROPSHIRE, Shifnal

A Study of Beautiful Porcelain and Pottery
Park House Hotel

RVS Enterprises is a small, privately run organization which caters to a discerning clientele (RVS stands for Rare, Vintage and Special). In 1980 the spring course offered a three-day study of outstanding porcelain and pottery which delighted china lovers by taking them to the newly reopened and extended City Museum and Art Gallery at Stoke-on-Trent. It houses the finest collection of ceramics in Britain and includes fine pieces from great factories such as Chelsea, Worcester, Minton, Derby and Spode. It's the first time in a century that these great collections have been collectively displayed. The tour of the magnificent galleries was conducted by Arnold Mountford, Director of Museums in Stoke-on-Trent and one of the world's foremost authorities on Staffordshire wares. A tour of the Worcester porcelain factory was led by Henry Sandon, Curator of the Worcester Porcelain Museum, and John Sandon, who works with a leading London auctioneering company, helped tour members identify the fine wares at other factories. A highlight of the course was an evening meal at Weston Park, the Earl of Bradford's elegant home, in company with the Curator, Michael Tebbutt, who also conducted a tour of the house. Only twenty-five places were available. The autumn course was held at Stratford-upon-Avon. Over the weekend members visited one of the most breathtaking collections in private hands. Worcester porcelain expert Henry Sandon and furniture restorer Eric Revill were guest speakers, and accommodation was in the historic Falcon Hotel. Similar tours will be offered in 1981; write for details.

RVS Enterprises, Hilton House, Norwood Lane, Meopham, Kent DA13 0YE. Telephone: (0474) 812171. Director: Judy Watts. Duration: weekend, March. Price: £84 per person (1980). Includes lectures, visits, entry fees, full board with bath. Single room supplement £3 (1980). VAT extra.

See also: CRUISING: INLAND WATERWAYS.

CHINA

WILTSHIRE, Marlborough

China Restoration
1 Basic China Restoration
2 China Restoration Workshop
Marlborough College Summer School

Thanks to the development of new materials and methods there's been a big advance in the repair and restoration of china in recent years. The basic restoration course deals with several techniques which use readily available materials and tools, including cleaning, sticking, modelling and overpainting. Talks and demonstrations go hand-in-hand with practical work. The course also prepares you to tackle more elaborate work on your own.

The workshop course, a direct follow-up of the first course, lets you work on your own pieces. The emphasis is on advice rather than formal teaching and assumes some previous training in basic methods. Your tutor on both courses is James Barrett, a restorer in the antique trade and a craft teacher for the Inner London Education Authority.

For details of accommodation see ARCHAEOLOGY.

Marlborough College, Summer School, Marlborough, Wiltshire. Telephone: (0672) 53888. Secretary: Glynis Lewis. Duration: 1 week, 1 19–25 July, 26 July–1 August; 2 2–8 August. Price: £155.25 per person private room (est); £126.50 dormitory; children under 14 years £103.50. Includes course fees, accommodation, holiday insurance, service and VAT. The college can also arrange accommodation at a hotel in town, room with private bath £195.50 (est).

See also ARCHAEOLOGY, FISHING, FURNITURE RESTORATION, MUSIC, SCULPTURE.

CHURCHES AND CATHEDRALS

ESSEX, Colchester

Churches and Cathedrals
1 Suffolk Churches
2 Cathedrals and Greater Churches
Flatford Mill Field Centre

Since Suffolk alone possesses 500 medieval churches, sporting details from every architectural period from Anglo-Saxon to late Perpendicular, Flatford is an excellent base for the study of parish churches.

The first course looks at the history, architecture and furnishings of Suffolk's splendid parish churches; the second course takes you to magnificent cathedrals such as Ely and Norwich, as well as other monastic sites of the region,

King's College Chapel at Cambridge and some of the fine wool churches.

For details of Flatford Mill Field Centre and accommodation see PAINTING.

Flatford Mill Field Centre, East Bergholt, near Colchester, Essex CO7 6UL. Telephone: (0206) 298283. Warden: F. J. Bingley. Duration: Wednesday to Wednesday, 1 1–8 April; 2 7–14 October. Price: £84 per person per week (1981). Includes course, full board; bring linen. No VAT.

NORFOLK, Norwich

Churches
Lansdowne Hotel

David O'Connor, lecturer in Medieval Art at the University of Manchester, will guide you on a tour of the outstanding Gothic churches of Norfolk. Norwich alone has more pre-Reformation churches than London, York and Bristol combined. Even the smaller churches are fas-

cinating, particularly so when explored with an informed guide. Some, such as Ranworth, have priceless medieval relics on display.

Leisure Learning Weekends, Embassy Hotels Ltd, Station Street, Burton-on-Trent, Staffordshire DE14 1B7. Telephone: (0283) 66587. Organizer: Gordon Hopper. Duration: weekend 10–12 July. Price: £48 per person (1981). Includes 2 nights full board with bath, lectures, service and VAT.

See also CASTLES AND HISTORIC HOUSES, LITERATURE, PHOTOGRAPHY, POTTERY.

WILTSHIRE, Salisbury

Churches and Abbeys
Philipps House

Mr Penny, a member of the Royal Archaeological Institute, is host to a programme that includes coach excursions to the majestic cathedrals of Winchester, Salisbury, and the smaller 12th century cathedral at Bristol; the abbeys at Romsey, Amesbury and St Mary Redcliffe, Edington Priory and St Lawrence at Bradford-on-Avon.

Accommodation is in Philipps House, built in 1817, where in addition to single, twin rooms and dormitories, there's a self-contained suite for four (adults only) consisting of two twin bedded rooms with bath and kitchenette.

Philipps House, Dinton, Salisbury, Wiltshire SP3 5HJ. Telephone: (0722 76) 208. Sponsors: Holiday Fellowship, 142/144 Great North Way, London NW4 1EG. Telephone: (01) 203 3381. Duration: 1 week, July. Price: £72 per person (1981). Includes full board. VAT extra.

For further details of Holiday Fellowship, see under WALKING, *Loch Awe.*

YORKSHIRE, York

Yorkshire's Minsters and Monasteries
St John's College, York

No other region in England boasts Yorkshire's wealth of monastic remains and outstanding minster churches. On this course, you study in detail York Minster itself, one of Europe's most impressive Gothic churches. There'll be numerous guided visits to the Minster and lectures on its history, stained glass, the Cistercian Order in Yorkshire and the general development of medieval monasticism as expressed in art and architecture. You'll also make a number of excursions to outstanding buildings such as the spectacular abbey ruins of Fountains and Rievaulx, Mount Grace and the minster churches of Beverley, Howden and Ripon. It's hoped to include a visit to Ampleforth too, to see how a present day Benedictine abbey works.

Association for Cultural Exchange, 9 Emmanuel Road, Cambridge CB1 1TW. Telephone: (0223) 65030. Duration: 11–18 July. Price: £110 per person (est). Includes tuition, 4 nights accommodation, dinner, bed, breakfast and two lunches, all visits, return travel from London. No VAT.

See also ARCHITECTURE, THEATRE GOING.

CIGARETTE WITHDRAWAL

HERTFORDSHIRE, Tring

Cigarette Withdrawal
Champneys at Tring

Kick the nicotine habit at Champneys.
This luxuriously appointed health centre,
set in 170 acres of rolling hillside 600 feet
up in the Chilterns, provides a smoking
withdrawal course supervised by experts.
The treatment, run by former stockbroker
Ian Hutchinson, lasts an hour a day for
four days. It's the aversion method which
has proved highly successful in the United
States. Hutchinson's method concentrates
on attacking the psychological urge to
smoke rather than any physical need.

According to him, in spite of the fact that
nicotine is addictive it need only take two
cigarette-free days for physical cravings
to disappear.

Champneys is one of the best equipped
health and beauty centres in the country.
Facilities include a heated indoor pool,
saunas, physiotheraphy unit, a fully
equipped gymnasium and a beautician's
department. In the evening there are
films, talks and fashion shows to help
take your mind off lighting up. The price
quoted is for the full health course; cigarette withdrawal is just one of the many
programmes available.

*Champneys at Tring Health Resort, Tring,
Hertfordshire HP23 6HY. Telephone:
(044 27) 73155/6 or (044 27) 3351. Duration: all year, 7 days or longer (usually
Sunday to Sunday). Price: singles £200–
£310 per week (est). Includes four-poster
bed, private bath, diets, treatments and all
meals. VAT extra.*

See also HEALTH AND BEAUTY.

CINEMA AND VIDEO

CHESHIRE, Burton

Video Workshop
Burton Manor College

Burton Manor, an adult short-course college, is a fine Edwardian sandstone mansion built by Henry Gladstone, son of the Prime Minister. Set in twenty acres of attractive gardens and parkland, it has a hard tennis court, a putting green and a croquet lawn, all available to course members. You can study a wide range of subjects – creative, recreational and academic – in this lovely building, now equipped with all the amenities of a good hotel. There's a fully licensed bar and wine is available in the dining room. Most bedrooms are singles but there are some doubles. All are equipped with washbasins, bedside lamps, electric razor sockets and central heating.

Beginners and those with some experience – as well as professional actors – can benefit from the video workshop. Instructors Allan Kingsbury and Siri Taylor will lead a small group in the production of a television play or drama programme from first reading through to final take. You'll cover technical aspects of production such as camera work, vision and sound mixing, microphones, editing, graphics and lighting, using a variety of video equipment.

Burton Manor College, Burton, Wirral, Cheshire L64 5SJ. Telephone: (051) 336 2262. Principal: Allan Kingsbury. Duration: 13–15 February. Price £30 per person (est). Includes tuition, full board (twin room) and VAT.

See also ASTRONOMY, DANCE, ECOLOGY, FURNITURE RESTORATION, GARDENING, LANGUAGES.

DORSET, Bournemouth

Video Production Course
The Video School

Make your own movie at home or for business. These courses are aimed at the serious amateur film maker, though no previous experience is necessary. The course takes you step by step through the procedures of shooting, with indoor and outdoor lighting, simple sound mixing, interview techniques and basic editing. The small classes (three or four people) ensure individual attention and give you a chance to bring up specific problems. The modern equipment is of professional standard and its use is included in the fee. The organizers try to avoid the use of technical jargon – thus enabling you to pass on what you learn to colleagues. It's an ideal course for adventurous executives with imaginative video schemes in mind.

The school is two minutes from the sea and less than twenty minutes drive from the New Forest and the fine countryside of Dorset and Hampshire. Field trips are organized if weather permits. Accommodation arranged in various local hotels is included.

The Video School, 36 Lorne Park Road, Bournemouth, Dorset BH1 1JL. Telephone: (0202) 28786. Director: Paul St John Misso. Duration: weekends all year. Price: £95 (est). Includes 1 night in single room, breakfast, course, and VAT.

EIRE, COUNTY CORK, Cork

Cork Film Festival

See the stars and the best new films on pre-release at one of Europe's best-known film festivals. Don't miss the fringe events because they too will show you what's being done by amateurs and independents.

This all-inclusive holiday is a package which gives free membership of the Film Festival Club (where the stars let their hair down under the influence of Irish hospitality), bed and breakfast for eight nights (twin accommodation) in a registered guest house, free transfer to and from your accommodation on arrival and departure and tickets to all the Festival's main screenings. Founded in 1955 by Dermot Breen, the Cork Film Festival attracts many actors and actresses as well as devotees who come because of the lively atmosphere and the chance to talk shop. This is one of those rare opportunities for the film buff to meet the film maker.

Ross Anderson, Cork Film Festival, 38 MacCurtash Street, Cork, Eire. Telephone: (021) 502221. Duration: 8 days, October. Price: £87 per person (est). Includes tickets to all major screenings, membership of Film Festival Club, transport to and from lodgings on arrival and departure, 8 nights bed and breakfast in a registered guest house, service and VAT. £155 (est) for same deal but with 8 nights bed and breakfast in a Grade A hotel.

KENT, Canterbury

Film Summer School
University of Kent

If you're a film buff, here's your chance to explore the ins and outs of independent film-making. You'll examine its relationship to mainstream and avant garde cinema and look critically at the political and aesthetic significance of independent cinema's history. You don't need specialist knowledge but should be willing to do some preparatory reading from suggested background texts to get the most from the lectures and numerous film screenings (at the Institute's fully equipped theatre). Regular staff will conduct most seminars. They are supplemented by additional tutors with particular areas of expertise.

Accommodation is on campus in modern single study bedrooms. A limited number of £30 bursaries are available for UK students and the unemployed.

The British Film Institute, Education Department, Summer School, Secretary, 81 Dean Street, London W1V 6AA. Telephone: (01) 437 4355. Duration: 1 week, late July to August. Price: £100 per person for UK students (est), £130 for overseas students (est). Includes all tuition and full board.

CLAY MODELLING

SHROPSHIRE, Ludlow

Clay Modelling
Ashford Studio

Stephen Coote is a working sculptor and trained teacher who lives in a 16th century Tudor farmhouse in this quiet Shropshire village. In his adjoining studio, once a cart-shed, he runs a flexible and informal programme of clay modelling and plaster-casting for beginners, cold casting in resin bronze, and vinyl or silicone rubber moulding for the more advanced. To take full advantage of these advanced techniques you should bring along one or two finished models ready for casting. Either full or half-day classes are available. Demonstrations and talks are followed up with practical work, so you'll go home at the end with a sculpture you've made yourself as a souvenir of the holiday. You can also take home moulds and casts. Courses are restricted to four students so there is plenty of individual attention.

Students stay *en famille* with the Cootes. There's a large twin-bedded room with private bathroom, and two single rooms with hand basins.

Ashford Studio, Ashford Carbonell, Ludlow, Shropshire SY8 4BX. Telephone: (058474) 314. Proprietors: Stephen and Sheila Coote. Duration: 1 week, April to October. Price: £115 per person (est); £105 (est) if you book before 31 March. Includes tuition, all materials – except silicone rubber (optional) – and full board from Sunday dinner to Saturday breakfast.

CLIMBING

HIGHLAND, Aviemore

Rock Climbing
Glenmore Lodge

Glenmore Lodge, near Aviemore, is the Scottish Sports Council's National Training Centre. It aims to foster high standards in mountaineering, skiing, canoeing and sailing by training the already-skilled as instructors, and by introducing novices to these sports. The Lodge, in the foothills of the Cairngorms, was the first purpose-built outdoor activity centre in Britain. It accommodates sixty people in rooms for four and boasts a comfortable lounge, library, lecture room, shop, laundry and showers. You can buy a complete range of technical equipment from the Lodge store or bring your own. One essential is a good standard of physical fitness.

The 1980 rock climbing programme included an introductory course where novices could learn belaying, ropework, protection systems and route planning. After preliminary work on small cliffs and the Lodge's climbing towers, an expedition was formed to climb multi-pitch routes on larger crags. For the past two years there's been a popular spring course held on sea cliffs in Cornwall with instruction at all grades, and all camping, climbing and cooking gear provided on site. A hut-based course on the Black Cuillin of Skye provided challenging middle standard rock climbing.

Scottish Sports Council, 1 St Colme Street, Edinburgh EH3 6AA. Telephone:

(031) 225 8411. Duration: June to September. Price: £75 (1980) Spring Rock Climbing; £145 (1980) Introductory Rock Climbing; £150 (1980) Skye Rock Climbing. Includes tuition, accommodation, all meals, equipment, in-course transport. VAT extra. Deposit of £20 required. Other activity courses also available, send for brochure. 1981 dates and prices not final at time of going to press.

ISLE OF SKYE, Glenbrittle

1 Basic Rock Climbing
2 Intermediate Rock Climbing
Glenbrittle Youth Hostel

These climbing courses are offered under the auspices of the Scottish YHA. The hostel is ideally situated half a mile from the sea, with easy access to the western side of the Black Cuillin, where aspiring climbers will find some of Scotland's best ascents and ridge walks. Guides are there to help you get the most enjoyment from these mountains. The basic course introduces beginners to modern belaying and protection techniques, such that by the end of the course students can be leading climbs. The intermediate course introduces those with previous climbing experience to self-rescue techniques and the use of advanced equipment. If you want you can have a go at artificial climbing too.

Gerry Ackroyd, Cuillin Guides, Stac Lu, Glenbrittle, Isle of Skye, Highland, Scotland. Telephone: (047 842) 289. Duration: 5 days, 4 April–26 September. Price: 1 £55 per person (1981); 2 £65 per person. Includes instruction and all equipment. Accommodation at Glenbrittle Youth Hostel booked through Cuillin Guides. Price: £1.70 (est) per person per night 16–20 year olds; £2.05 (est) per person per night for over 20s. Includes bed only, cook all own meals. Participants must be members of YHA. Many other courses; write for brochure to Scottish YHA, National Office, 7 Glebe Crescent, Stirling FK8 2JA.

WALES, GWYNEDD, Capel Curig

Rock Climbing
Plas y Brenin

This basic rock climbing course is designed to teach absolute beginners or those with limited experience to feel relaxed and confident with rock and rope. With a ratio of one instructor to two students you get maximum individual attention and a full six days of action in a variety of North Wales' best rock climbing areas. You'll be encouraged to develop your initiative so that by the week's end you should be ready to set off on further rock climbing adventures on your own.

For details of the centre see MOUNTAIN SKILLS.

Booking Department, Plas y Brenin, Capel Curig, Betws-y-Coed, Gwynedd, Wales LL24 OET. Telephone: (06904) 214. Administrator: Roger Orgill. Duration: weekly, April to October. Price: £105 per person per week (1981). Includes tuition, *full board and VAT. Equipment issued free, minimum age 16. Special week for 14–16 year olds, August, September, October. Price: £95 per person per week (1981).*

See also CANOEING, MOUNTAIN SKILLS.

CLOCKS

WEST SUSSEX, Fittleworth

Clock Repair
The Old Rectory

Here's your chance to learn the basics of clock repair in a pleasant relaxed atmosphere. You'll be taught how to clean the mechanism and such esoteric tricks of the trade as the repair of pivots, rebrushing of worn holes and the repair of pallets. Along the way you'll also learn what these terms refer to! Bring along a clock of your own if you wish, so that if you have a long-stopped grandfather clock this is a great opportunity to have it examined by experts.

For details of the Old Rectory see SENIOR CITIZENS: CRAFTS.

The Old Rectory, Fittleworth, Pulborough, Sussex RH20 1HU. Telephone: (079 882) 306. Proprietors: Brenda and Graham Salmon. Duration: 5 days Monday to Friday in September. Price: from £44 per person (1981) in a twin room, from £50 per person in a double room. Materials and VAT extra. Bring a clock.

See also CASTLES AND HISTORIC HOUSES, GENEALOGY, MUSIC, ORNITHOLOGY, QUILTING AND PATCHWORK, SENIOR CITIZENS.

WEST YORKSHIRE, Mickelthwaite

Clock Making
Mickelthwaite Studio Workshops

Teacher Robert Ellwood and his wife Jan, a professional caterer, conduct studio workshops which feature a wide variety of programmes. The clock making course, run by designer-craftsman Brian Franks, will show you how to make your own reproduction, solid hardwood, bracket clock. It's a programme designed for amateur wood workers, and materials are charged at cost. Students are divided into groups of ten to ensure individual attention.

Accommodation, in modernized single and double rooms with hot and cold water, is in the 17th century water mill used for teaching and on two floors of the mill owner's house.

Mickelthwaite Studio Workshops, Holroyd Mill, Beck Road, Mickelthwaite, Nr. Bingley, West Yorkshire. Telephone: (08766) 2464. Proprietors: Robert and Jan Ellwood. Duration: weekend mid-October. Price: £45 per person (est). Includes tuition, equipment and full board in double or twin bed rooms, from Friday dinner to Sunday tea. Materials extra, charged at cost.

See also WOODWORKING.

COLLAGE

WALES, DYFED, Llandysul

Collage
Yr Hen Ysgol

The Welsh hamlet of Aberbanc, near the Teifi Valley, is the perfect unspoilt rural setting for the craft centre owned and run by John and Mary Lloyd-Jones. He's a well-known rug weaver, she's a painter and tapestry weaver whose work has been purchased for both public and private collections. They offer individually tailored weekly courses for eight students in fabric collage, as well as hand-loom and tapestry weaving, spinning, batik, patchwork and painting. Individual instruction is supplemented by an excellent library on painting and textiles and an extensive colour slide collection. The Lloyd-Jones will also take you on visits to local woollen mills and to the Welsh Woollen Industry Museum.

Yr Hen Ysgol, Aberbanc, Llandysul, Dyfed, Wales. Telephone: (0559) 370771. Proprietors: Mary and John Lloyd-Jones. Duration: weekly, 1 June–30 September. Price: £11 per person per day (1981). Includes tuition, lunch and VAT. Self-catering accommodation £5 per day (single). 4 berth caravan £25 per week. Other local accommodation available on request. Transport can be arranged from Carmarthen Station or Newcastle Emlyn bus station.

COLLECTING

HERTFORDSHIRE, Tring

Philatelic Course
Pendley Manor Centre

Fancy something for your stamp collection? Try a philately weekend at Pendley Manor in Hertfordshire. This course of illustrated talks by experts Wally Rodger, Oliver Goodes and others also gives you a chance to display your own collection and possibly catch a glimpse of a few rarities. There's lots of opportunity for informal discussions.

The Pendley Manor Adult Education Centre is set amidst lawns and trees in the quiet Hertfordshsire countryside. Accommodation is in double and single rooms (a limited number) with shared facilities. There's also a dining hall and a licensed bar.

Pendley Manor Centre, Tring, Hertfordshire HP23 5Q2. Telephone: (044 282) 2481. Duration: 23–25 January. Price: £24 per

person. Single room supplement £1.50. Includes tuition, full board. VAT extra.

See also CREATIVE WRITING, GARDENING.

WEST SUSSEX, West Dean

Collecting
1 Antiquarian Books and Book Collecting
2 Collector's Workshop
West Dean College

Bibliophiles flock to Stanley Brett's courses. He's a mine of fascinating information and has trouble escaping eager questioners at the end of his classes. You'll study pre-1800 books, with reference to the skills, tools and materials used by early printers and binders. Aspects of collecting such precious items will also be discussed. Bring your own books for examination and discussion.

Bernard Price is your host for the Col-lectors' Workshop. He'll give a series of illustrated talks on furniture, pottery, porcelain, books, paintings, water colours and silver. Again, you're welcome to bring items for identification and discussion.

For details of West Dean College, see ART APPRECIATION.

West Dean College, West Dean, Chichester, West Sussex PO18 0QZ. Telephone: (024363) 301. Duration: 1 6–8 March; 2 27 February–1 March. Price: £39.50 per person (1981). Includes tuition, full board and VAT. Single room supplement £3.

See also ART APPRECIATION, CALLIGRAPHY, CANEWORK, THEATRE GOING, UPHOLSTERY.

Cookery

BERKSHIRE, Winkfield

Residential Cookery Courses
Winkfield Place

This is a good chance to do some really creative cooking and enjoy a holiday at Winkfield Place, a charming Georgian country house, at the same time. Up to forty men and women spend three mornings of the course on practical cookery, working in pairs to prepare a three course meal. A typical menu might be cream of cucumber soup, spiced fish with stuffed tomatoes, petits pois and Gateau Chantilly. Voilà – it's lunchtime!

Each afternoon there are demonstrations on how to prepare a dinner party, a buffet supper and a Sunday lunch. One evening is devoted to wine followed by a tasting session. On the fourth day there's a flower arranging demonstration (the school was started by Constance Spry) followed by a practical session – which you needn't attend but extra cooking cannot be substituted.

Winkfield Place is a school, not a hotel, so there are no private bathrooms; some of the larger bedrooms house four to six students during term time. During these courses they're used as singles or doubles. Guests have the use of a hard tennis court and heated outdoor pool. Fees include residence, tuition and materials.

Winkfield Place, Winkfield, Windsor, Berkshire SL4 4RN. Telephone: (034 47) 2904. Secretary: Mrs Beryl Sitch. Duration: 5 days, April, July, August. Price: £107.50 per person (1980). Includes tuition, equipment, materials, full board in a single room from Monday tea to Friday tea, and VAT. £101 (1980) per person for friends sharing twin room. Non-residential fee £70.50. Bring apron, notebook, pencil and flower scissors if you have them. 1981 dates and prices not available at time of going to press. Write for brochure.

DEVON, Chagford

Cookery Courses
Gidleigh Park Hotel

Paul and Kay Henderson sometimes call their imposing Tudor style country house hotel, set in thirty acres of riverside woodland, a restaurant with rooms. They're right. The high standard of cuisine offered by this enterprising American couple has made it one of the most popular restaurants in the West Country. In the four-day course Kay assisted by the hotel's other chef John Webber (former sous-chef at the Dorchester) will instruct up to ten intermediate level household cooks in fundamentals such as stock and pastry doughs, as well as the increasingly

popular nouvelle cuisine. At the end of the course you'll have a repertoire of sixteen to twenty dishes suitable for dinner parties. The emphasis is on practical work rather than demonstration and at the end of the day after a light lunch, you'll dine together on the results of your day's efforts. Each course includes two wine tasting sessions. What's more, by the time you leave you'll have sampled around fifteen different cheeses. The Hendersons also run winter wine tasting weekends; they're fully booked for 1981, but will be repeated every year.

Gidleigh Park Hotel, Chagford, Devon PQ13 8AH. Telephone: (06473) 2225 or 2367. Proprietors: Paul and Kay Henderson. Duration: 4 days, Monday to Thursday, November to March, dates on application. Price: singles £50 per person per day (est), doubles £45 per person per day (est). Includes tuition, equipment, all materials, full board and service. VAT extra.

LONDON

Holiday Cookery Courses
Leith's School of Food and Wine

Prue Leith of cookbook, television and newspaper fame originally opened this school so aspiring students could learn to cook for a living. Now she offers special holiday courses for the serious amateur based on her firm conviction that anyone with intelligence and application can learn to cook remarkably well. Both the one and four week holiday courses are split into beginners and advanced categories. The emphasis in both, however, is on the use of good, fresh ingredients rather than complicated preparation methods.

'Food', as Ms Leith says, 'should make you hungry, not impress you with its ornateness'. Her secrets in buying, preparing and serving food will stand you in good stead ever after.

Leith's School of Food and Wine, 36A Notting Hill Gate, London W11 3HX. Telephone: (01) 229 0177. Registrar: Christine French. Duration: 1 or 4 weeks, 9 January–2 October. Write for course details. Price: £122.50 per person for 1 week, £402.50 for 4 weeks (1981). Includes tuition, materials and literature. Accommodation is not provided. Leith's suggest you contact Mrs Brand at 'Universal Aunts' (Telephone: (01) 730 9834) or Mr and Mrs Macleish of 'Beds and Homes' (Telephone: (01) 637 3251) for recommended hostels and private rooms. Also the Portobello Hotel, 22 Stanley Gardens, London W11 2NE (Telephone: (01) 727 2777) is a 5 minute walk from the school. Price: singles £21–£25 per night (est), includes room with private shower and breakfast. VAT extra.

NORTHAMPTONSHIRE, Brackley

Nicola Cox Cookery Demonstrations
Farthinghoe Fine Wine and Food Ltd

Nicola Cox, 1972 winner of the Sunday Times Cook of Britain competition, offers cooking demonstrations from the specially-designed kitchen in her charming country home at Farthinghoe. Up to twenty-six guests can attend the sessions which include a morning demonstration from 10.00 a.m. to 12.30 p.m., a three-course lunch (including a glass of one of wine merchant husband Simon's fine vintages) and an afternoon session from 2.00 to 4.00 p.m. The demonstrations cover a wide range of subjects; French country cooking, international specialities, game cookery and dinner party dishes can all be tailored to meet your particular interests – and you get to sample Mrs Cox's creations.

They also run residential gourmet weekends, nine guests only, where you'll combine concentrated cooking demonstrations with the opportunity to eat and drink well in the relaxed atmosphere of the Old Rectory. These weekend sessions include a wine talk and tasting before your gourmet four-course dinner. The Coxes arrange local accommodation for non-residential courses.

Farthinghoe Fine Wine and Food Ltd, Old Lane, Farthinghoe, Brackley, Northamptonshire. Telephone: (0295) 710018. Proprietors: Nicola and Simon Cox. Duration: 1 day, February to June, October to December. Price: £10.30 per person (1980). Includes 2 demonstrations, lunch and VAT. Accommodation list available on request. 1981 programme not final at press time. Send SAE for brochure.

CREATIVE WRITING

CAMBRIDGESHIRE, Burwell

Song Writing Course
Burwell House

Country and Western is one of the most distinctive forms of music to emerge from America. If you're a honky tonk fan, this is an opportunity to study country and western song writing under the expert tutelage of Terry McKenna, 1978 and 1979 winner of the Country Music Songwriter of the Year award. The course covers all aspects of songwriting so you can concentrate on your own main areas of interest. Song construction, styles and patterns, song publishing, recording rights, plagiarism protection, and how to make demo tapes will all be discussed. Participants should be able to play guitar or piano.

The course is held at Burwell House, an attractive 19th century house set in three acres of gardens and maintained as a short-term residential education centre. It retains the friendly atmosphere of a large family house and accommodates up to twenty-four students.

Burwell House, Burwell, Cambridgeshire CB5 0BA. Telephone: (0638) 741 256. Warden: Michael Pike. Duration: 27–29 March. Price: £29.90 per person per weekend (1981). Includes tuition, full board and VAT.

DEVON, Beaworthy
WEST YORKSHIRE, Hebden Bridge

Writing Courses
1 Totleigh Barton, Devon
2 Lumb Bank, West Yorkshire
The Arvon Foundation

Arvon is an exciting venture devised, directed and entirely conducted by established artists. Its aim is simple: to provide an opportunity for small groups of up to fifteen to meet, consult and live with two artists (novelists, poets, playwrights, painters or musicians). The atmosphere is completely informal and everyone pitches in to help with the cooking and daily chores. Artists who've already participated include Beryl Bainbridge, David Benedictus, Ted Hughes, Brian Patten and Alan Sillitoe. Some of the writers who'll be acting as tutors in 1981 include Melvyn Bragg, Fay Weldon, Stan Barstow and Anthony Thwaite. All courses run five days (usually Thursday to Tuesday) and there are about thirty a year, mostly held between May and October. You can discuss your work daily with the tutors and in the evenings everyone gets together to read their own material or extracts from the works of artists of their choice.

In Devon you stay at Totleigh Barton, a large thatched farmhouse dating from the 11th century set in isolated farmland on the River Torridge. It's been fully renovated, has central heating and a well-equipped kitchen, stonne-flagged main dining rooom with refectory table, a library and a lounge. A barn has been

converted for use as a performance studio.

Lumb Bank in Yorkshire is a 19th century mill owner's house owned by poet Ted Hughes. It's set in twenty acres of steeply sloping pasture land which runs down to a thickly wooded valley. The house has been fully modernized and accommodates up to sixteen in three bunk-bedded rooms. An adjacent barn has been converted into a workshop/studio.

1 The Arvon Foundation, Totleigh Barton, Sheepwash, Beaworthy, Devon EX21 5NS. Telephone: (040923) 338. 2 The Arvon Foundation at Lumb Bank, Heptonstall, Hebden Bridge, West Yorkshire HX7 6DF. Telephone: (042284) 3714. Duration: 5 days April to October. Price: £55 per person (est). Includes tuition, full board.

HERTFORDSHIRE, Tring

Creative Writing
Pendley Manor Centre

Only fifteen applicants will be accepted for this course to ensure individual attention from the distinguished tutor Dr Roger Manville, a visiting Professor of Film from Boston University. He has over forty books to his credit including biographies of Charlie Chaplin, Sarah Siddons and Annie Besant and has written many radio and television scripts.

Pendley Manor is an impressive country mansion now maintained as an adult education centre. You have use of spacious formal gardens, a lounge, TV room and the cellar bar. Its gracious cultured atmosphere has been the setting for adult education courses since 1945.

Pendley Manor Centre, Tring, Hertfordshire HP23 5QZ. Telephone: (044 282) 248. Duration: 29 June–3 July. Price £45 (est) per person. Includes tuition and full board, single room supplement £1.50. VAT extra.

See also COLLECTING, GARDENING.

LEICESTERSHIRE, Loughborough

Craft of Writing
Loughborough University

If you've got a way with words this course is designed to help you clarify your ideas about the whole range of aims and methods of writing. Mrs July Burrows of the Open University will lead tutorials, writing and study periods and seminars for the reading of your work (always optional). You'll examine passages from published works for content and technique but the main emphasis is on writing as an art. There'll also be some tips on commercial aspects plus two guest lectures from professional writers. (It's not essential to have a typewriter but if you have a portable bring it along.)

For details of accommodation see SCULPTURE.

Centre for Extension Studies (BR), University of Technology, Loughborough, Leicestershire LE11 3TU. Telephone: (0509) 63171 extension 249/213. Duration: 2–8 August. Price: £105 per person per week (est). Includes tuition, full board and VAT.

See also CAR MAINTENANCE, NEEDLEWORK, SCULPTURE.

SUSSEX, Chichester

Writers' Workshop
The Earnley Concourse

This weekend series runs throughout the year. After the 'Introductory Writers' Workshop' in May, each subsequent course looks at a separate theme. In turn, these cover the Novel, Freelance Writing, Poetry and the Radio Story, followed by a writers' forum for newly-published authors.

For details of the Concourse see ANTIQUES.

The Earnley Concourse, Nr. Chichester, Sussex PO20 7JL. Telephone: (0243) 670392/670326. Duration: 2 or 4 days, April to January. Write for details. Price:

£40 (est) (2 days), £70 (est) (4 days) per person. Includes tuition, accommodation (in twin room with bath) and all meals. VAT extra.

See also ANTIQUES, FLOWER ARRANGING, FOLK/JAZZ, LANGUAGES, MUSIC, PUPPETRY, SURVIVAL TRAINING, WINE TASTING.

WARWICKSHIRE,
Stratford-upon-Avon

Creative Writing Weekend
The Fold

There are two courses here, both valuable for aspiring and for published writers. The weekend begins with a convivial Friday evening dinner, followed by a lively *conversazione*. Sessions will be held on Saturday morning and evening as well as Sunday morning, leaving two after-noons free for your own writing, or for more informal discussions. Bring along your own work – short stories or poetry perhaps – if you'd like to discuss these, or come as a sympathetic listener or critic.

For details of Holiday Fellowship see WALKING, *Loch Awe.*

Holiday Fellowship, 142/144 Great North Way, London NW4 1EG. Telephone: (01) 203 3381. Leader: Trude Dub. Duration: weekend 3–5 April. Price: £26–£27 (1981). Includes tuition, accommodation and all meals (from Friday dinner to Sunday lunch). VAT extra.

See also BOWLS, BRASS RUBBING, ECOLOGY, FOLK MUSIC, GENEALOGY, JEWELLERY, ORIENTEERING, THEATRE GOING, WALKING, YOGA.

CROCHET

NORTHAMPTONSHIRE, Irchester

Crochet with James Walters and Sylvia Cash
Knuston Hall

If you're proficient at crocheting established patterns but want to express yourself your tutors James Walters and Sylvia Cash will encourage latent creative talents. You'll deal mainly with the techniques of crochet but also study selection of yarns and be introduced to handspinning and home-dyeing. Bring examples of your own work (even if unfinished) if you have any, for discussion at the introductory session, as well as a range of crochet hooks, scissors, tape measure, needle, notebook and pencil and as many odd balls of yarn as you can for experimenting.

Both your tutors, who've worked as partners since 1977, are crochet designers. They specialize in imaginative and exclusive clothes for individual clients and often use their own handspun and dyed yarns. They've also collaborated on books and publications, including the comprehensive manual 'Crochet Workshop'. James has appeared on the BBC2 TV series 'Knitting Fashion'.

Accommodation is in bedrooms for two or three with curtained wash-basins.

Knuston Hall, Irchester, Wellingborough, Northamptonshire NN9 7EU. Telephone: (09334) 2104. Principal: I. F. Fraser. Duration: 3–5 April. Price: £23.50 per person (1981). Includes tuition, full board in shared rooms. Bring soap and towel.

CROSS-COUNTRY SKIING

HIGHLAND, Aviemore

Ski Touring,
Categories A, B and C
Highland Guides

If you're of average fitness and enjoy walking, you should enjoy ski touring. Like walking, you take it at your own pace. Until the mid 19th century cross-country skiing was a major form of winter travel in Norway and the forerunner of downhill skiing. (Central Europeans adapted it to suit steep Alpine slopes.) Touring skis are much lighter and thinner than Alpine ones and the boots are much lighter and more flexible; equipment varies according to terrain. The lightest skis, boots and bindings are used for low level, easy terrain while heavier, less flexible equipment is used for hilly country.

All three courses at this Spey Valley centre cover techniques such as diagonal stride and double poling; star, kick, step and skating turns; downhill skiing and, for the more advanced, the telemark. Route planning, snow types and waxing are also included.

Category A is geared to casual hill walkers and families with some hill-walking experience (no skiing experience required). Minimum age thirteen, while those over sixteen can be unaccompanied.

Snow cover permitting, you'll explore the valley forests and the easier slopes and finish with the Great Northern Corries of the Cairngorms.

Category B is designed for regular summer and winter hill walkers, mountaineers and backpackers. Minimum age seventeen, no previous skiing experience necessary. You'll explore hill and mountain country, especially, weather permitting, the high plateaux of the Cairngorms.

If you've completed previous Highland Guides' Ski Touring Courses, or had previous cross-country skiing experience, Category C offers a chance to improve your technique on mountainous terrain. You can join on a daily basis but must do a minimum of three days. It's non-residential but Highland Guides are happy to supply you with a list of nearby accommodation. Average weekly cost of bed and breakfast is £35.

Highland Guides, Inverdruie, Aviemore, Highland PH22 1QH. Telephone: (04 79) 810 729. Duration: Sunday to Friday, January to April. Price: from £16 per person (est). Includes 5 days instruction, guiding, waxes and VAT. 6 days ski hire £14. Anoraks, over-trousers, goggles etc, can be hired. Accommodation list on request (e.g. £38.50 per person per week (est) bed and breakfast).

See also MULTI-ACTIVITY.

CRUISING: COASTAL

AROUND THE BRITISH ISLES

Coastal Cruising
Orpheus

The 353 foot ocean-going luxury cruiser *Orpheus* will transport people round the British coastline in style, complete with daily excursions inland with two distinguished guest lecturers on a tour of some of the country's most outstanding old buildings and gardens. You'll visit the Orkneys, Shetlands, Outer Hebrides, Isles of Scilly and Guernsey; and sites such as Hadrian's Wall, the Ring of Kerry, Caernarvon Castle and the enchanting tropical gardens of Inverewe.

Accommodation aboard fully air-conditioned *Orpheus* is top-quality. Her vast deck space is large enough for every one of her 315 passengers to be on deck in a chaise-longue without feeling crowded. Amenities below include a comfortable library/writing room, beauty salon and boutique. The spacious cabins are designed for two or three occupants, all with showers, WCs (a few have baths), telephone and radio. You embark at Southampton and transport to and from London is included in the coast.

Swan Hellenic, 237/238 Tottenham Court Road, London W1P 0AL. Telephone: (01) 636 8070. Duration: 2 weeks, July. Price: from £605 per person (est). Includes 14 nights in a 3 berth cabin, all meals, excursions, entrance fees, guides, transport London to Southampton. Children under 12, 20% reduction.

See also ARCHAEOLOGY, ARCHITECTURE.

STRATHCLYDE, Kirn

Coastal Cruising in the West of Scotland
West Highland Cruises

Cruise the spectacular scenery of the West Highlands in the comfort of a private yacht. The good ship *Dumaras* accommodates up to twelve guests and provides such civilized comforts as a lounge, dining room, bar (no licensing restrictions), two sun decks, TV, a cassette player and a well-stocked library. Regular cruises include a three-day tour around Mull with overnight stays at Bunessan and Tobermory; a nine-day tour of the Skye coastline; and a nine-day cruise of the Outer Hebrides. New cruises will visit the Isle of Arran and Kyles of Bute and Inverary. The schedules are flexible, so if passengers on the latter trip would like to visit the Duke of Argyll's Inverary Castle home this can be included. All entertainment, except water-skiing, is included and this can also be arranged at a reasonable fee. The boat carries two launches; one for water skiing, the other for fishing. All meals plus afternoon tea and evening hot drink are included.

West Highland Cruises Co, Winclaves, Kirn, By Dunoon, Strathclyde PA23 8DT. Telephone: (0369) 3167. Director: Stuart Balfour Bisset. Duration: April to September. Price: from £60.50 per person (1981) 3

day cruise, to £264 per person (1981) 9 day cruise. Includes entertainment and full board.

WESTERN SCOTLAND

Coastal Cruising in the West of Scotland

The sheltered waters along Scotland's ruggedly beautiful West Coast provide some of Britain's finest sailing. Choose from a variety of cruising holidays for parties of four to six either under sail or by motor yacht, all manned by expert crews. Most boats are available for charter by small groups but individuals can sometimes be accommodated. One trip guaranteed to delight ornithologists is a cruise to St Kilda beyond the Outer Heb-

rides, where thousands of seabirds nest. Historical cruises visit islands such as Iona, where St Columba introduced Christianity to Scotland 1300 years ago, and Gigha, with its spectacular gardens established by Sir James Horlick. You'll also be delighted by the abounding animal and birdlife in these parts. Rates for charter vary according to boat size, from £770 for four upwards for a week, inclusive of accommodation, catering, fuel and crew.

Tourist Promotion (Scotland), 36 Castle Street, Edinburgh EH2 3BN. Telephone: (031) 226 6692. Duration: weekly in season. Price: from £770, four people per week up to £2200, six people per week (est). Includes crew, fuel and full board.

See also FESTIVALS, SHOOTING.

CRUISING: INLAND WATERWAYS

EIRE, COUNTY CLARE, Kildare

Cruising the River Shannon
Corma Cruises of Killaloe

Unwind as you cruise quietly up the River Shannon, whose 160 miles of tranquil inland waters invite you to relax and dream. Corma Cruises rent boats that accommodate from two to six people. They have five basic types of easy-to-handle craft, all fuelled by economical, duty-free diesel and equipped with boarding ladder and complete safety equipment, plus a small dinghy that tows behind. You have your own fresh water system and bedding, towels, cutlery and kitchen equipment are provided. Fishing rods, bicycles and even a skipper are available for hire. The company has a breakdown service arrangement with companies en route in case of emergency. Prices vary seasonally.

Corma Cruises Ltd, Lakeside Marina, Killaloe, County Clare, Eire. Telephone:

(061) 76251. Duration: all year. Price: (Irish pounds) from £295 (est) per 6 berth cruiser per week (low season), to £470 (est) (high season June to August); from £100 (est) per 2 or 3 berth cruiser (low season) to £189 (est) (high season June to August). Fishing rods, bicycles, sailing dinghy and skipper are also available for hire.

EIRE, COUNTY LEITRIM,
Carrick-on-Shannon

Cruising

Carrick Craft operate two marinas on the River Shannon, one at the popular boating centre of Carrick itself, the other further south at Banagher. Cruisers vary in size from the two-berth Dublin Class to the eight-berth Galway and Longford Classes. All have showers, toilets, bedding, gas cooker, hot and cold water, cutlery, electric light and a small refrigerator. Send for their excellent 'Captain's Handbook' which tells you

everything you'll need to know about what to bring and how to run your ship.

The company will transport you to and from Dublin Airport to Carrick-on-Shannon, or to Banagher for £14 return (£7 for children under twelve).

Carrick Craft, PO Box 14, Reading, Berkshire RG3 6TA. Telephone: (0734) 22975. Director: Marie Thomas. Duration: all year. Price: (in Irish pounds) from £285 (1981) per 5 berth cruiser per week (low season), to £495 (1981) per week (high season, 21 June–22 August); from £150 (1981) per 2 berth cruiser per week (low season), to £245 (1981) per week (high season, 21 June–22 August). Includes VAT. Available for hire are bicycles at £8 per week, fisherman's dinghy and outboard for £20 per week.

EIRE, COUNTY LEITRIM,
Carrick-on-Shannon

Shannon River Cruises
Weaver Boats at Carrick-on-Shannon

Cruise a leisurely course through the green heartland of Ireland on one of Europe's finest holiday waterways – the River Shannon. Just ask the skipper to stop along the way if you want to swim, pick wild flowers, fish, sketch, row about in the boat's dinghy, or do some cycling – it's that kind of holiday. Fishing tackle and bicycles can be rented locally, either at Carrick or villages along the way. Average rental prices, £3 per day bicycles, £1 per day, tackle.

'Palo Alto', your specially converted barge, boasts five two-berth cabins, each with hand basin, electric light and ample bedding. There's seven feet of headroom throughout, and the quiet diesel engines provide steady power with no pitch or roll. The cook/hostess on board justly prides herself on feeding passengers well.

The turf-burning stove in the main cabin is often the focal point of an evening or you may want to go ashore to one of the many music pubs along the way.

Weaver Boats Ltd, Carrick-on-Shannon, County Leitrim, Eire. Telephone: Carrick-on-Shannon 204. Director: Donnaca Kennedy. Duration: 1 week Saturday to Saturday, May to September. Price: £520 per week 4 people, £610 per week 6 people, £700 per week 8 people (est). Includes crew and full board and VAT.

NORFOLK

Boating Holiday
Boat Enquiries Ltd

Skipper yourself on Britain's delightful inland waterways, or enjoy the luxury of a hotel-boat cruise. Boat Enquiries Ltd will send you a large, well-illustrated brochure with details of a comprehensive range of cruising holidays and the various craft available. Comforts such as hot and cold running water, baths or showers, a bar, heating and comfortable public lounges are standard on hotel-boats. There's accommodation for eight, ten or twelve passengers in private cabins and a small crew does all the work. If you choose to be your own captain you'll be given full instructions on necessary chores such as working the locks and navigation. No previous experience is necessary – it's not only easy, it's fun.

One example from the many on offer is a six-day cruise on the *Cavendish*, a seventy-foot-long hotel-boat which accommodates ten passengers for a relaxed cruise through the Norfolk Broads. Amenities include a shower, toilet and washbasin in each cabin, full-length wardrobe and dressing table, heaters, sun deck, a well-stocked bar and a wide selection of books. There are many stops along the way to take in local sights and, of course, on the 'Skipper Yourself' holidays you can follow your own whims completely.

Boat Enquiries Ltd, 43 Botley Road, Oxford OX2 OP2. Telephone: (0865) 51161. Director: A. D. MacDonald. Duration: 6 days May to September. Price: £145 per person (1981). Includes full board and VAT.

THAMES VALLEY

Actief Barge Cruising Holidays

What better way to enjoy the scenic Thames Valley than by river cruise. The *Actief* is a luxuriously converted Dutch Steel barge, the largest vessel sailing the Upper Thames. A maximum of twelve passengers can sleep in twin or single rooms or luxury suites. The suites are double the size of the standard cabins and one boasts a king-size double bed. All six cabins contain private toilets, washbasins and showers. You'll enjoy the facilities of a first class hotel and cordon bleu cuisine and fine wines add to the delights of the voyage. The ship cruises at a steady four knots and stops so that you can make daily excursions to some of the manor houses and lovely villages for which the area is famed.

RVS Enterprises (ABC), Hilton House, Norwood Lane, Meopham, Kent DA13 0YE. Telephone: (0474) 812171. Director: Judy Watts. Duration: 6 days, April to October. Price: from £280 per person (est). Includes cruise and full board. VAT extra.

See also CERAMICS.

VARIOUS

Canal Cruising
Galleon World Travel

These cruises operate in conjunction with Inland Waterway Cruises Ltd and cover almost every waterway in the extensive British network. Six narrow boats work in pairs and depart from a different point each week – see Galleon's brochure for a detailed schedule. Each of these 'floating hotels' is gaily painted with traditional floral designs and accommodates up to twelve passengers.

You can help work the locks and swing bridges en route; otherwise just put your feet up and relax. The boat will stop along the way so you can explore villages and visit riverside inns.

You might spend a weekend exploring some of the more isolated canals around Swansea, or the ports of the now disused Glamorganshire canal. On the Monmouthshire, Brecon and Abergavenny canal systems you can visit the Risca Irrigation Centre and the recently restored locks at Cwmbran. You'll also have a chance to cruise the delightfully rural Brecon and Abergavenny Canal.

The cost of the week includes accommodation with private bath at the Royal Hotel, Cardiff, and all meals.

Galleon World Travel Association Ltd, Galleon House, King Street, Maidstone, Kent ME14 1EG. Telephone: (0622) 63411 or (01) 859 0111. Duration: 1 week, 18 April–19 September. Price: £120 per week (1981). Includes accommodation and all meals from Saturday dinner to Sunday breakfast. Extra mandatory insurance of £2.25 per person.

See also ANTIQUES, GARDENS, HISTORY, PONY TREKKING, SURFING.

CURLING

GRAMPIAN, Grantown-on-Spey

Competition Curling
Seafield Lodge Hotel

Curl away your days in the grandeur of the Highlands. The Scafield Lodge Hotel arranges curling breaks in conjunction with the nearby Aviemore Ice Rink just up the valley. Take advantage of the free transport to and from the rink on Saturdays. Each season, there are over half a dozen open competitions ranging from the prestigious Johnny Walker Silver Plate to the Pernod Cup and the Seafield Lodge Trophy. Most of these are open to any four curler team.

Originally a country mansion, this comfortable hotel has a television lounge, bar and sun lounge for your indoor enjoyment. Try your luck on the putting green and there's also excellent local fishing on the River Spey (renowned for its salmon and trout) on the local association's water (open to visitors). A private beat can sometimes be arranged at extra cost. The hotel also runs special fishing holidays, these include instruction for beginners, while Aviemore's nearby ski slopes are a winter attraction for all comers.

Seafield Lodge Hotel, Grantown-on-Spey, Grampian PH26 3JN. Telephone: (0479) 2152. Proprietor: Nigel Grant. Duration: 3 days, Friday to Sunday, November to February. Dates on application. Price: £31–£60 per person (1981). Includes ice charges, transport to and from ice rink on Saturday, lunch on Saturday and 2 nights bed, breakfast and dinner. VAT extra.

TAYSIDE, Kinross

Curling Package
The Green Hotel

Come curling in Kinross. The Green Hotel runs curling packages which include two days full board plus three games of curling and participation in the Weekend Championship (if it's on while you're there).

The hotel, off the M90, is just twenty-five minutes' drive from Edinburgh. There's an indoor 50 foot heated swimming pool, bars, gardens, an 18 hole golf course and, of course, the indoor curling rink. Nearby there's Loch Leven, 3500 acres of fine trout water. Fishing arrangements and hire of equipment can be organized by the hotel at extra cost. Among other facilities nearby (not included) are pony trekking, horse riding, gliding and some of the world's finest golf courses (St Andrews is twenty-four miles away, Gleneagles just sixteen). Kinross House and Loch Leven Castle are both within fifteen minutes drive.

The Green Hotel, Kinross, Tayside, Scotland KY13 7AS. Telephone: (0577) 63467. Manager: D. Wilkie. Duration: 2 days, October to May. Price: £38 per person (1981). Includes 3 games curling and participation, 2 days full board, service and VAT.

CYCLING

NORTH YORKSHIRE

Historic and Scenic Cycle Tour

Pedal your way past the natural beauties of scenic North Yorkshire and use your rest stops to enjoy the splendour of some of the country's most outstanding abbeys and stately homes. You'll be given a suggested itinerary for the eight day/seven night tour and will stay in guesthouses or hotels along the route.

You'll arrive at the guesthouse in Helmsley on Saturday night. It's in a small market town on the edge of the moors and boasts a 13th century castle and a beautiful ghost, reportedly a nun, who haunts Canons Garth, a 16th century building off the market square. Collect your cycle next day and set off for Rievaulx and its spectacular ruined abbey. Over the next six days you'll visit Byland Abbey with its famous stone carvings and glazed tiles; Hutton-le-Hole, with its fine folk museum; Castle Howard, the most magnificent historic home in Yorkshire; the village of Grosmont where you can see old steam and diesel engines being repaired in a large locomotive shed and Dalby Forest where the forest drive laid out by the Forestry Commission treats you to marvellous scenery.

Freedom of Ryedale Holidays, 23a Market Place, Helmsley, Yorkshire YO6 5BJ. Telephone: (0439) 70775. Duration: 8 days by arrangement (starts Saturday) all year. Price: £82 per person (est). Includes 6 days cycle hire, luggage transfer from Helmsley to Pickering, Moorsrail ticket from Gramont to Pickering, map of area and route suggestions; 7 nights bed, breakfast and VAT. Entrance fees extra.

See also RAILWAYS, WALKING.

DANCE

CHESHIRE, Burton

Dance
Burton Manor College

Dancers will find many ways to express themselves in the courses on offer at Burton Manor. For instance, the 1980 Free Dance Workshop, directed by Judy Bird and Brenda Guest, explored ways of becoming fit, supple and relaxed while enjoying yourself in the process. No previous experience of any form of dance technique is necessary because the workshop caters for enthusiasts rather than experts. The 1980 jazz dance course, tutored by Veronica Lewis and guest teachers, welcomed both beginners and those with more dance experience in a programme which combined technique, composition and rhythm sessions. For details of the 1981 courses send SAE for brochure.

For details of Burton Manor see CINEMA AND VIDEO.

Burton Manor College, Burton, Wirral, Cheshire L64 5SJ. Telephone: (051) 336 2262. Principal: Allan Kingsbury. Duration: weekends. Price: £15 per person per day (until April 1981). Includes tuition, full board in twin room and VAT.

See also ASTRONOMY, CINEMA AND VIDEO, ECOLOGY, FURNITURE RESTORATION, GARDENING, LANGUAGES.

DERBYSHIRE, Matlock

Dance History
Nonsuch at Matlock College of Education

Try tripping the light fantastic medieval-style. These courses give students an understanding of the origins of early dance and an impression of the social and historical setting in which they thrived. They're of particular interest to teachers and actors, amateur or professional, who are interested in producing or performing in period plays. Four to six hours of tuition daily includes general classwork (with demonstrations) and practical work in informal groups.

Matlock is surrounded by some of Derbyshire's finest countryside and is within range of several fascinating historic houses. Some afternoon time is left free for excursions, as well as for private study and impromptu music-making.

The college provides accommodation in separate study bedrooms. All meals are self-service in the dining hall and there's a club bar. Other facilities include washing machines, drying room, DIY hairdressing salon and reference library.

Bring comfortable, loose-fitting clothes (leotards and skirts are not obligatory). Dance shoes should have flexible soles and little or no heel. If you have period costume do bring it.

Nonsuch Summer School in Early Dance and Early Music, 16 Brook Drive, London SE11 4TT. Telephone: (01) 735 8353. Manager: Peggy Dixon. Duration: 1 week, beginning 15 August and 22 August. Price: £90 per person (est). Includes tuition and full board in single study bedrooms. No VAT.

DORSET, Bournemouth

Come Dancing
Highcliffe Hotel

Learn the latest dances and add new steps to your old favourites. Respond each morning to coaching in the intricacies of modern ballroom dancing, Latin American favourites and the latest disco crazes. All levels are catered for. After dinner till midnight there's an opportunity to show off your new moves to the music of a live band.

The large hotel overlooks the bay. There's a games room, indoor/outdoor play areas and a nanny service. One of the three bars is strategically placed beside the heated open air pool. If you've got any surplus energy after a day on the dance floor, the sauna, solarium, 9 hole putting green and tennis court should keep you busy. Each bedroom has TV, radio, and tea and coffee making facilities.

Highcliffe Hotel, West Cliff, Bournemouth, Dorset BH2 5DU. Telephone: (0202) 27702. General Manager: Christopher Smith. Duration: weekends, January to April. Price: £45.50 per person (1981). Includes coaching, full board, Friday dinner to Sunday lunch, service and VAT. Children under 12 sharing parents' room are free.

See also GOLF, HEALTH AND BEAUTY.

LANCASHIRE, Chorley

Weekend of Dance
Lancashire College

This weekend offers you an opportunity to enjoy dance in its many forms. Of particular interest to dance students and teachers, it also caters for those who are interested in dancing just for fun. Course Director Barbara Lipscomb will lead you through an exploration of traditional, modern, classical and contemporary dance forms by means of practical work which combines technical discipline and free expression.

For details of Lancashire College see WINE TASTING.

Lancashire College, Southport Road, Chorley, Lancashire PR7 1NB. Telephone: (025 72) 76719. Courses Secretary: Jill Calder. Duration: weekend in October. Price: £29 per person (est). Includes tuition, full board. No VAT. Lancashire residents £2 reduction.

See also LANGUAGES, WINE TASTING.

DISABLED

CORNWALL, Bodmin

Education and Adventure Holidays
Churchtown Farm Field Studies Centre

At Churchtown Farm even the most severely disabled can sail a yacht, paddle a canoe, climb rocks or go hiking. The centre is a specially converted farm which accommodates forty-eight students in four-bedded rooms in a mixture of purpose-built residential blocks and converted traditional stone barns. There's a well-equipped laboratory, a classroom with visual aids, a library and a photographic dark room. The dining hall and common room are in the old barn area and there's an indoor heated pool. All buildings are linked by the imaginative use of ramps and a covered concourse. A well-laid path system means wheelchair users can move freely in the grounds, where you'll find a nature reserve with pond and bird hides and a botanic garden.

At Puddle Farm, a short walk away, you can see cows, sheep, pigs, goats and a small milking parlour. The farm allows groups to become involved in the day to day activities of agricultural life. There are no age limits and all degrees and types of handicaps are accepted. (The very severely disabled should be accompanied by an assistant.) Courses are taught in environmental sciences and a wide range of natural history subjects, rural studies and adventure and leisure pursuits. Outdoor activities concentrate on water sports such as boating, canoeing, fishing and sailing – all take place on the nearby River Fowey. Rock climbing is taught at Bodmin Moor and pony treks are made to the moor and the coast. Hiking and camping often feature in these courses. Field study courses take students to the seaside, moor, ponds and woods. Birdwatching, photography, pottery, painting and enamel work are available along with many other activities.

Churchtown Farm Field Studies Centre, Lanlivery, Bodmin, Cornwall. Telephone: (0208) 872148. Warden: Dr Mike Cotton. Duration: Wednesday to Wednesday all year, course dates on application. Price: £50 per person per week (November to February), £80 per person per week (March to October) (1981). Includes tuition, accommodation, all meals, transport from nearest station and VAT. Reduction for children. For full details, send SAE for brochure.

CUMBRIA, Keswick

Disabled
The Calvert Trust Adventure Centre

Here's an opportunity for the disabled to safely explore a wide range of outdoor activities in one of the country's most spectacular and scenic outdoor recreation areas. The centre is a traditional Cumbrian building specially adapted to accommodate mixed groups of up to twenty-seven, in two and three bedded rooms. It's designed for wheelchairs, and plenty of staff and helpers are on hand. Amenities include specially adapted bathrooms, showers, two dining rooms, a lounge (with TV), a well-stocked library and a large games hall. You'll enjoy the panoramic views of Bassenthwaite Lake and nearby fells.

The centre is open mid-January to mid-November for archery, angling, birdwatching, hill walking and nature trails (many of the trails take wheelchairs). Canoeists have the use of single and double canoes, and equipment for groups of up to twelve; while sailing courses give an all-round introduction to boating. Riding instruction is given in indoor and outdoor training areas; there's swimming in a heated indoor pool; and rock climbing instruction takes place on a nearby crag where enthusiasts can learn basic principles such as rope handling and belays. Films and talks on a wide variety of topics are part of the evening programme. If you play a guitar or other musical instrument, bring it along for evening sing-alongs.

The Calvert Trust Adventure Centre, Little Crossthwaite, under Skiddaw, Keswick, Cumbria CA12 4QD. Telephone: (0596) *72254. Warden: Emrys Evans. Duration: February to November. Price: standard course £76 per person (est), Saturday to Friday. Midweek course £50.60 per person (est), Monday to Friday. Weekend course £25.30 per person (est), Saturday and Sunday. Includes tuition, full board and VAT. Each group or individual will require to be accompanied by care staff/helpers in an adequate ratio to their needs.*

DISTILLERIES

GRAMPIAN

Whisky Trail
1 Glenfiddich
2 Glenfarclas
3 Tamdhu
4 Strathisla

Take to the Whisky Trail through the Scottish countryside. This particular sixty-two mile trail takes in four malt whisky distilleries in the Grampian region, and can last from four to six hours, depending on your stamina, and how many distilleries you wish to see. At each distillery, you'll be conducted round by knowledgeable guides, and be able to sample their wares. There's also a chance to visit the lovely village of Tomintoul, one of the highest in Scotland.

Department AHC, Department of Leisure, Recreation and Tourism, Grampian Regional Council, Woodhill House, Ashgrove Road West, Aberdeen AB9 2LU, Grampian. Telephone: (0224) 682222. Duration: 1 all year, Monday to Friday 10.00 a.m. to 12.00 p.m., 2.00 p.m. to 4.00 p.m.; 2 all year, Monday to Friday 9.00 a.m. to 4.30 p.m.; 3 May to September, Monday to Friday 10.00 a.m. to 12.30 p.m., 1.00 p.m. to 4.30 p.m.; 4 June to September, Monday to Friday 9.30 a.m. to 11.30 a.m., 1.00 p.m. to 4.00 p.m. Accommodation list on request.

DO-IT-YOURSELF

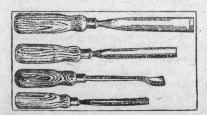

HAMPSHIRE, Ower

DIY Laminating
New Forest Lodge

Home handymen have a chance to explore the many possibilities of formica, particularly how to cut, bond and trim this versatile, durable material. De-

monstrations will suggest how to make the best use of it at home.

On the edge of the New Forest, the lodge is known as Vine Inn to the locals, a name which dates back to its 16th century origins. Your cordial hostess, Penny Cooke, gets the course off to a friendly start with a sherry reception.

DIY Weekends, 7 Stratford Place, London W1A 4YU. Telephone (01) 629 6618 ext 220. Co-ordinator: Lydie Bielak. Duration: weekend, 16–18 January. Price: £49.90 per person (1981). Includes course, full board in twin room with bathroom, service and VAT.

See also ORNITHOLOGY.

OXFORDSHIRE, North Stifford

Do-It-Yourself Weekend:
Lighting and Electrical
Oxford Europa Lodge

If the lighting in your home leaves you baffled this course, which offers instruction in basic electrical repair and extension work, will help. The mysteries of flexes, fittings, circuits and fuses are explained and there's discussion on various aspects of good lighting. Roy Day, the host for the weekend, welcomes you with a sherry reception on Friday evening at 7.30 p.m. After dinner he presents a DIY slide show.

The Europa is a modern hotel set in its own attractive grounds near Oxford. Each of the comfortable, gold-toned rooms has a private bathroom, TV, radio, telephone, and tea and coffee making facilities.

DIY Weekends, 7 Stratford Place, London W1A 4YU. Telephone: (01) 629 6618 ext 220. Co-ordinator: Lydie Bielak. Duration: weekend, 30 January–1 February. Price: £47.50 per person (1981). Includes course, full board (twin room with bathroom), service and VAT.

DRAMA

BERKSHIRE, Eton

Theatre Courses
1 Shakespeare
2 Modern Theatre
3 Drama Studio Games
Eton College

These are all half-day courses, although you can combine two to make a full day's programme or substitute half-day instruction for any of the school's many sports activities (see ARCHITECTURE for details).

The Shakespeare course provides a lively introduction to the work of the Bard and should appeal to non-experts from sixth formers to mature students.

Modern Theatre deals with the theory and practice of directing, acting, lighting and design. You'll look at key writers, major theorists such as Stanislavski and contemporary directors such as Peter Brook.

The Drama Studio Games will give you a chance to work out improvisations and flex your theatrical muscles in a delightfully informal group.

Independent Summer Schools, Southfield, Bath Road, Marlborough, Wiltshire SN8 1PA. Telephone: (0672) 54222. Director: Brian Ashley. Duration: Sunday to Saturday, August, Price: £150 (est). Includes full board, single room, tuition, service and VAT. Children under 17 must be accompanied by an adult.

See also ARCHITECTURE, LITERATURE.

GLOUCESTERSHIRE, Cheltenham

Drama

1 Adult Summer School
2 Junior Summer School
1 St Mary's and St Paul's Colleges
2 St Paul's College

The British Theatre Association offers valuable year-round courses in all aspects of theatre – acting, stage management, production, design, lighting, make-up, voice and movement. The junior summer school is a seven day residential course for over-fourteens held at St Paul's College. The adult residential course for actors, directors and stage managers is held at both St Paul's and St Mary's Colleges.

British Theatre Association, Training Department, 9 Fitzroy Square, London W1P

6AE. Telephone: (01) 387 2666. Organizers: Peggy White (Junior Course), Jane Hackworth-Young (Adult Course). Duration: 1 13–22 August; 2 22–29 July. Price: 1 £150 per person (1981); 2 £100 per person (1981). Includes tuition, full board and VAT.

DRESSMAKING

AVON, Bath

Dressmaking

Under the auspices of the Association of British Craftsmen Deirdre Trenchard teaches dressmaking to beginners and intermediate students. She also spins and weaves, does batik, and natural and chemical dyeing in the large, well-appointed studio attached to her elegant Georgian house up behind Bath's famous Royal Crescent. You're sure to have a memorable week in this cultured attractive home, furnished with fascinating antiques and *objets d'art*. Count on at least four hours' instruction a day and stay in either the double or single bedroom reserved for course members. Full details of how, when and where to arrive will be sent to you once you've booked your week with Deirdre.

Avocations (Bristol Crafts) Ltd, 37 Coombe Bridge Avenue, Bristol, Avon BS9 2LT. Telephone: (0272) 686417. Director: Gerald Richardson. Duration: 1 week, all year. Price: £117 per person per week (1981). Includes tuition, use of equipment, full board twin; single supplement 15% extra. No VAT.

See also BATIK, ENAMELLING, NEEDLEWORK, STAINED GLASS, TAPESTRY, WOODWORKING.

CUMBRIA, Bassenthwaite Lake

Adapting to Fashion
Higham Hall

In a follow-up to her successful TV series, Betty Foster will personally show you how to create your own fashions from a basic master pattern. The course is suitable if you're a beginner but want to get off to a good start. All necessary equipment will be supplied.

For details of Higham Hall see ART APPRECIATION.

Higham Hall, Bassenthwaite Lake, Cockermouth, Cumbria CA13 95H. Telephone: (059 681) 276. Warden: Peter Hadkins. Duration: 13–15 March. Price: £24 per person (1981). Includes tuition, 2 nights accommodation, all meals. Cumbrian residents £2 reduction. Minimum age 18.

See also ART APPRECIATION, MUSIC, WAR GAMES.

DEVON, Beaworthy

Dressmaking
Lower Forda

Lower Forda is a charming 300-year-old farm cottage complete with sheep, ducks, pigs, chickens, a large orchard, a soft fruit garden and a vegetable garden. Your resident hostess, Nina Skinner, makes skilful use of all these assets and produces her own butter, cream and cheese. She's also experienced in candlemaking, crochet, canework and spinning. Mrs Skinner,

who has taught crafts in North Devon Community Centres for over nine years and is a qualified City and Guilds cook, has other qualified tutors to help and demonstrate at her 'Learn a Craft' courses.

The atmosphere's homely and relaxed at Lower Forda. The structured format is the timetable – you'll work from Monday to Thursday from 9.30 a.m. to 12.30 p.m. and also in the evenings. In addition to dressmaking you can try soft-toy making, rag dolls, gingham embroidery and patchwork. There isn't much demand for spinning but if you're interested Mrs Skinner will be delighted to pass on her skills.

Lower Forda, Shebbear, Beaworthy, North Devon. Telephone: (04 0928) 218. Principal: Nina Skinner. Duration: 6 days, April to September. Price: from £75 per person (1981). Includes 4 days tuition and full board. Materials and outings extra. Transport from coach stop 25p per person.

See also QUILTING AND PATCHWORK.

KENT, Folkestone

Dressmaking Summer School
1 Design your own Clothes
2 Dress Design Workshop
Shepway Arts Centre

The Arts Centre, part of the Shepway Adult Education Centre, holds regular exhibitions of contemporary artists and craftsmen, including such notables as Jacob Epstein and Henry Moore. It also presents regular professional chamber and choral concerts, plus lectures, films, drama and poetry readings. And it offers the use of a wide range of excellently equipped studios to people of all ages from rank beginners to the very experienced from age ten upwards. All tutors are qualified, practising artists and craftsmen.

The first course mentioned here is run by successful freelance designer Jennifer Bateman, who offers a beginner's course for dressmakers who are competent but haven't yet experimented or created their own designs. There'll be lectures and demonstrations to illustrate how you can evolve a variety of styles from one basic pattern. In 1980, students were asked to bring along Simplicity Pattern No. 7073,

plus pencil, tissue paper, normal sewing aids and a length of material. *Pattern Adaptation*, by Gary Jacobi and Kitty Todor, is a recommended but not essential text book (available from public libraries).

The Design Workshop is an advanced course for those who've done some flat pattern cutting or pattern adaptation. You can work on any form of dress designing you choose – such as using ideas based on sewing machine techniques or designing for a particular type of fabric (border prints or saris, for example). You'll be helped with pattern cutting and making up your garment, but Miss Bateman won't be teaching these skills from scratch. You should bring a basic pattern, normal sewing aids, pencil, tissue paper and fabric.

The Arts Centre, New Metropole, The Leas, Folkestone, Kent CT20 2LS. Telephone: (0303) 55070. Secretary: Sheila Nash. Duration: 1 28 June–3 July; 2 5–10 July. Price: £25 per person per week (est). Includes tuition. Bring sewing aids and material. Accommodation in Folkestone: guest houses £35 (est); hotels £64 (est). Includes breakfast and dinner.

See also JEWELLERY.

ECOLOGY

CHESHIRE, Burton

Local Woodland Ecology
Burton Manor College

In 1980 Dr Robert Bunce led a fascinating look at the complex ecosystem to be found in the nearby woodland. Woodlands both local and national were studied, concentrating mainly on the flora and practical field work was included. The same year, Dr Derek Bell headed a study of plant ecology, illustrating basic principles with the investigation of a

number of contrasting plant communities. Students visited freshwater ponds and streams and woodland and heathland in the Wirral. A description of types of life found was followed up with discussion of experimental results and environmental factors which influence plant distribution. For details of the 1981 course, send SAE for brochure.

For details of Burton Manor see CINEMA AND VIDEO.

Burton Manor College, Burton, Wirral, Cheshire L64 5SJ. Telephone: (051) 336

2262. Principal: Allan Kingsbury. Duration: weekend. Price: £15 per person per day, £17.70 (est) after 1 April 1981. Includes tuition, full board in twin room and VAT.

See also ASTRONOMY, CINEMA AND VIDEO, DANCE, FURNITURE RESTORATION, GARDENING, LANGUAGES.

CORNWALL, Newquay

Ecology
Beaconsfield House

Mrs W. Crowther, well qualified in biological sciences and meteorology, leads a group of twenty-five in the study of a variety of natural habitats. You'll explore the natural course of development from marine environments through dune and salt marsh to woodlands, and you'll go by coach to the Lizard, Fowey, Mousehole, Newlyn and several estuaries. Bring a magnifying glass, identification books, clipboards and plastic bags for specimen collecting.

Beaconsfield House, off the main street in Newquay, overlooks a beautiful bay, and has direct access to the beach opposite the house. Amenities include three lounges and a ballroom. Priority will be given to families with children and meal times can be arranged to suit all ages. Some high chairs and cots are available.

For details of Holiday Fellowship see WALKING, *Loch Awe.*

Holiday Fellowship, 142/144 Great North Way, London NW4 1EG. Telephone: (01) 203 3381. Booking Department. Duration: 1 week, July. Price: from £95 per person (est). Includes full board, instruction, excursions. Service and VAT extra. New members £10 subscription.

See also BOWLS, BRASS RUBBING, CREATIVE WRITING, FOLK MUSIC, GENEALOGY, JEWELLERY, ORIENTEERING, THEATRE GOING, WALKING, YOGA.

CUMBRIA, Sedbergh

The Ecology of Caves
Whernside Cave and Fell Centre

The cave as a living environment is a subject often neglected by the sporting caver. This weekend is a lively introduction to the fascinating life to be found in caves, how lifeforms survive in such a daunting environment and the factors that affect them. Suitable for cavers and for fit naturalists.

For details of Whernside see CAVING AND POTHOLING.

Yorkshire Dales National Park, Whernside Cave and Fell Centre, Dent, Sedbergh, Cumbria LA10 5RE. Telephone: (05875) 213. Warden: M. K. Lyon. Duration: 3 days, May. Price: £30 per person (1981). Includes tuition, use of equipment, full board and VAT. Transport from Oxenholme Station £2.50 each way (requires 7 days' notice).

See also CAVING AND POTHOLING, WALKING, WILDLIFE.

DEVON, Bovey Tracey

Wildflower Week
Coombe Cross Hotel

Take a fresh look at the delights of the colourful vegetation of the South Devon hills in early summer; river valleys and nearby seashore. You'll be taken by minibus to several sites famous for their very rare flowers. Your guide/lecturer is keen ecologist Mrs Lillian Ghent, a recorder for the Botanical Society of the British Isles. A hand lens is useful, wellington boots vital and a camera worth toting.

Coombe Cross Hotel, Bovey Tracey, Newton Abbot, Devon TQ13 9EY. Telephone: (0626) 832476. Proprietor: Misses Anne and Elizabeth Hebditch. Duration: 7 days 2–9 July. Price: £138 (est) per person. Includes guide, transport in the field, accommodation in twin room (add £10.50 for single and/or private bath), all meals, service and VAT. Bring a hand lens and wellington boots.

See also BRIDGE, CASTLES AND HISTORIC HOMES, GARDENS, ORNITHOLOGY.

WALES, DYFED, Haverfordwest

Seaside Ecology
Dale Fort Field Centre

This centre runs one-week courses throughout the year on different aspects of ecology. There are too many to list but topics include 'The Atlantic Islands', with a visit to Lundy to study the seabirds (suitable for beginners); 'Seaweeds and Seashores', a course for informed amateurs who'll examine various shores around Dale Fort; 'Studies on Ancient and Modern Sediments of Pembrokeshire', designed for students with some geological training; and 'Ecology of Seabirds', advanced courses for teachers, university students and the informed amateur ornithologist on the breeding biology of seabirds. On this one you'll visit the offshore islands of Skomer and Skokholm in the centre's boat. The emphasis in the first part of this course is on seabirds while songbirds and the techniques of bird-ringing are considered in the second.

Students stay at Fort Dale, a converted fort on a narrow peninsula jutting into the Atlantic. The rugged coastline makes this an ideal spot for courses such as these. There are double rooms for up to thirty-six visitors; the rest stay in dormitories. Since lunch is always a packed meal be sure to bring a sandwich box and a thermos.

Dale Fort Field Centre, Dale, Haverfordwest, Dyfed, Wales SA62 3RD. Telephone: (064 65) 205. Warden: David Emerson. Duration: 1 week, February to November. Price: £84 per person (1981). Includes tuition, use of all facilities and equipment, and full board in dormitories or double rooms. Transport extra. No VAT. Send to Warden for details of courses and essential equipment to bring; there's a lot.

ENAMELLING

DUMFRIES AND GALLOWAY, Moniaive

Enamelling
Crossford Craft Studios

One of the two studios in this former country school has been converted into a graphics studio for drawing, painting, screen printing and enamelling. The other is now a workshop with potter's wheel, kiln, stone polishing gear and multi-purpose machinery (bench drill, belt, sander, power jigsaw etc.).

It's a casual course – you and ten to twelve other students may spend as much time as you please on any of these crafts, with appropriate tuition. The studio is open from 10.00 a.m. to 9.00 p.m. on weekdays, 10.00 a.m. to 5.00 p.m. at weekends, with tuition available six hours a day – six days a week. If course members are interested the school can arrange visits to local craftsmen's workshops.

Crossford Craft Studios, Schoolhouse, Crossford, Moniaive, Dumfries and Galloway, Scotland. Telephone: (038 782) 410. Proprietor: Duncan Devlin. Duration: 1 week, July to August. Price: £45 per person per week (1981). Includes tuition, and use of studios for 1 week. Students 20% discount. Accompanied children 11–16 50% discount. Accommodation at Crossford £45 per person per week. Includes full board double. At local farmhouse £52.50 per person per week. Includes full board with packed lunch. Self-catering cottages £48 per week sleeping 3 to 6. Camping at studios £3.50 per week.

See also POTTERY.

EAST ANGLIA

Enamelling

Learn enamelling from expert Peter Campbell while staying as a guest in his marvellous 12th century country home – once part of a Benedictine monastery – in a sleepy market village on the Norfolk/Suffolk border. The studio is situated in a converted barn in the extensive grounds. Peter also teaches oil and water-colour painting.

There are two single and two double bedrooms and two bathrooms for the exclusive use of guests plus the run of the large house with its huge farmhouse-style kitchen/dining room, a good library and sitting rooms. Once you've booked your week's course, ABC will send you full details of how to get there.

Avocations (Bristol Crafts) Ltd, 37 Coombe Bridge Avenue, Bristol, Avon BS9 2LT. Telephone: (0272) 686417. Director: Gerald Richardson. Duration: 1 week, all year. Price: £117 per person per week (1981). Includes tuition, full board (twin), single room supplement 15% extra, plus a small supplement for use of enamelling kiln. No VAT.

See also BATIK, DRESSMAKING, NEEDLEWORK, STAINED GLASS, TAPESTRY, WOODWORKING.

FALCONRY

GLOUCESTERSHIRE, Newent

Falconry
Birds of Prey and Falconry Centre

By the close of this twelve-day course, even a complete beginner will know enough about the ancient sport of falconry to be able to cope singlehandedly with a bird. You'll be shown how to train and handle a falcon and study housing, maintenance, health, and breeding birds in captivity.

Birds of Prey and Falconry Centre, Newent, Gloucestershire GL18 1JJ. Director: Philip Glasier. Telephone: (0531) 820286. Duration: 12 days, November to February. Price: £150 per person (est). Includes tuition. Accommodation available at local inn. Price: £15 per person per night, full board.

FARMHOUSE HOLIDAYS

COUNTRYWIDE

Down on the Farm
Country Farm Holidays

A farmhouse holiday is the perfect way to see some of Britain's loveliest countryside. You can enjoy the best of country life – good food, fresh air and wide open spaces – and relax in informal comfort. Children love the atmosphere and the animals, and mums can let someone else do the cooking. (Self-catering holidays are also available.) Your hostess will also be happy to babysit. Country Farm Holidays will send you an attractively illustrated brochure so you can choose from the wide range of places available: idyllic half-timbered cottages, mellow stone buildings, lovingly restored mills, barns and granaries. Swimming pools and tennis courts feature at some locations.

One charming example is Offley Hoo Farm, a 16th century beamed farmhouse nestled in a dell on the edge of the Hertfordshire village of Hitchin. There's a tennis court, a pond for children's fishing and a pony for experienced riders. West Middleton Farm in Yorkshire, by way of contrast, is an impressive 18th century stone-built house on a 107 acre cattle and arable farm. It offers commanding views with trout fishing and rough shooting available on the farm.

Country Farm Holidays, The Place, Ham Lane, Powick, Hereford and Worcester WR2 4RA. Telephone: (0905) 830899. Contact: Andrew Grieve. Duration: all year. Price: farmhouse from £55 per person per week (1981). Includes full board and VAT. Self-catering cottage from £30 per person per week (1981). Reductions for children. Send 20 pence in stamps for brochure.

NORTHERN IRELAND

Farm and Country Holidays

The Northern Ireland Farm and Country House Association puts out an illustrated book on establishments owned and run by members. Mrs S. W. Lyttle in Ballygawley, for example, owns a thatched cottage built in 1720. Now centrally heated, it has three bedrooms for let between May and September. Children and dogs are welcome and babysitting can be arranged.

In Ballyclare Mr and Mrs Bradford's seventeen-acre farm is conveniently close to a leisure centre and golf, fishing and horse riding can be arranged nearby.

Mrs M. McClure at Crumlin runs a modern, centrally heated farmhouse set in fifty-two acres near good trout fishing. Her home baking 'can't be beat'. Two bedrooms are available, one double and one family.

Also in Crumlin, Mr and Mrs A. Peel open their listed Georgian farmhouse and two hundred acres to guests. Amenities include grass tennis courts (with resident tennis coach) and an indoor games room. Open mid-January to mid-December.

Northern Ireland Farm and Country House Holidays Association, Greenmount Lodge, 58 Greenmount Road, Gortaclare, Omagh, County Tyrone, Northern Ireland. Telephone: (066 284) 325. Secretary: Mrs Frances Reid. Duration: some farmhouses open all year. Prices: £4–£8 per person per day for bed and breakfast (est). £6–£11 for bed, breakfast and dinner (est). Write to Secretary for the Association's book, also available from British Tourist Authority and Northern Ireland Tourist Board.

FESTIVALS

EDINBURGH

Edinburgh Festival Budget Holidays

Edinburgh hums in August as the world famous Edinburgh Festival of Music and Drama gets under way. Visitors from all over the world flock to Scotland's capital for the fabulous three-week run of artistic and cultural highlights, making tickets and accommodation hard to come by. You can bypass this problem by choosing a holiday based on recommended private home or guest house, bed and breakfast accommodation for either three or seven nights. These packages include a grand tour of the historic city, particularly the Castle, St Giles Cathedral, the Royal Mile and the Palace of Holyrood House; an unlimited bus travel pass; the choice of one of four other tours of Edinburgh and environs; and a ticket to the spectacular Military Tattoo. A full-day coach tour to Loch Lomond and the Trossachs is also part of the seven day holiday. Book your own tickets for main events – very few theatre tickets are usually available on the night.

Tourist Promotion Scotland, 36 Castle Street, Edinburgh EH2 3BN. Telephone: (031) 226 6692. Duration: 4 or 8 days, 16 August–6 September (1981). Price: £94.80 per person for 8 days (est). Includes transport pass, 1 day coach tour, ticket for Tattoo, 7 nights bed and breakfast (twin rooms in selected guest house or private home) and VAT. 4 days costs £51 per person (est), same deal but for 3 nights only, without the coach tour to Loch Lomond.

See also CRUISING: COASTAL, ROYAL BRAEMAR AND FESTIVALS TOUR, SHOOTING.

LOTHIAN, Dalkeith

Highlights of the Edinburgh Festival
Newbattle Abbey College

These popular long-established courses provide visits to selected performances from the Edinburgh Festival programme preceeded by introductory lectures each morning. You'll also visit one of the principal Festival exhibitions. Fees include all tickets and transport. In 1980 the courses started and finished on a Saturday. After provisional registration you're sent a detailed programme of events and thereafter a non-returnable deposit of £20 is required.

For details of accommodation see
ANTIQUES.

Newbattle Abbey College, Dalkeith, Lothian EH22 2LL. Telephone: (031) 663 1921/2. Duration: weekly, 22 August–5 September. Price: £149.50 per week (est). Includes full board, theatre tickets, transport. No VAT.

See also ANTIQUES, CASTLES AND HISTORIC HOUSES, MUSIC, PAINTING.

SCOTLAND

Royal Braemar and Festivals Tour

This programme gets off to a grand start with a two-day guided tour of Edinburgh, which includes a performance of the world famous Military Tattoo and visits to the Castle and St Giles Cathedral. Then you'll head north by luxury coach to Pitlochry for an evening performance at the Festival Theatre and dinner at the theatre restaurant. Then on to Braemar where you'll enjoy the piping, Highland dancing and caber tossing from reserved seats in the covered stand; the Royal Family often attend. Along the route your party will visit a distillery as well as Blair Castle and Scone Palace.

Tourist Promotion Scotland, 36 Castle Street, Edinburgh EH2 3BN. Telephone: (031) 226 6692. Guide: Jean Duncan. Duration: 7 days, August to September. Price: £313.55 per person (1981). Includes all tickets and entrance fees, transport, 7 nights accommodation in twin rooms with bath (single room supplement £3 per night), all meals and VAT.

See also EDINBURGH FESTIVAL BUDGET HOLIDAYS.

FISHING: COARSE

EIRE, River Shannon

Coarse Fishing in Ireland

The deep, slow-moving Shannon has few equals anywhere in the world as a coarse fishing ground. There are many large lakes on its 160 mile length and its depths yield the legendary Irish pike (these sometimes reach a weight of thirty plus pounds) as well as fine tench, bream, rudd, roach and dace. There's a permanent open season for coarse fishing, although March to October is your best bet. Fishing here is free as it is almost everywhere in the Republic.

Joe Walsh offers a fishing package with a choice of four areas – Tulla, Athlone, Shannonbridge and Ballinasloe; you can choose one, two or all four. The price of the holiday includes a return ticket for you and your car or, if you travel by air, a self-drive Ford Escort with unlimited mileage. Your accommodation can be hotel (with private bath) or guest house. Prices vary with accommodation and season. No permits required.

Joe Walsh Tours Ltd, Ireland House, 150 New Bond Street, London W1Y 0AQ. Telephone: (01) 493 3201. Duration: 6 nights,

all year. Price: doubles £85 to £125 (1980) by sea. Includes return ticket for car (any length) and passengers; 6 nights bed and breakfast. By air £119 to £170 (1980), same deal but includes return air fare from Blackpool or Liverpool (extra from other UK airports) and unlimited mileage in self-drive car. Rod hire can be arranged in advance (approximately £1 per day per rod).

See also GOLF, HORSE-DRAWN CARAVAN.

FISHING: GAME

BORDERS, Coldstream

Game Fishing
The Milne Graden Fishings

The Milne Graden Fishings are close to Coldstream at the junction of Bannock Burn with the River Tweed about fifty miles from Edinburgh. There are four rods on a single-bank beat of seven miles and the use of two boats is included. Although the fishing rights are from the north (Scottish) bank only, you benefit from an arrangement with the Tillmouth Park Hotel by which fishing on two miles of the beat opposite hotel property is permitted for both parties on alternate days.

The area hasn't been fished much recently but knowledgeable local anglers expect a yield of about thirty salmon per season. The beat tends to hold more fish in

the autumn, with the Fairy Well pool your best bet for sea trout in July and August.

The salmon season runs from 1 February to 30 November inclusive. Rights are for fly fishing for the whole season with spinning permitted from 16 February to 14 September. If you need a boatman there's an additional charge of £11 per day. Arrange your own accommodation, possibly in one of the eight self-catering cottages on the estate, some of which are right on the river. All are comfortably furnished and heated with TV and all 'mod cons'. They'll sleep up to eight people. The Tillmouth Park Hotel is just five miles away.

Book through William Quarry, Hardwood House, Reston, Berwickshire. Telephone: (031) 226 7431 day; (03904) 323 evenings. Duration: 1 February–30 November salmon, 16 February–14 September trout.

*Prices: £13.20 per rod per day 1 February–
30 April; £5.50 per rod per day 30 April–
14 September; £16.50 per rod per day 14
September–30 November. VAT extra.
Boatman (if required) £11 per day (est).
Accommodation: for self-catering telephone Captain J. D. Hotham (0289)
82321. Tillmouth Park Hotel, Telephone:
(0890) 2255. Prices: approximately £30 per
person per day (est). Includes room with
private bath, all meals, service and VAT.
Collingwood Arms Hotel, Telephone:
(0890) 2424. Price: £18.50 per person per
day (est). Includes room, all meals, service
and VAT. Rod hire available £1 per day.*

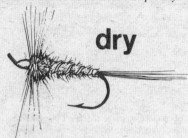

dry

BORDERS, Peebles

Fishing
*1 Trout Fishing Courses
2 Trout Fishing Holidays*
Tontine Hotel

Twenty-three miles from Edinburgh, this
hotel has been the town's main inn since
it was built in 1808. Despite modernization,
it retains outstanding original features
such as the Adam-style dining room. All
thirty-seven bedrooms offer private bath,
colour TV, radio, telephone and tea/coffee
making facilities. You can fish on thirty
miles of the River Tweed on both holidays.

*Tontine Hotel, High Street, Peebles, Bor-
ders, Scotland. Telephone: (0721) 20892.
Duration: 1 April to May, Friday night to
Sunday afternoon; 2 April to September, 4
days mid-week. Price: 1 £64 (est). Includes
all fees, accommodation, all meals (packed
lunch); 2 £103.50 (est) April and May, £108
(est) June to September. Includes accommodation, meals (as above), fishing fees. £6
reduction for non-fishers. Prices include
VAT.*

CUMBRIA, Holmbrook

Game Fishing
Lutwidge Arms Hotel

This well-known fishing hotel on the
River Irt has been run by the Simpson
family for three generations. Their motto
proclaims that 'We like to see our guests
catch fish' – and you stand an excellent
chance of doing just that. The hotel owns
one of the finest stretches of water in
northwest England, with twenty-two
holding pools. In low water you can
actually see hundreds of salmon and sea
trout from your bedroom window. Brown
trout fishing is also available in many
nearby tarns and lakes at reasonable
charges. You have twenty-four-hour use
of individual lock-up tackle rooms, a
clothes dryer and a deep freeze, so you
can get your catch home as fresh as the
day it was caught. Permits and River
Board Licences are sold at the hotel (£4
per day, £18 per week). The salmon and
sea trout season runs from 1 April to 31
October, brown trout from 20 March to
15 September. The fishing beat is five and
a half miles and this is fished by up to
eighteen rods (catches of up to eighteen
pound salmon). No tackle for hire.

The hotel's light, airy rooms all have
hot and cold water, night storage heaters,
teamaking facilities and electric blankets.

*Lutwidge Arms Hotel, Holmbrook, Cum-
bria CA18 1UH. Telephone: (09404) 230.
Proprietor: Colin Simpson. Duration: 1
April–31 October, salmon and sea trout;
20 March–15 September brown trout.
Price: £9.50 single bed and breakfast (est);
£97.50 bed, breakfast and dinner per
person per week (est). Includes full board
and VAT. A North West Water Authority
licence is mandatory, price and details on
application.*

wet

HAMPSHIRE, Southampton

Fishing
1 Fly Fishing
2 Grayling Fishing
Cotswold Hotel

Fulling Mill has its own three-mile stretch of the River Itchen which offers some of the finest brown trout fishing in Britain. You can confidently expect to land at least a one and a quarter pounder. The two-day break includes fishing on Saturday or Sunday, two nights accommodation with dinner and a lunch box with wine. The three-day holiday includes trout fishing on Saturday and Sunday, accommodation with dinner on Friday, Saturday and Sunday, and two packed lunches with wine.

There's excellent unlimited grayling fishing on the Lower Water at Fulling Mill. This package includes accommodation with dinner on Friday and Saturday and a lunch box with wine.

You stay in the modern Cotswold Hotel, near Southampton University. The eighty rooms all boast colour TV, central heating, telephone, radio and tea and coffee making facilities. A popular dinner dance is held on Saturday nights.

Cotswold Hotel, Highfield Lane, Portswood, Southampton SO9 1YQ. Telephone: (0703) 559555. Duration: 1 2 or 3 days, Friday, Saturday or Sunday, 1 April–31 October; 2 2 nights, Friday and Saturday, 1 November–31 March. Price: 1 £54–£60 per person (1981), depending on stretch of river. Includes 1 day fishing, 2 days accommodation and dinner, and 1 lunch. £88–£100 (1981) for 2 days fishing and 3 days accommodation and dinner and 2 lunches; 2 £38. Includes 1 day fishing (Saturday only), 2 days accommodation and dinner, and 1 lunch.

HIGHLAND, Aviemore

Fly Fishing Course
Post House

The Post House Hotel is an ideally located base in the spectacular Spey Valley for the multitude of outdoor activities around Aviemore. Fly fishing is one of the area's big draws and this course will leave you in great shape to take advantage of it. Your expert instructor will start you off gently, teaching rod, reel and line construction and how to choose tackle that's right for you. Then you'll move on to casting practice and finally plunge right into the fast-moving waters of the Spey to learn approach and wading techniques. You'll also cover fly-tying, how to handle a landing net, watercraft, entomology and spinning. The beat fished is around two miles long and this is usually fished by around six rods (ghillies are free for the first two days).

The Post House, Aviemore Centre, Aviemore, Highland PH22 1PH. Telephone: (0479) 810771. Duration: 5 days, any Sunday to Thursday, May to October. Price: £180 per person (est). Includes tuition, tackle hire, transport from centre, permit, 5 nights accommodation, breakfast and dinner. Children under 14 sharing parents' room £56.40 per child (est) (same deal but meals extra).

See also GOLF, SAILING, WINDSURFING.

HIGHLAND, Aviemore

All-Round Fishing
1 Salmon Fishing Holiday
2 Salmon Fly Fishing Course
3 Three-Day Crash Course in Fly Fishing
4 Two-Day Crash Course
5 Pike Fishing Holiday
Osprey Fishing School

Proprietor and chief instructor Jim Cornfoot, a fly fishing enthusiast since the age of ten, teaches the traditional casting methods he learned as a lad for both beginners and long-time fishermen at his school. The River Spey and local lochs are your classroom; salmon, sea trout, brown trout, rainbow trout and pike are your reward for learning well. You'll unravel the mysteries of fly lines, rod and reel construction, learn how to choose the right tackle, water craft and wading. An introduction to spinning for both game and coarse fish is included and other aspects of fishing can be covered on request. The school provides rod, reel, waders and all required tackle (they prefer to let you use their balanced tackle sets).

The Fishing Centre, Aviemore Centre, Aviemore, Highland, Scotland. Telephone: (0479) 810767/810911. Proprietor: Jim Cornfoot. Duration and prices: 1 February to September, Monday to Saturday, £120 per person (1981); 2 April to November, Monday to Friday, £85 per person (1981); 3 April to November, Monday to Wednesday, £48 per person (1981); 4 April to November, Saturday and Sunday, £40 per person (1981); 5 April to December, Monday to Friday, £65 per person (1981). Includes tackle, tuition, fishing permit, instructor and transport to water. Accommodation at the centre extra, bed and breakfast, bunkhouse (sharing) £3.50; at house, £4.50, per person. Hotels, guest houses, camping and caravan sites are in the area.

TAYSIDE, Killin

Salmon Fishing Break
Killin Hotel

The hotel is perched on the banks of River Lochay at the western end of Loch Tay in old Perthshire. They supply a boat with outboard motor and two days fishing instruction to help you land the salmon and trout that abound in the hotel's own waters.

No permits are needed for hotel residents (otherwise they cost £6 per day). The fishing beat is along thirteen miles of Loch Tay (at the western end) and this is never fished by more than thirteen rods. Ghillies can be hired for £8 per day and they will occasionally lend tackle.

Killin Hotel, Killin, Tayside, Scotland FK21 8TP. Telephone: (05672) 296. Manager: Dennis Proctor. Duration: 7 nights, all year, closed November–14 December. Price: £229 (est) January to April, £212 (est) May to September, £206 (est) September to October. Includes 2 days tuition, 6 days fishing with boat and outboard, 7 nights accommodation and all meals.

WALES, CLWYD, Llangollen

Go Fishing Holidays
Hand Hotel

This modernized coaching inn on the River Dee offers a week's fishing on thirteen miles of trout water and six miles of salmon water plus expert tuition from a local professional. You can get all Water Authority licences for the Dee and five nearby lakes, and pay angling club fees, at the hotel which also provides maps and guides.

The hotel's one-hundred-yard beat is free to residents (usually fished by around three to four rods). Salmon from eight pounds and trout from four pounds are the usual catch. No hire of tackle at hotel.

For further details of the hotel see GOURMET.

The Hand Hotel, Llangollen, Clwyd, Wales LL20 8PL. Telephone: (0978) 860303 or Best Western (01) 940 9766. Duration: 7 days, 1 March–30 September. Price: £20.80 per person per day for trout, £23.95 per person per day for salmon (1981). Includes maps and guides, club fees and licences, all meals and VAT.

See also COOKING.

WALES, POWYS, Lake Vyrnwy

Trout fishing
Lake Vyrnwy Hotel

This large, old-fashioned sporting hotel has been a comfortable base for keen fishermen since the 19th century. Lt Colonel Sir John Baynes runs it as much like a private house as possible. Food is traditional country house fare which makes good use of the kitchen garden and, of course, fresh-caught trout – you'll see trays of the day's catch laid out before dinner. The hotel holds sole fishing rights on Lake Vyrnwy and stocks it to supplement natural breeding.

It's strictly fly-fishing with proper fly rods and reels only, and no flies over one and a half inches allowed. Recent catches: 1610 brown trout in 1979; 491 rainbow trout, average weight one pound; best catch in 1979, a rainbow trout of 3 lb 10 oz and a brown trout of 5 lb 8 oz. The limit is eight trout per rod per day, ten inches for brown trout, eleven inches for rainbow trout. Virtually all fishing is done from boats (free to hotel residents). Each fishing guest is put in charge of one boat. The hotel will store up to eight of your catch in its deep freeze. You'll need a Severn River Board licence, obtainable at the hotel.

Lake Vyrnwy Hotel, via Oswestry, Salop SY10 0LY. Telephone: (069 173) 244. Proprietors: Mrs J. F. Moir and Lt Col. Sir John Baynes. Duration: all year except mid January to 1 March. Price: low season £1.25 per half day, £2 per day; high season £3 per day, £1.75 per half day. Accommodation £11 per person per day (est), room,

breakfast and dinner. Includes service and VAT. Winter Bargain Break special rate 1 November–1 May £32 per person. Includes 2 nights full board, commencing with dinner on any one day. Excludes Christmas, New Year and Easter.

WILTSHIRE, Marlborough

Fly Fishing
Marlborough College

This is an intensive course held in the college grounds on Marlborough's own stretch of the upper River Kennet and on a specially constructed trout lake. Your tutor, Michael Hanford, is a National Angling Council Instructor with over thirty years experience of game fishing in many countries. He'll give you expert instruction in casting techniques, types of rod, flies and general river history. With prior notification, you can arrange to hire rod and tackle for £1 per day. No permit required. The beat is approximately three miles long (one bank) and is fished by twelve rods. Brown and rainbow trout are the main catch.

Marlborough College Summer School, Marlborough, Wiltshire SN8 1PA. Telephone: (0672) 53888. Secretary: Glynis Lewis. Duration: 7 days, 19–25 July, 26 July–1 August and 2–8 August. Price: £126.50 per person (est) in dormitory, £155.25 in private room. Includes tuition, accommodation and all meals. Hire of rods and equipment extra, and must be arranged in advance.

See also ARCHAEOLOGY, CHINA, FURNITURE RESTORATION, MUSIC, SCULPTURE.

FISHING: SEA

EIRE

Sea Fishing Holiday

If you're a sea angler you're sure to find what you're looking for off Ireland's 3000 miles of coastline. Aer Lingus will fly parties of six from Liverpool to Cork or Shannon, provide you with a self-drive minibus on unlimited mileage and arrange either three or seven nights accommodation at any of five sea fishing centres: Clifden, Fenit, Kinsale, Cobh and Dungarvin. Then it's up to you to see if you can top Irish record catches for blue shark (206 lb), conger (72 lb), cod (42 lb), bass (17 lb) or monkfish (69 lb). In early winter there's top-class fishing for specimen flounder, bass and flatfish. Both shore anglers and deep sea fishermen will find ideal locations. Generally speaking, sea angling on the west and south-west coast is similar to that around Devon and Cornwall, and you can use similar tackle.

Costs vary with season and accommodation; supplements apply from UK airports other than Liverpool.

Aer Lingus Holidays, 52 Poland Street, London W1. Telephone: (01) 439 7262. Duration: 3 or 7 nights, all year. Price: £119.60–£140.90 per person for 3 nights (est); £167.50–£209 per person for 7 nights. Includes return air fare to Cork or Shannon (from Liverpool; other airports in UK extra), self-drive minibus (for 6 people)

with unlimited mileage, 3 or 7 nights bed, breakfast, dinner, service and VAT. Boat charter from approximately £35–£92 (est) per day extra. Tackle hire can be arranged in advance (approximately £1 per day per person).

WALES, DYFED, Aberystwyth

Offshore Sport Fishing
Belle Vue Royal Hotel

Here's a chance to spend a day with the only offshore salt water sport fishing fleet on the west coast. The purpose-built fifteen-ton vessels cover a twenty-mile radius and a normal trip lasts seven to ten hours, depending on the tides. You'll have an excellent chance of catching shark, tope and turbot.

Recently modernized, the substantial Belle Vue Royal Hotel is on the sea front overlooking Cardigan Bay and local amenities include an 18 hole golf course.

Belle Vue Royal Hotel, Aberystwyth, Dyfed, Wales SY23 2BA. Telephone: (0970) 617558, or Best Western (01) 940 9766. Manager: Phillip Clements. Duration: 2 nights (weekends preferable) 1 April–31 October (1981). Price: £45 per person (1981). Includes boat trip, 2 nights accommodation, breakfast, dinner and 1 packed lunch. Tackle hire £1 per day per person.

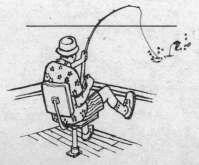

FLOWER ARRANGING

GLOUCESTERSHIRE, Redmarley

Flower Arranging
Flower Design of Britain

Rona Coleman, winner of many international awards and author of *Basic Floristry* and *The Senior Florist*, offers professional and non-vocational courses in her well-equipped country studio. Her own apartment is sometimes free, otherwise she will recommend addresses within three miles or refer you to a friend who offers much-sought after accommodation because she's a fantastic cook and hostess.

The vocational courses, open to students at all levels, prepare you to meet the high standards of national floristry examinations and include hospital and gift arrangements, bridal design, funeral design, buying and salesmanship. The non-professional 'Leisure and Pleasure' course offers practical work, lectures and demonstrations on designing with dried, silk and garden flowers, foliage and other natural materials. The dates for this course are flexible, as Ms Coleman prefers to work out a mutually convenient time with prospective students.

Flower Design of Britain, The Old Schoolhouse, Payford Bridge, Redmarley, Gloucestershire. Telephone: (0531) 820809. Proprietor: Rona Coleman. Price: professional courses £65 per person per week. Includes tuition and materials. Non-vocational courses £3 per hour tuition, materials extra. Bring scissors, knife, kitchen roll, plastic bags, cloth. Accommodation list on request (e.g. £10.50 per person per day full board (1980)). No VAT.

SUSSEX, Chichester

Flower Arranging
1 Flower Arrangement and Basic Floristry
2 Christmas Flower Decorations
The Earnley Concourse

If the subtle art of flower arranging appeals Basic Floristry at the Earnley Concourse is hard to beat for beginners while the more experienced will have plenty of

opportunity to sharpen their skills. You'll learn to create simple but effective bouquets and corsages (a useful talent for parties and weddings) while next Christmas you can one-up your neighbours with your own door garland. The Christmas Flower Decoration course uses simple and inexpensive materials such as ribbon, crêpe paper and dried plants to demonstrate other floral arrangements for the festive season.

For details of the Concourse see ANTIQUES.

The Earnley Concourse, Nr Chichester, Sussex PO20 7JL. Telephone: (0243) 670392/670326. Duration: 1 2 days, June; 4 days, 2–6 March. 2 2 days, 31 October–2 November. Price: £44.10 per person for 1 and 2 for 2 days (est). Includes tuition, materials and full board in a single room with bath; £72.70 for 4 day course (1981). VAT extra.

See also ANTIQUES, FOLK AND JAZZ, LANGUAGES, LITERATURE, MUSIC, POETRY, PUPPETRY, SURVIVAL TRAINING, WINE TASTING.

WEST MIDLANDS, Wolverhampton

Flower Arranging
Pendrell Hall

Learn how to make best use of dried and fresh materials, accessories and artificial flowers. Mrs Bentley of the Baswich Flower Club is your tutor and she'll demonstrate how to make Christmas decorations and dried arrangements and how to use them for maximum effect. Fresh material is provided while added supplies are on sale. Bring scissors/secateurs, glue or similar, Polyfilla (interior), cutting out scissors, Sellotape, textile material for a wall hanging, thick cardboard for backing and gold and silver spray.

For details of Pendrell Hall see LANGUAGES.

Pendrell Hall College of Residential Adult Education, Codsall Wood, Nr Wolverhampton WV8 1QP. Telephone: (090 74) 2398. Secretary: Mrs S. Whitehead. Duration: 3 days, December. Price: £24 per person (est). Includes tuition, some materials and full board for 3 days in a single room, £20.50 if you share a room. Other materials for sale at college. Reduced rates for West Midland residents.

See also LANGUAGES, WINE-TASTING, YOGA.

FLYING

BUCKINGHAMSHIRE, Booker

Come Fly With Us
Wycombe Air Centre

Want to try your hand at piloting a Cessna? Then head for Wycombe Air Centre, a flying school based at Wycombe Air Park (formerly Booker) high in the Chiltern Hills thirty miles from London. Anyone can arrange a trial lesson without obligation to continue the course. The lesson includes a day's membership with the centre, a full pre-flight briefing with a qualified instructor, a flight in a modern Cessna training plane during which you actually handle the controls and fly the aircraft yourself and a debriefing after-

wards. If you decide to go ahead and apply for a PPL (Private Pilot's Licence), the centre's course provides the required thirty-five to forty hours in the air under the direction of a qualified instructor; and parallel ground training.

Your flying instruction is given in dual control aircraft on flights that last forty-five to sixty minutes. Depending on the weather if you train full-time (on a daily basis) you can complete the course in three to six weeks. If you're unable to do this the centre suggests you spread your training over six months. Before you go solo you'll need to take a simple medical examination (glasses wearers qualify). Advanced training and instructors' courses are also available.

Wycombe Air Centre Ltd, Wycombe Air Park, Booker, Nr Marlow, Buckinghamshire SL7 3DR. Telephone: (0494) 25378. Manager: Richard/ Gyselynck. Price: £15 (1980) trial lesson, includes VAT. Other prices on application – from £35 per person per hour (est). Flying costs

are particularly subject to variations in fuel prices and the price indicated may change greatly. Accommodation available at airfield £3 per night plus VAT, or local guest house; list available from centre.

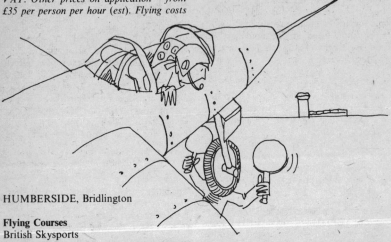

HUMBERSIDE, Bridlington

Flying Courses
British Skysports

You're in good hands when you fly with British Skysports. Chief Instructor Ginger Lacey is an ex-RAF Squadron Leader who gained fame as a war ace when he scored the most kills in the Battle of Britain. You're started off with a one-hour trial lesson in a Cessna 150. A total of forty hours' flying is the requirement for a Private Pilot's Licence; you can spread your flying time with the centre over as long a period as you wish. The bleakly beautiful Yorkshire moors make an ideal setting for beginner pilots.

For details of British Skysports Centre see PARACHUTING.

British Skysports, Bridlington Aerodrome, Bridlington, Humberside. Telephone: (0262) 77367. Instructor: Ginger Lacey. Duration: all year. Price: £32 per hour (est). Flying costs are particularly subject to variations in fuel prices and the price indicated may change greatly. Includes tuition and VAT. Bunk bed accommodation £1.15 per night (1981), bring sleeping bag.

Folk Music

CUMBRIA, Keswick

English Folk Music, Dance and Song
Derwent Bank

This programme is kept deliberately flexible to suit the various interests of the thirty-four guests. Cyril Jones teaches all types of English social dance traditions from the 17th century onwards. Iris Jones leads sing-a-round sessions of old and new folk songs and there's a resident musician who'll direct sessions if you're interested in playing folk music.

Derwent Bank is the most popular of

all the Holiday Fellowship centres so you'll have to book early to be sure of a place. Its extensive grounds run down to the shores of Derwent Water and you can hire boats nearby.

For details of Holiday Fellowship see WALKING, *Loch Awe.*

Holiday Fellowship, 142/144 Great North Way, London NW4 1EG. Telephone: (01) 203 3381. Duration: 1 week, October. Price: £69–£83 (est). Includes tuition, events and full board accommodation in twin rooms. VAT extra.

See also BOWLS, BRASS RUBBING, CREATIVE WRITING, ECOLOGY, GENEALOGY, JEWELLERY, ORIENTEERING, THEATRE GOING, WALKING, YOGA.

DEVON, CUMBRIA, NORTH WALES

Folk Camps

Ordinary family camping holidays can mean a lot of work for parents. The Folk Camps Society (FCS) answer is camping holidays where you're provided with three full meals a day, organized children's entertainment from 6.00 to 9.00 p.m. and late evening singing, dancing and folk music. Rain – the camper's nightmare – needn't bother you on one of these holidays thanks to large marquees with wooden floors where you can attend morning workshops in country dancing, guitar, square dancing and sword or clog dancing. Toilet facilities and hot and cold water are provided. At the Nutwell Court Camp in Devon, you can also study crafts such as painting, pottery and corn dolly making.

Folk Camps Society Ltd, Folk House, 10 Richmond Road, Exeter, Devon EX4 4JA. Telephone: (0392) 77285/6. Duration: July to August. Price: from £35 per person per week (est). Includes tuition, all activities, camp site, all meals and VAT. Reduction for children. Bring tent. 1981 prices and dates not final at press time. Write for brochure.

EAST SUSSEX, Alfriston

Folk Week
North Barn

North Barn is an isolated cluster of typical Sussex flint buildings with oak beams, nestling in a fold of the South Downs – so you can sing and play as loudly as you like without disturbing the neighbours. It's a holiday designed for seventeen to thirty-year olds and informality is the keynote. You'll all pitch in, serving yourself at meals and helping to clear up afterwards.

Most activities are in the evening. Visit local folk clubs and craft centres, watch folk films and enjoy a special evening of Folk Custom and Ritual. Highlights include a midnight ramble, a barbecue on the beach and available Folk Festivals.

Holiday Fellowship, 142/144 Great North Way, London NW4 1EG. Telephone: (01) 203 3381. Leader: David Lloyd. Duration: 1 week, July and August. Price: £68–£74 (est). Includes events and full board. VAT, excursions to local folk festivals and travel to North Barn (nearest station Eastbourne) are extra.

SOMERSET, Crowcombe

Come Dance, Play and Sing
Halsway Manor

Halsway Manor is a residential Folk Centre for the practice and enjoyment of dancing, singing and the arts in general. Courses usually take place over a summer weekend or week. The Manor itself is worth a visit. Nestled at the foot of the Quantock Hills with magnificent views of Exmoor it's a spacious red sandstone building which dates from the 14th century with subsequent additions. The hall, lounge and library are oak panelled and a pleasant landscaped garden stretches below the terrace. Halsway Manor can accommodate up to forty-six in rooms for two to five people with heating and wash-basins (soap and towels supplied). In summer there's a full programme of varied activities. Past programmes have included courses on songs, instruments and dances from medieval and Elizabethan England; madrigals (taught by Alistair Jones, Bristol Cathedral School's Director of Music) and a 'have a go' workshop weekend, led by Gay Gayler, when students can play, dance and sing. Members of the English Folk, Dance and Song Society are entitled to a five per cent reduction.

Halsway Manor Society Ltd, Crowcombe, Taunton, Somerset TA4 4BD. Telephone: (09848) 274. Manager: Ruth Cavill. Duration: weekly and weekends, all year. Price: 1 week £87.72 per person (est). Weekend £30.10 per person. Bed and breakfast £9.25 per night. Includes tuition, events, full board accommodation (in rooms for 2–5 people) and VAT. Children aged 2–6 sharing parents' room pay half adult weekend rate, children aged 7–14 pay two-thirds adult weekend rate.

FOLK AND JAZZ

SUSSEX, Chichester

Folk and Jazz
1 Jazz Beginners' Weekend
2 Jazz Summer School
3 Folk Weekend
4 Jazz Weekend
The Earnley Concourse

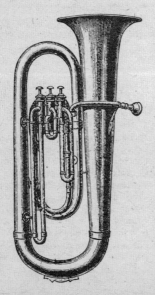

The Jazz Beginners' Weekend course is sweet music for all concerned. Groups divide into appreciation sessions for non-players and practical Dixieland sessions for the rest. At the end of the weekend there's a rip-roaring jam session where you can show your stuff. If you play mention your instrument on application.

During the Summer School students split into modern and traditional jazz groups. You'll hear all about the colourful history of both forms, take a couple of outings and put on a concert for a finale.

The Folk Weekend demonstrates how every variety of vocal and instrumental music has developed from folk song. Examples are chosen from all over the world.

After be-bop came Ray Charles, the Adderly Brothers and Horace Silver. Take a close look at this period over the Jazz Weekend and tackle the music yourself in workshop sessions.

For details of the Concourse see ANTIQUES.

The Earnley Concourse, Nr Chichester, Sussex PO20 7JL. Telephone: (0243) 670392/670326. Duration: 1 weekend in May; 2 1 week July; 3 weekend in October; 4 weekend in November, 20–22 March (1981). Price: £36.10 per person (until 1 April 1981), £39.70 (est) after April) for 1,

3 and 4. Includes tuition and two days full board (twin room with private bath). 2 £116.50 (est). Includes all tuition, excursions and 7 days full board (twin room with private bath); £85.50 without private bath. VAT extra. Bring your own instruments.

See also ANTIQUES, FLOWER ARRANGING, LANGUAGES, LITERATURE, MUSIC, POETRY, PUPPETRY, SURVIVAL TRAINING, WINE TASTING.

FOXHUNTING

CUMBRIA, Lake Ullswater

Foot Foxhunting
Glenridding Hotel

Glenridding's foxhunt with a Lakeland Fell Pack is a traditional local event and an attempt to control the fox population to make the area safe for lambing time. As it involves following the chase over hill and down dale you have to be super fit to follow the whole hunt. However, the hotel can give you the hunt's course, and you can join it at will.

The Glenridding Hotel stands at the head of Ullswater, one of Britain's most beautiful lakes. The village has an alpine atmosphere, with its crisp clear air and mountain scenery. It's the ideal centre for fell walking, climbing, sailing, fishing and riding. Glenridding is owner-run and boasts thirty-three cheerfully furnished rooms, most with bathrooms and showers *en suite*; three are luxury suites.

Glenridding, Lake Ullswater, Nr Penrith, Cumbria CA11 0PB. Telephone: (08532) 228/224. Manager: John Melling. Duration: September to April. Price: £35 per person (est). Includes 2 nights, room, breakfast, dinner and VAT.

NORTH YORKSHIRE, Pickering

Hunting Holidays
High House

Hunt in the Ridings of Yorkshire. Parties of up to five (all over eighteen, with riding experience) are welcome at this 18th century farmhouse in the centre of the North Yorkshire Moors National Park. A stay of six days is suggested, starting on Monday, ending on Sunday, two of which are spent fox hunting. (The local hunt meets on Tuesdays and Saturdays.) Trail riding over the moors is organized on other days. Guidance and advice is given on all aspects of hunting.

Accommodation is in twin and single rooms, all with hot and cold water. (Adjacent bathrooms, separate showers and WC.) The farmhouse has a pleasant lounge with a log fire where guests mingle in an informal atmosphere. For hunting, bring along a black jacket and black hard hat (though tweed jacket with collar and tie is acceptable with the local hunt).

High House, Rosendale Abbey, Nr Pickering, North Yorkshire. Telephone: (07515) 471. Proprietor: Alice Rawlings. Duration: Monday to Sunday, November to March. Price: from £240 per person (est). Includes 2 hunting days, 6 nights full board, and VAT.

FURNITURE RESTORATION

CHESHIRE, Burton

Furniture Restoration
Burton Manor College

Professional restorer Michael Bennett leads this intensive introduction to the restoration of antique furniture, with particular reference to techniques for revising finishes and matching repairs to the colour and patina of existing finishes. There'll be little or no theory on its own – all processes are demonstrated and you follow up with practical work. There's also an opportunity to discuss repairs to your own antique furniture.

For details of Burton Manor, see CINEMA AND VIDEO.

Burton Manor College, Burton, Wirral, Cheshire L64 5SJ. Telephone: (051) 336 2262. Principal: Allan Kingsbury. Duration: 1 week, June. Price: £17.70 per person per day (est). Includes tuition, full board in twin room and VAT.

See also ASTRONOMY, CINEMA AND VIDEO, DANCE, ECOLOGY, GARDENING, LANGUAGES.

WILTSHIRE, Marlborough

Antique Furniture Restoration
Marlborough College

Furniture maker Alan Solly will lead you through a brief outline history of furniture from the 16th century including a look at tools and materials. Students are encouraged to bring along a smallish antique, such as a small chair, to repair. You'll learn how to dismantle, repair and reassemble it in your tutor's large High Street workshop while Alan introduces you to tricks of the trade such as repairs to feet, beading, surface repairs, veneering, reupholstering, French polishing and 'fade and fudge' work.

For details of accommodation see ARCHAEOLOGY.

Marlborough College Summer School, Marlborough, Wiltshire. Telephone: (0672) 5388. Secretary: Glynis Lewis. Duration: 7 days, 19–25 July, 26 July–1 August. Price: £166.75 per person (est). Includes tuition, tools, materials and full board in a private room from Sunday afternoon to Saturday morning. Hotel accommodation £207 per person (est). Dormitory accommodation £138 (est). Children under 14 in dormitory accommodation £115. Bring your own antique to repair.

See also ARCHAEOLOGY, CHINA, FISHING, MUSIC, SCULPTURE.

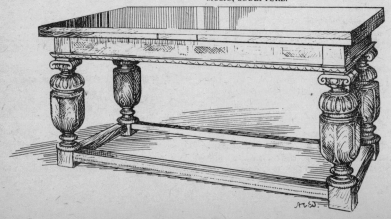

GARDENING

BEDFORDSHIRE, Woburn

Gardening: Design and Renewal
Maryland College

This residential course will help you plan the layout of a new garden or re-plant an established one. Lectures and demonstrations cover site preparation, soil management and the selection of suitable plants, shrubs, trees etc. for particular conditions. Your green thumb has never had so much fun.

Maryland College, Woburn, Milton Keynes, Bedfordshire MK17 9JD. Telephone: (052 525) 688. Lecturer: Leslie Jones. Duration: weekend, 3–5 April. Price: £27.25 per person (1981) (£24.25 Bedfordshire students). Includes tuition, accommodation (mainly single rooms) all meals (from Friday dinner to Sunday lunch). Bring your own towel.

See also LACEMAKING, LANGUAGES, PHOTOGRAPHY.

CHESHIRE, Burton

Home Gardening
Burton Manor College

In 1980 tutor Alan Smith led a weekend home gardening course which covered lawn care, use of a cold greenhouse, bedding plants, alpine plants and rock gardens. There was also a day course on ornamental trees and shrubs.

For details of Burton Manor *see* CINEMA AND VIDEO, and for details of 1981 gardening courses send SAE for brochure.

Burton Manor College, Burton, Wirral, Cheshire L64 5SJ. Telephone: (051) 336 2262. Principal: Allan Kingsbury. Duration: weekend. Price: £17.70 per person per day (est). Includes tuition, full board (twin room) and VAT.

See also ASTRONOMY, DANCE, ECOLOGY, FURNITURE RESTORATION, LANGUAGES, CINEMA AND VIDEO.

DEVON, Torquay

Garden Lovers Weekend
Imperial Hotel

The Imperial offers you the chance of a gardener's lifetime – to hear Percy Thrower and other of Britain's best-known gardeners, lecture on the raising of flowers, fruit and vegetables, plus invaluable tips on work in the greenhouse and with houseplants. You'll also go with them to visit some of Devon's most outstanding gardens.

A weekend highlight is to partake of one of the hotel's famed gastronomic dinners on Saturday night, accompanied by vintage wines. Other cocktail parties and a dinner dance will further entertain you, while Sunday afternoon is devoted to discussing your own particular gardening problems.

The Imperial Hotel, Torquay, Devon. Telephone: (0803) 24301. Duration: weekends, 8–11 May, 10–13 July, 14–18 September. Price: £125 per person (est) (according to room, all have private baths). Includes lectures, 3 nights accommodation, all meals (from Friday dinner to Monday breakfast) and service. VAT extra.

See also ANTIQUES, GOURMET, MUSIC.

COUNTY DURHAM, Stanley

Four Seasons
Beamish Hall

This is a series of four linked weekend courses covering each season, particularly valuable in total yet any one is self-contained and worthwhile in its own

right. For instance, 'Summer in Your Garden' covers lawn care, summer colour, raising plants and summer salads, vegetables and fruits, tips on how to cope with pests, disease and weeds, and even suggestions on garden leisure activities.

For details of accommodation see MUSIC.

Beamish Hall, Stanley, County Durham DH9 0RG. Telephone: (0207) 33147. Lecturer: R. McParlin. Duration: 4 weekends, mid April, early July, also Autumn and Winter. Price: £19.55 per person per weekend (until 1 September 1981) (reduced rates for County Durham residents). Includes tuition, accommodation, all meals (from Friday dinner to Sunday lunch). 10% reduction if you book all 4 weekends. No VAT.

See also ARCHAEOLOGY, ASTRONOMY, JEWELLERY, MUSIC.

HERTFORDSHIRE, Tring

1 Alpine Gardens
2 Happy Gardening
Pendley Manor

Time you got to grips with your garden? Try a gardening weekend at the Pendley Centre. Philip Waters, lecturer in Horticulture at Harrow College of Further Education, runs courses which cover all aspects of gardening. Illustrated talks cover everything from Care of Lawns to Greenhouse Management and there's a coach trip to the Savill Gardens (charge extra).

Accommodation is in the modern student bedsits of this Adult Education Centre. This has many modern facilities including launderettes, bath and showers on all floors, kitchenettes and licensed bars.

Pendley Manor, Station Road, Tring, Hertfordshire HP23 5QZ. Telephone: (04 4282) 2481. General Manager: John McKenna. Duration: 1 2 days March; 2 2 days June. Price: 1 £10.50 per person (est); 2 £24 per person (1981). Includes tuition and full board. VAT extra. Single room supplement £2.

See also COLLECTING, CREATIVE WRITING.

GARDENS

CORNWALL, Falmouth

Spring Gardens
Somerdale Hotel

See Cornwall's celebrated Spring Gardens at their best. These owe their reputation to the special climate of Cornwall, whose coast is washed by the Gulf Stream, and the rich mineral soil of this westerly peninsula. Three full-day and two half-day coach tours take you to celebrated gardens such as Cotehele, Glenduran and Trelissick. There's also an evening talk by a leading gardening personality.

Your base is the two star Somerdale Hotel which boasts a six course dinner each evening and twice weekly dancing.

Somerdale Hotel, Falmouth, Cornwall. Enquiries: Galleon World Travel Association Ltd, Galleon House, King Street, Maidstone, Kent ME14 1EG. Telephone: (0662) 63411 or (01) 859 0111. Duration: late March to late April. Price £98 per person per week (est). Includes accommodation with private bath, all meals, transport and VAT.

See also ANTIQUES, CRUISING: INLAND WATERWAYS, HISTORY, PONY TREKKING, SURFING.

CORNWALL, Fowey

Spring Gardens
Fowey Hotel

April is the perfect time to see some of England's finest southern gardens in the company of Fred Shepherd, Chairman of the Cornwall Garden Society. This guided tour includes such horticultural gems as Glendurgan, Cotehele, Lanhydrock, Trelissick, a number of private gardens and the Probus Demonstration Centre. There's an evening lecture on the night of your arrival and other instructional talks suitable which will interest both amateurs and specialists.

You'll stay at the three star Fowey Hotel overlooking the entrance to the town's picturesque fishing harbour.

Fowey Hotel, Fowey, Cornwall. An Oxford University course. Enquiries: Isis Seminar, Coombe, Gratious Street, Selbourne, Alton, Hampshire GU34 3JE. Telephone: (042 050) 228. Director: Lt Col. A. H. Gye. Duration: 1 week, late April. Price: £172 per person (est). Includes full board accommodation, guided excursions, lectures, transport and VAT.

DEVON, Bovey Tracey

Holidays for Garden Lovers
Coombe Cross Hotel

Rambling, secluded and presided over by the Misses Hebditch, Coombe Cross Hotel stands on the edge of Dartmoor. From here you go by minibus to visit famous gardens such as the 14th century Tiltyard at Dartington Hall, Castle Drogo and others less well known. The choice of gardens varies with the season, and some, such as Marwood Hill's water garden, and Fernwood (privately owned), are not regularly open to the public. Others, like Andrew's Corner, a small garden 1000 feet up on Dartmoor, are so far off the beaten track you'd be unlikely to find them without the assistance of your three expert guide-lecturers. A highlight of the programme is the day trip to the Isles of Scilly to visit Tresco's magnificent tropical gardens. Bring slides of your own garden for discussion, and your National Trust card if you're a member.

Coombe Cross Hotel, Bovey Tracey, Newton Abbot, Devon TQ13 9EY. Telephone: (0626) 832476. Proprietors: Anne and Elizabeth Hebditch. Duration: 1 week end of March, early May, early June, mid July, early October. Price: £150 per person (est). Includes double room, all meals, transport, entrance fees, guided tuition, service and VAT. Single room supplement £10.50 per person.

See also BRIDGE, CASTLES AND HISTORIC HOUSES, ECOLOGY, ORNITHOLOGY.

DUMFRIES AND GALLOWAY
Gatehouse of Fleet

Scottish Gardens
Murray Arms Hotel

See the great gardens of Scotland in bloom. This early June holiday is under the direction of garden-lovers Mr and Mrs Anthony Wolfe, who have lived in this area for many years. Guided visits cover such classic gardens as Culzean, Threau, Arbigland, Castle Kennedy and the famous Logan Botanic Gardens. Trips to the more private gardens of Steadstone, Bannlourie, Bargany, Corsock House and Brooklands are also included. The selection depends on the owners' willingness to open on any given day.

Guests arriving by rail are met at Dumfries Station, then there's a reception/dinner at the Murray Arms in Gatehouse of Fleet.

The Murray Arms Hotel, Gatehouse of Fleet, Dumfries and Galloway, Scotland. An Oxford University course. Enquiries: Isis Seminar, Coombe, Gratious Street, Selbourne, Alton, Hampshire GU34 3JE. Telephone: (042 050) 228. Director: Lt Col. A. H. Gye. Duration: 29 May–3 June. Price: £147 per person (1981). Includes full board, accommodation, guided excursions, lectures, transport, entrance fees and VAT.

See also GOLF.

OXFORDSHIRE, Oxford

Garden History
1 Historic Gardens
2 Gardens: Victorian to Modern
Oxford University

'Beauty is truth, truth beauty,' – that is all ye know on earth, and all ye need to know. Was Keats perhaps referring to an English garden? Here's your chance to find out. Drink in the beauties of the great Victorian garden at Cliveden and its notable modern additions, the pleasing layout at Hidcote and Sezincote where you can appreciate modern horticultural work in an ancient setting. You'll visit several private gardens as well. Included in this course is a talk by Hal Moggridge on contemporary garden design. He'll also be happy to answer questions on your own garden design problems.

Oxford's splendid Magdalen College will be home during your course. Evening activities are arranged for you such as organ recitals in the College Chapel, visits to College libraries and book exhibitions (featuring books relevant to the course) arranged by Blackwells', the celebrated Oxford booksellers.

Isis Seminar, Coombe, Gratious Street, Selbourne, Alton, Hampshire GU34 3JE. Telephone (042 050) 228. Organizer: Lt Col. A. H. Gye. Duration: 1 week, 1 7–12 September; 2 21–27 September. Price: £170 per person (est). Includes course, full board, entry fees, service and VAT.

STRATHCLYDE, Island of Seil

Gardens Week
Dunmor House

Dunmor House is a licensed hotel on the rugged coastal hill farm of Dunmor. It overlooks the sea to the Inner Hebrides, and offers real country house accommodation for up to twenty-three guests. You'll be given a suggested itinerary of outstanding gardens and in a week you might visit Inverary Castle, Achamore, Arduaine, Crarae and more. Many of the gardens of Argyll are at their best in spring, so a special spring tour is offered in 1981 with a ten per cent reduction on the normal tariff. If you come to Dunmor House for any seven-day period between 1 May and 18 June, you'll receive a proposed daily itinerary, route map and any other relevant information. During the week you could visit nine outstanding gardens and travel through stunning West Highland scenery to get there. You'll return each evening to the warmth and comfort of your hotel and one of its fine dinners.

Dunmor House, Island of Seil, By Oban, Strathclyde PA34 4RF. Telephone: (08523) 203. Proprietor: Lt Commander Hugh Campbell-Gibson. Duration: 7 days during 1 May–18 June. Price: from £137.50 per person per week (1981). Includes a weekly itinerary, map, full board and VAT.

STRATHCLYDE, Strachur

Gardens and Castles
Creggans Inn

The Creggans Inn is a perfect centre for touring famous Scottish gardens as so many are within easy reach – Inverary, Benmore, Crarae, Gigha, Ardkinglas, Isle of Bute, Eckford, Glenarn, Carradale, Easdale, Loch Lomond and Glencoe. The warming Gulf Stream and south westerly winds mean that even sub-tropical plants such as palms, tree ferns and magnolias flourish in the West of Scotland. Mid-April to the beginning of June is the period when Argyll's gardens are at their most magnificent.

The Creggans Inn is a lovely little hotel on Loch Fyne, owned by Sir Fitzroy and Lady Maclean who've made extensive, tasteful improvements to the original inn. Lady Maclean personally supervises all the menus; her well-known best-selling cookery book gives a hint of the culinary delights in store in the hotel dining room.

The Creggans Inn, Strachur, Strathclyde, Scotland. Telephone: (036 986) 279. Proprietors: Sir Fitzroy and Lady Maclean. Price: from £18 single (est), £35.50 double (est). Includes bed and breakfast, information on where to go, and VAT. 10% service charge added.

GENEALOGY

SUSSEX, Fittleworth

Family History
The Old Rectory

Tracing your family tree can be a fascinating (though sometimes shocking) pursuit. This course is geared to the beginner who wants to discover his ancestry in the most efficient, economical way. Your tutor, Vice Chairman of the Sussex Family History Group, will help you to embark on this fascinating adventure with illustrated lectures, discussions and practical field work such as visits to a local record office and museum.

For details of accommodation see SENIOR CITIZENS.

The Old Rectory, Fittleworth, Pulborough, Sussex RH20 1HU. Telephone: (079882) 306. Directors: Graham and Brenda Salmon. Duration: 1 week course during July. Price: £85 per person (1981), double room accommodation, £95 single; with private bath £95 doubles, £107 singles. VAT extra.

See also CASTLES AND HISTORIC HOUSES, CLOCKS, MUSIC, ORNITHOLOGY, QUILTING AND PATCHWORK, SENIOR CITIZENS.

YORKSHIRE, Scarborough

Heads and Tales
Grovenor House

Tracing your ancestors and researching your family tree is an increasingly popular pastime. Bring with you any family documents or old family photos that might help in your research. You'll make exploratory excursions by coach to Hutton-le-Hole, Kilburn, York and Stedmore.

Grovenor House is near the railway and bus stations, and only a five-minute walk from the seafront. All rooms have hot and cold water and heating; in addition to the usual Holiday Fellowship Centre lounges, there's a ballroom with a separate games room opening on to a patio.

Grovenor House, Grovenor Road, Scarborough, Yorkshire. Telephone: (0723) 64955. Duration: 1 week beginning 14 June. Price: £84–£95 per person (est). Includes full board accommodation, exploratory excursions. VAT extra. Sponsors: Holiday Fellowship.

For further details of Holiday Fellowship see under WALKING, *Loch Awe.*

See also BOWLS, BRASS RUBBING, CREATIVE WRITING, ECOLOGY, FOLK MUSIC, JEWELLERY, ORIENTEERING, THEATRE GOING, WALKING, YOGA.

GEOLOGY

TAYSIDE, Enochdhu

Geology
1 Rocks and Minerals
2 Geology and Scenery
Kindrogan Field Centre

Learn about rocks among the rocky splendours of the Scottish Highlands. The course in Geology and Scenery, run by C. H. Dingwall, is aimed at all who are interested in Highland landscape and the rocks and process that have shaped it. There are also related courses in geographical fieldwork, mountains and the rocks and plants of the Tayside region. These courses are run for informed amateurs, undergraduates and teachers, but beginners would get a lot from them as well.

Accommodation is at the Kindrogan Field Centre in Tayside just a few miles north of the Highland Boundary Fault. Nearby there are several mountains over 3000 feet and a variety of glacial landforms – all of which are visited on organized trips. The accommodation is hostel style and you'll be expected to help with the meals and service. The centre's classrooms and fully equipped laboratories are used during the course.

The Scottish Field Studies Association, Kindrogan Field Centre, Enochdhu, Blairgowrie, Tayside PH10 7PG. Telephone: (025081) 286. Warden: Brian Brookes. Duration: 1 22–29 July, 26 August–2 September; 2 5–12 August. Price: £84 per person per week (est). Includes tuition, full board and VAT.

See also BOTANY, WILDLIFE.

GLIDING

GLOUCESTERSHIRE, Stroud

The Gliding Experience
Amberley Inn

This holiday offers the thrills, but no spills (hopefully), of unpowered flight. Your fee includes two nights' bed, dinner and full breakfast, plus a visit to the Bristol and Gloucester Gliding Club five miles from Amberley. Here you'll have instruction and twenty minutes' free gliding – at 2000 feet. If you're hooked and want to go up again, the rates are £5.50 a tow, and £1.60 for each twenty minute unit of gliding time.

Amberley Inn is a picturesque Cotswold stone building with welcoming log fires and a panoramic view of one of Great Britain's loveliest areas.

The Amberley Inn, Amberley, Stroud, Gloucestershire GL5 5AF. Telephone: (045 387) 2565, or Best Western (01) 940 9766. Duration: all year, any 2 nights. Price: £37.50 per person autumn/winter, £41 spring, £49 summer (slightly dearer midweek) (1981). Includes tuition, 20 minutes free gliding, 2 nights bed, breakfast, dinner, service and VAT.

TAYSIDE, Scotlandwell

Gliding Holidays
Scottish Gliding Union Ltd

The Scottish Gliding Union runs holiday gliding courses at Portnoak from April to September. One of these makes a good introduction to the sport, or can simply be a way of spending a week in the open air (literally!) doing something different. Training is given in two-seat dual control gliders under the guidance of experienced qualified instructors. You'll be one of a small group and will help with general activities such as ground handling the gliders and retrieving and laying the launch cables. If the weather prevents gliding arrangements will be made for indoor lectures. Courses assemble at 6 p.m. Sunday and end with breakfast on the following Saturday. Temporary membership extends for one month after the course's end so you can continue to fly as a member during that period. Simple bunkhouse accommodation is available at £3 per night, or you can camp in your own tent for 50p per night. Meals are served cafeteria-style in the clubhouse, and are paid for as taken.

Scottish Gliding Union Ltd., Portnoak Airfield, Scotlandwell, Tayside, Scotland, KY13 7JJ. Telephone: (0592 84) 543. Duration: 1 week, April to September. Price: £98 per person per week (est). Includes tuition, temporary membership and VAT. Bunkhouse accommodation £3 per person per day (1981). Meals extra, available at clubhouse. Deposit of £10 required.

GOLD PANNING

HIGHLAND, Golspie

Goldpanning with Ghillie
Golf Links Hotel

Want to pan for gold? You can strike it rich a lot closer to home than you think. Major Dewar of Ghillie Personal Travel will meet you at Inverness Station and drive you to the Golf Links Hotel; and every day he'll take you and a guide to a lovely Highland burn to pan for the glittering flakes that flow through these rushing streams. You'll have a packed lunch, and return to an excellent dinner. The local pipe band plays for guests one evening, while another features a surprise 'Scottish Entertainment'. All of this plus meals, transport, instruction, and room with private bath are included in the cost. Golf and fishing can be arranged.

Ghillie Personal Travel, 64 Silverknowes Road, East Edinburgh EH4 5NY. Telephone: (031) 336 3120. Duration: 1 week, April, May, June. Price: April £130, May and June £145 per person (1981). Includes tuition, travel from Inverness Station and in the field, shared room with bath (singles add £12), and all meals. VAT extra.

See also ROCK HUNTING.

GOLF

CHANNEL ISLANDS, GUERNSEY, L'Ancresse

Golf
Royal Guernsey Golf Club

Go golfing in Guernsey. Members of any recognized golf club are welcome to play at the Royal Guernsey Golf Club and make use of their many excellent facilities. Their course, situated at the northern end of the island, is bounded by the beautiful bays of L'Ancresse and Grand Havre, with long rolling beaches on two sides.

You can stay at the L'Ancresse Lodge Hotel, just beside the golf course itself and overlooking the bay. The hotel has spacious dining rooms with sea views, bars, TV room and facilities for packed lunches and bike hiring.

The Royal Guernsey Golf Club, L'Ancresse, Guernsey, Channel Islands. Telephone: (0481) 46523/44001. Secretary: Geoffrey Nicolle. Green fees: £7 per day, £19.50 per week (est). Accommodation: L'Ancresse Lodge Hotel, L'Ancresse Bay, Guernsey. Telephone: (0481) 44328. Proprietor: Donald Sims. Price: £10 to £12 per person per day (est).

DEVON, Northam

Golfaway Anyday
Yeoldon House Hotel

Your stay at this cosy hotel, marvellously situated overlooking the River Torridge, includes one day's golfing at the Royal North Devon course at Westward Ho! It's the oldest 18 hole course in England (1864). It was recently used for the Martini championship where players included such famous names as Brian Barnes, Neil Coles and Christie O'Conner. The club has hosted the Amateur Championship several times and in the 1950s one of its own members, the Hon. Michael Scott, won that Championship.

You can spend another day at Saunton near Barnstaple, which has two 18 hole courses set among the sand dunes, a top-notch clubhouse and facilities. The gourmet fare at Yeoldon House is a big draw and highly popular with golfing, entertainment and political celebrities.

Yeoldon House Hotel and Restaurant, Durrant Lane, Northam, near Bideford, Devon EX39 2RL. Telephone: (02372) 4400/6618. Proprietors: Chris and Judi Fulford. Duration: any 3 nights, October to March (1980/81). Price: £58 per person in winter (1980/81), £71 spring (weekdays), £73 weekends (1981). Includes 2 days green fees, 3 nights bed, breakfast and dinner, service and VAT. Golf clubs can usually be hired from £1 per round.

See also GOURMET, ORNITHOLOGY.

DORSET, Bournemouth

Highcliffe Thirty Sixer
Highcliffe Hotel

This all-inclusive holiday at one of the south coast's premier four star hotels offers two rounds of golf, including one on a championship course (Queens Park or Meyrick).

The hotel's extensive grounds, overlooking the sea, include a heated swimming pool, hard tennis court, putting green and sauna/solarium. There's good pub ale and Magnum's, the hotel's own night spot, is open six nights a week for late dancing.

For further details of accommodation see DANCING.

Highcliffe Hotel, Bournemouth, Dorset. Telephone: (0202) 27702. Manager: Christopher Smith. Duration: late October to late May. Price: singles £46 to £48.50 (1981) for any two days. Includes bed and English breakfast, lunch and dinner, plus two rounds of golf. Golf clubs can be hired at the club for approximately £1 per round, golf balls free from the Hotel. Price includes service and VAT.

See also DANCE, HEALTH AND BEAUTY.

DUMFRIES AND GALLOWAY, Gatehouse of Fleet

Golf
Murray Arms Hotel

The Murray Arms, built in 1642 as a coaching inn, is still an hotel of warmth and character where you can enjoy a drink with the locals – who'll be sure to let you know that the great national bard, Robert Burns, wrote 'Scots Wha Hae' while staying here. Your holiday includes two days green fees at a nearby 9 hole golf course, and of course the marvellous countryside in the heart of 'Burns Country' is yours for free.

Murray Arms Hotel, Gatehouse of Fleet, Dumfries and Galloway, Scotland. Mana-

ger: Mr R. Raphael. Telephone: (05574) 207 or Best Western on (01) 940 9766. Duration: 3 nights 1 November–31 May excluding all Bank Holidays. Price: £66.50 per person (1981). Includes accommodation, all meals from dinner on day of arrival to breakfast on day of departure, plus 2 days green fees. (No hire of golf clubs.) Prices include VAT.

EIRE

Golfing in Ireland
Various Locations

Ireland's lush countryside has 250 golf courses and averages one championship course to every fifty miles of motoring. From this putter's paradise, Joe Walsh has selected five centres for you to choose from, each conveniently near one of the outstanding golf clubs at Ballybunion and Killarney in County Kerry; Lahinch in County Clare; County Sligo Golf Club; the Bundoran, County Donegal; and, around Dublin, the Royal Dublin, the Hermitage, Clontarif and Howth. Green fees are surprisingly reasonable (usually around £2 per round). Lessons from a club professional cost about £2.50 each. Be sure to bring showerproof clothing, golf shoes and a light bag of clubs, as caddies are not always available. Visitors are welcome to use the clubhouse and facilities; courses are seldom crowded and waiting is virtually unknown during the week.

Joe Walsh Tours Ltd, Reservations Department, Ireland House, 150 New Bond Street, London W1Y 0AQ. Telephone: (01) 493 3201. Duration: 6 nights, January to December. Price: doubles travelling by sea £109.25–£143.75; by air £159–£194 (1981). Includes bed and breakfast, shared room with bath or shower, car hire included in air fare. Prices include VAT.

See also FISHING: COARSE, HORSE DRAWN CARAVANS.

GRAMPIAN, Banff

Golfing Break
County Hotel

At this impressive Georgian house over-looking the Moray Firth you'll sleep in a four-poster bed, get in one round of golf a day at either Duff House Royal or Royal Tarlair (depending on the season).

The County Hotel, Banff, Banffshire, Grampian, Scotland. Telephone: (02612) 2846, or Best Western on (01) 940 9766. Duration: March to November. Price: singles from £36 (est) for any 2 days. Includes dinner, bed and breakfast, plus one round of golf per day; hire of golf clubs approximately £1 per round.

HIGHLAND, Aviemore

Golfing Holidays
The Post House

This package offers a marvellous deal for children – just the ticket if Junior's keen to take to the links. The charge is only £10 per child and includes green fees to Bant of Garten (six miles away) or Grantown (thirteen miles) golf courses. Under this scheme, you share a room with any children you bring, and pay for their meals as taken. Your dinner and breakfast are included in the fee.

The Post House, Aviemore Centre, Aviemore, Highland PH22 1PJ. Telephone: (0479) 810771. Duration: any Sunday to Thursday inclusive from end of May to early October. Price: £130 per person (est). Includes 5 nights, Scottish breakfast, dinner and green fees. £10 per child for children under 14 sharing parents' room. Includes 5 nights plus 4 days green fees, meals extra. Guests must provide their own equipment and transport. Club facilities available. Prices include VAT.

NORFOLK, Norwich

Getaway Golf
Barnham Broom Hotel and Golf Club

Combine the fun of golfing on an 18 hole, par seventy-two championship course with the pleasure of a weekend away from it all at this fine forty bedroom hotel set in 120 acres of grounds. In the summer months you'll enjoy the large outdoor swimming pool, while a sauna is available all year round. This is a new hotel with many amenities.

Barnham Broom Hotel and Golf Club, Barnham Broom, Norwich, Norfolk NR9 4DD. Telephone: (060 545) 393 or Best Western on (01) 940 9766. Duration: all year, 2 nights weekends only. Price: £38.50 per person (est). Includes bed and breakfast, dinner, 1 lunch plus 4 rounds of golf. Hire of golf clubs from £1 per round. Price of holiday includes VAT.

See also SKID CONTROL.

SUFFOLK, Aldeburgh

Golfing Bargain Break
Brudenell Hotel

Picturesque Aldeburgh on the North Sea and the river Alde has been, since 1948, host of the annual internationally famous music festival. It also boasts an 18 hole golf course, and there's another two miles north, at Thorpeness. Both courses, on light sandy soil, are drier for play during the winter and spring than most clubs further inland. The Brudenell is a modernized Victorian hotel on the sea front; all forty-seven rooms have private bath, TV and telephone. There is good sailing on the river and the hotel has a thirty-foot sailing boat for hire (£16 daily).

The Brudenell Hotel, The Parade, Aldeburgh, Suffolk IP15 5BU. Telephone: (072 885) 2071. Manager: Mr H. Clacy. Duration: October to May, Monday to Friday. Price: from £42 per person (1981). Includes 2 days accommodation, all meals and green fees.

YORKSHIRE, Harrogate

Go Golf
Hotel St George

This holiday has been designed by golfers for golfers, with lots of little extras to make your holiday memorable. You'll be welcomed as a guest for the day at the Moor Allerton Golf Club, an outstanding course designed by Robert Trent Jones. Before you tee off, you'll get twenty-five balls for practice on the driving range. Lunch in the Members' Club House is included and if you're still feeling energetic you have free use of their seven tennis courts, two snooker tables and bowling green. There's also a sauna.

The package includes green fees at Pannal Golf Course – 18 holes and 6568 yards, standard scratch score 71, the scene of many major tournaments. You'll also get a Dunlop golfball, a personalized ball marker and half a bottle of wine.

For details of accommodation see ANTIQUES.

Hotel St George, Ripon Road, Harrogate, Yorkshire HG1 2SY. Telephone: (0423) 61431 or Best Western (01) 940 9766. Proprietor: John Abel. Duration: 3 nights, all year round. Price: £86.50 per person (1981). Includes 1 day's green fees, 3 nights bed, breakfast and dinner, 1 lunch, service and VAT. Hire of golf clubs for £1 per round.

WALES, DYFED, Gwbert-on-Sea

Golfing Getaway
Cliff Hotel

You can see the sea from every tee when you use this cliff-top hotel's free 9 hole golf course. For a mere £3.50 a day you can play Cardigan's 18 hole course. The hotel is renowned for its cuisine and has many facilities, including bars, a TV lounge and ballroom.

Cliff Hotel, Gwbert-on-Sea, Dyfed, Wales SA43 1PP. Telephone: (0239) 3241. Duration: any 2 days 26 October–22 May.

Price: from £36 (1981). Includes bed, breakfast and dinner each day, plus one lunch. Golf free on hotel's course; £3.50 extra per day to play on Cardigan's 18 hole course, hire of golf clubs approximately £1 per round.

WALES, POWYS, Llandrindod Wells

Hotel Metropole Golf Tournament
Hotel Metropole

Hotel Metropole's two-day golf package entitles you to play at the Llandrindod Wells Golf Club each day. Or you could opt for the tournament weekend and a chance to more than cover your modest expenses – prizes exceed £200. You can practise and limber up for free on Friday, and then try your skill against members of the local golf club in the open Stableford Competition on Saturday. There's another competition on Sunday morning too. The weekend fee includes dinner, breakfast, accommodation, all golf, a Saturday night dance and farewell lunch on Sunday.

Hotel Metropole, Llandrindod Wells, Powys, Wales LD1 5DY. Telephone: (0597) 2881/2. Duration: golf package available all year any 2 days Monday to Friday. Golf Tournament 13, 14, 15, March 1981. Prices: Golf Tournament £37.50 (1981). Includes 2 nights, breakfast and dinner each day and all golf. Golf package: summer £37.50, rest of year £29.50. Includes bed, breakfast and dinner each day; room with private bath, and all green fees. VAT included. Bring golf clubs.

WEST MIDLANDS, Coventry

Summer Golfing Bargain Break
The Post House

Treat yourself to a two-day break centred on golf courses just ten minutes from your hotel in the Forest of Arden's beautiful Packington Park. Test your skills on the 9 hole par three course, or the more challenging 18 hole par seventy-two course, where many a putter has come to grief at the cleverly placed trout lakes.

The Post House, Rye Hill, Allesley, Coventry, West Midlands CV5 9PH. Telephone: (0203) 402151. Duration: May to September. Price: singles £45 (est); non-playing guests £35.50 (est) (single room £2.50 extra (est)) for any 2 days. Includes room with private bath, colour TV, breakfast and dinner, green fees. Special prices for children. Hire of golf clubs from £1 per round. Golfers asked to wear ties in clubhouse.

GOURMET

DEVON, Northam

Gourmet Weekend
Yeoldon House Hotel and Restaurant

Cordon Bleu chef Judi Fulford supervises these weekends in her charming country house hotel. The extensive grounds and sweeping view of the River Torridge make an idyllic setting for the imaginative cuisine, a mixture of English, Continental and original specialities that makes good use of the best of fresh local produce, including duck, trout and salmon. The five-course menus change daily to take advantage of what's in season, but the traditional Sunday roast luncheon is always followed in the evening by a candlelit smorgasbord.

There are plenty of opportunities to work up an appetite or walk off surplus calories. The Fulfords will gladly supply you with a list of nearby sailing, bird-watching, pony trekking and fishing facilities, and they also offer a golf weekend.

The centrally heated rooms all have radio, TV and bathroom *en suite*. Prices vary depending on which two nights of the weekend you book.

Yeoldon House Hotel and Restaurant, Durrant Lane, Northam, near Bideford, Devon, EX39 2RL. Telephone: (02372) 4400/6618. Proprietors: Chris and Judi Fulford. Duration: first weekend of each month, October to March (1980/81) or any weekend for pre-booked parties of six or more. Price: £46 per person (1981). Includes full board from Friday dinner to Sunday lunch, service and VAT. £39 per person for Saturday dinner to Monday breakfast; £59 per person for Friday dinner to Monday breakfast.

See also GOLF, ORNITHOLOGY.

DEVON, Torquay

Gastronomic Weekend
Imperial Hotel

It was in 1961 that this grand hotel began its now famous tradition of gastronomic weekends. Distinguished chefs from various countries are invited to the Imperial

to present their interpretations of the best in regional specialities, to be accompanied by appropriately distinguished vintages of wine. The weekend includes some form of theme-related entertainment; a feast of Venetian dishes, for instance, was accompanied by an exhibition of the latest Maserati and de Tomasco cars. You may also expect such diversions as champagne receptions, cabarets, ballroom dancing, excursions to Devon beauty spots, films and cooking demonstrations by visiting chefs.

The Imperial Hotel, Torquay, Devon. Telephone: (0803) 24301. Duration: selected weekends, all year. Send for details. Price: £103–£138 per person (1981), according to room. Includes 3 nights accommodation in a room with private bath, all meals and wine, receptions, tastings, demonstrations from Friday afternoon to Monday morning and service. VAT extra.

See also ANTIQUES, GARDENING, MUSIC.

fishing and golf, and there are horse-drawn canal trips, and a local steam railway. All rooms have private bath and colour TV.

The Hand Hotel, Llangollen, Clwyd, Wales LL20 8PL. Telephone: (0978) 860303 or Best Western on (01) 940 9766. Proprietor: David Morris. Duration: weekends, all year. Price: £44 per person (est) in autumn and winter, slightly higher spring and summer. Includes banquet and entrance tickets, room with private bath, all meals from Friday p.m. to Sunday lunch, service and VAT. Transport on excursions extra.

See also FISHING: GAME.

WALES, CLWYD, Llangollen

Medieval Breakaway Weekend
Hand Hotel

The weekend gets off to a rousing start with a medieval banquet on Friday night at Ruthin Castle (reputedly haunted). Tuck into a lavish four-course feast washed down with goblets of wine, and enjoy the medieval-style entertainers. Then it's back to the Hand Hotel for the night, and to nearby Chester on Saturday for an hour long tour of the historic town and a one-hour visit to its fascinating British Heritage Museum. The hotel sends you off with a packed lunch fortified with wine or lager, and welcomes you back to a candlelit dinner dance.

Sunday's highlight is a morning visit to Vale Crucis Abbey and the famous Plas Newydd (Llangollen) on the Menai Straits. You can take a packed lunch, or return to the hotel for your midday meal.

A modernized former coaching inn, the Hand Hotel stands on the River Dee in the lush Llangollen Vale. It has its own

WALES, DYFED, St Davids

1 Penwythnos Gwyl Dewi Sant
2 2nd Annual French Gastronomic Weekend
Warpool Court Hotel

Wine and dine at Warpool Court on the historic unspoilt peninsula of ancient Menevia. Resident proprietors David and Grahame Lloyd believe in the personal touch and since 1969 they've been putting their beliefs into practice. The menu consists only of the freshest local produce and features fruit and vegetables from their own kitchen garden as well as fresh fish from nearby Milford Haven. It's all prepared to very high standards.

If you think there's no such thing as Welsh cuisine try their Cawl Bryn-y-Garn (a lamb and vegetable broth with Caerphilly cheese). Welsh specialities aside, the cuisine here is international and ranges from such gourmet classics as filet mignon beaunaise to their own original *crêpes* Dylan Thomas (scallops cooked in a cream and champagne sauce).

They also have country house weekends and chamber music weekends which feature superb music by such internationally famous groups as the Bartok and Aeolian String Quartets.

The hotel is set amidst green fields within champagne cork popping distance of the sea and the hotel's many facilities include an indoor heated swimming pool and even a hotel boat (the *Langouste*) for exploring the rugged local coastline. The area is also renowned for its bird life and wild flowers and you can enjoy long walks through spectacular scenery along the Pembrokeshire National Park Coastal Path. This is culture in style (with not a vulture in sight.)

Warpool Court Hotel, St Davids, Dyfed, Wales. Telephone: (043 788) 3000. Proprietors: Grahame and David Lloyd. Duration: 1 27 February–1 March; 2 3–5 April. Price: £46.25 per person per weekend (1981). Includes lectures, full board, service and VAT.

HANG GLIDING

EIRE, COUNTY DUBLIN, Glenageary

Hang Gliding
Airsports, Ireland

The exhilaration of hang-gliding has led to it being dubbed the 'Ultimate Sport'. On this course you'll gradually build up experience on low, gentle slopes, then progress to higher hills, using training methods evolved from the British and American Hang Gliding Associations' recommendations. As you progress, you'll use the latest available training gliders. Since there are never more than six students to one instructor, trainees get lots of individual attention. For courses held on weekends (beginning at 10.00 a.m. on Saturdays) you assemble in front of Dun Laoghaire Town Hall. Since training sites vary with wind direction, you then travel together by minibus. Travel time is used to discuss flight theory, site and weather conditions.

Airsports Ireland Ltd, 60 Hillcourt Road, Glenageary, County Dublin, Eire. Telephone: (01) (0001 from England) 852 856. Contact: Jennifer Hudson. Duration: all year, weekend course. Price: £21 per person per day (est). Includes tuition, travel from Dun Laoghaire to flying site, third party insurance and any damage to gliders. Bed and breakfast accommodation around Dun Laoghaire extra. Bring crash helmet (a few are available), boots with good ankle support, warm waterproof clothing and a packed lunch. Minimum age 16. Written parental consent for those under 18. Students need to be reasonably fit.

GRAMPIAN, Braemar

Hang Gliding
1 Introductory Course
2 Basic Course
3 Advanced Course
Cairnwell Hang Gliding School

Launch yourself on a hang gliding course at Cairnwell Mountain in Scotland. Gustav Fischnaller runs courses for all levels, based on syllabuses drawn up by the British Hang Gliding Association. Before launching you on solo flights, experts will instruct you in flying terminology, basic aerodynamics and all necessary principles. Within four days you should be making skilful turns and crosswind take offs. Equipment is included in the cost but pupils requiring insurance should make contact in advance with the BHGA-appointed insurance broker, Reggie Spooner, at Clifton House, Bath Road, Cowes, Isle of Wight (Telephone: Cowes 2305/6).

Accommodation is available at the Fife Arms Hotel nine miles away, where facilities include a sauna, children's playroom, restaurant and bars. The hotel is also within easy reach of Braemar, Balmoral Castle and the ski slopes of Glenshee.

Cairnwell Hang Gliding School, Cairnwell Mountain, Braemar, Grampian AB3 5XS. Telephone: (03383) 628. Proprietor: Gustav Fischnaller. Price: 1 2 days, £40 per person (1981); 2 4 days, £70 per person; 3 3 days, £40 per person. Accommodation at the Fife Arms Hotel, Mar Road, Braemar, 9 miles from the school. Telephone: (03383) 644. Price; doubles £28 (est), with bath £33.50 (est) per couple, singles £17 (est), with bath £22.50 (est). Includes breakfast and VAT.

WALES, POWYS, Crickhowell

Hang Gliding Holidays
Welsh Hang Gliding Centre

By the end of the week most people go solo, and if you've got a flair for this exhilarating sport you may well reach the British Hang Gliding Association's Pilot 1 standard. Everyone gets an Elementary Certificate. Every morning after breakfast you'll be collected from your local guest house and driven to the centre (a mile away) for a 9.30 a.m. start. First there's a theoretical lecture, then if the weather's unsafe for gliding, you'll practise other essential skills like parascending, land yachting and grass-skiing, to improve your coordination and judgement. Each group is made up of a maximum of five people. You'll lunch in a café or pub, or

picnic if the weather's fine. Then more instruction until 4.00 p.m. when you pack away the equipment and head back to the centre for a discussion, possibly with video recordings. You'll arrive back at your guest house about 6.00 p.m.

Welsh Hang Gliding Centre, New Road, Crickhowell, Powys, Wales. Telephone: (0873) 810019. Director: Gerry Breen. Duration: 7 day courses 16 March–18 October. Price: from £159 (1981). Includes all equipment and tuition, 6 nights bed and breakfast in a shared twin room (single rooms with bath/shower £32.50–£45 extra), lunches, transport from accommodation to flying site each day, and third party insurance. Bring warm, waterproof clothing. Prices include VAT.

WILTSHIRE, Marlborough

Hang Gliding Tuition
Birdman Flight Training School

Let Ashley Doubtfire launch you into space. Ashley, a recent chairman of the Hang Gliding Instructors' Association, staged the flying sequences for 'Tomorrow's World' and 'Nationwide', and also made the first test flights for Ken Messenger's 1978 Channel crossing.

This school offers a series of courses. The B1 (four day) and B2 (five day) start on Monday and work towards a Pilot

Certificate. (The B1 course can also be split over two weekends.) Beginners should opt for the useful A course – a two-day introduction to the sport, which covers pilot theory and includes some practical flying, sometimes solo, to give you an idea of what further tuition involves.

There are soaring courses especially for you if you've got your own glider. The school makes and sells Cherokee gliders (approximately £525 + VAT) and a new Commanche is being developed; second-hand gliders are sometimes available – ask for details.

Birdman Flight Training School, Milden-hall, Marlborough, Wiltshire. Telephone: (0672) 52909. Contact: Ashley Doubtfire. Duration: 2–6 day courses, all year. Price: from £50 to £145 (est). Includes equipment and training only (and VAT). The school provides a list of bed and breakfast houses nearby at £6–£7 per night which they'll book for you. Bring warm, waterproof clothing.

HEALTH AND BEAUTY

BEDFORDSHIRE, Henlow

Health Farm
Henlow Grange

Estonian-born Madame Leida Costigan has trained as a ballerina, worked as a physiotherapist, studied massage, manipulation and heat treatment in Paris and in Sweden and gained a thorough knowledge of beauty treatments and use of cosmetics in London. All this plus fluency in nine languages has helped make her beauty farm internationally popular. She and her husband have done a brilliant restoration job on the historic Georgian grange. Beginning in 1961 they restored the gardens (including the elaborate Italian Garden) to their former splendour, restored the century-old hand painted Chinese wallpaper in the Peacock Room; and created the sumptious Dolphin Room, complete with fountain and swimming pool. Apart from the main buildings there's the North Wing, a converted Tudor building. You can enjoy all the comforts of a first class hotel combined with a fully-equipped treatment centre run by highly qualified staff. Treatments available include heat bath (either sauna, steam or foam bath), body massage, G5 Vibro massage and infra-red lamp, face cleanse, massage, electrotherapy, manicure, pedicure, seaweed bath and hydrotherapy. Additional treatments available include Parafango volcanic mud treatments, paraffin wax baths, depilatory waxing etc. You're encouraged to take advantage of additional facilities such as table tennis, bicycle machines, billiards, tennis, badminton, archery, croquet and rowing.

Henlow Beauty Farm Ltd, The Grange, Henlow, Bedfordshire. Telephone: (0462) 811111. Duration: All year. Price: from £65 per person per day (est). Includes treatment, full board and VAT. From £220 per person per week (est). Includes full board and VAT.

BORDERS, Peebles

Health and Beauty Holiday
Stobo Castle

Tone up at the magnificent Georgian castle of Stobo, former country home of the Duchess of Dysart, which lies in the rolling hills of the Scottish Borders, looking across the River Tweed to the Eildon Hills. Built by architects Archibald and James Elliot in 1811, it's listed as having an exterior of special architectural importance. The interior has been completely renovated. Spacious private suites have turreted bathrooms, central heating and colour TV.

The highly qualified team of resident therapists is headed by Gaynor Winyard, former chairman of the Society of Health and Beauty Therapists. A maximum of twenty-six guests are cared for each week with a high degree of personal attention by staff. Amenities include a heated indoor swimming pool, therapy rooms and specialized cooking facilities. The castle even has its own private water supply from a pure mountain stream nearby.

Stobo Castle Ltd, Peebles, Borders, Scotland EH45 8NY. Telephone: (07216) 249. General Manager: Stephen Winyard. Duration: minimum stay 3 days, all year. Price: 3 days from £170 per person (1981); 7 days £345 per person. Includes treatments, consultations, diets, full board (single with bathroom). VAT extra. Transport charge from Edinburgh £7.50 per person.

DORSET, Bournemouth

Fun and Fitness
Highcliffe Hotel

Here's a way to combine a seaside holiday at the luxurious four-star Highcliffe with a disciplined start to a programme of good health. Begin your 'keep fit' regime with this introduction to a sensible programme and expert advice on your choice of diet. Enjoy too the free daily use of the Hotel's sauna/solarium and heated indoor pool.

For a description of the hotel and accommodation see DANCING.

Highcliffe Hotel, Bournemouth, Dorset BH2 5DU. Telephone: (0202) 27702. Manager: Christopher Smith. Duration: any 2 days late October to late May. Price: £43.50–£45.50 per person (1981). Includes accommodation, all meals and free use of sauna and solarium, and VAT.

See also DANCING, GOLF.

EIRE, COUNTY KILDARE,
Castledermot

Health and Beauty Clinic
Kilkea Castle Hotel

Get in shape at one of Ireland's oldest inhabited castles. Kilkea, ancestral home of the Fitzgeralds, dates back to 1180. Now it's a luxurious fifty-five bedroom hotel and one of Europe's most well-equipped health and beauty clinics. There are sections for men and women, including saunas, gymnasia, keep fit classes, plunge pools, massages, underwater massage, medicinal baths, ultra violet and infra-red treatments and, for the ladies, a complete and sophisticated beauty section. (Beauty treatments such as facials, leg waxing, eyelash tinting and manicures are extra.) Your individually tailored diet will include yoghurt, fresh fruit, wheatgerm and salads and you'll dine in the special health restaurant. Kilkea sits in a hundred acres of grounds. You can fish for trout in the River Griese which runs through the estate and afterwards tell your fishing stories in the atmospheric Cavalier Bar.

Kilkea Castle Hotel, Castledermot, County Kildare, Eire. Telephone: (0503) 45156. Duration: all year. Price: (in Irish pounds) from £120 per person per week (1981). Includes special course of daily keep fit and sauna, 1 underwater massage, 1 medicine bath, solarium course, 5 nights accommodation, dietary meals, service and VAT. Bring swimwear and shorts. Beauty treatments extra.

dual chalets set in the grounds. Champneys' carefully supervised cuisine is renowned. Be sure to bring a tracksuit, swimsuit and suitable clothing for country walks.

Champneys at Tring Health Resort, Tring, Hertfordshire HP23 6HY. Telephone: (04427) 3351. Duration: all year. Price: from £215 per person per week single (est), from £423.50 per person per week, room with bath (est). Includes treatment, diets, full board and use of recreational facilities. VAT extra.

See also CIGARETTE WITHDRAWAL.

HERTFORDSHIRE, Tring

Health and Beauty
Champneys at Tring

Holiday your way to health at Champneys in the Chilterns. This luxurious former Rothschild mansion is set in its own 170 acre estate 600 feet up in the Chiltern Hills. It's an ideal setting for a resort devoted to health and beauty. The emphasis here is on individual attention. Your health is thoroughly assessed on arrival, with a doctor's examination and an interview. Then a tailored treatment is designed to suit your special needs. This includes an individually tailored diet. Your daily life revolves around a judicious mixture of exercise and relaxation. The centre's exceptional range of facilities includes a heated indoor swimming pool, tennis courts, physiotherapy unit, saunas, ray-treatment rooms and a fully equipped gymnasium (all included in the cost). There's also a fully equipped beauticians' department which offers a comprehensive range of treatments including muscle toning, depilatory waxing, manicure and pedicure. There are lectures on all sorts of things, as well as films, fashion shows and casino nights. Their craft centre can introduce you to pottery, jewellery-making and painting.

Accommodation in the main house is of luxury standard with rooms overlooking the lawns and gardens or it's in indivi-

LANCASHIRE, Preston

Short Week Course to Beauty
Brooklands Country House Health Farm

Bounce back to health with Judith Brown at Brooklands. This fully equipped health farm, conveniently situated off the M5 and M6, has its own well-stocked kitchen garden and orchard which provide good fruit and vegetables through the year. In addition, Brooklands' high elevation and southern aspect gives it a fine view over the surrounding countryside.

Judith Brown is widely experienced in health and beauty work, and specializes in electrolysis. (This is the first health farm of its kind in the north-west.) She and her experienced staff have a wide range of facilities including a solarium, indoor heated swimming pool, massage

parlour and hairdressing salon. Her short stay courses of balanced health and beauty treatment aim to rejuvenate the body and invigorate all the systems which are 'run down' due to the pressures of modern life.

Guests should bring clothing suitable for indoor light exercise, swimwear and a warm dressing gown. Smoking is not encouraged, except in guests' own rooms.

Brooklands Country House Health Farm, Calder House Lane, Garstang, Nr Preston, Lancashire PR3 1QB. Telephone: (09952) 5162. Registrar: Judith Brown. Duration: all year, any three days and nights. Price: £95 (est). Includes single accommodation, all meals and treatments. VAT extra.

LEICESTERSHIRE, Ragdale

Health and Beauty Programmes
Ragdale Hall

Pamper yourself at Ragdale Hall with massage and a range of beauty treatments in the luxurious atmosphere of a grand country house. It is not a medical centre and treatments are entirely optional. The *table d'hôte* menus, which are included in the programme prices, are carefully chosen to provide a balanced meal, calorie-graded but mouth-watering. You can choose from a range of programmes; prices vary with duration and accommodation. All rooms have colour TV and a telephone. Additional treatments to those in the programme you choose can be booked at an extra charge. They include sauna, dietary consultation, Slendertone, infra-red, underwater massage, manicure and pedicure, bio-peeling, facials, Uvasun, make-up, wax treatments and eyelash and brow dye.

Ragdale Hall, Ragdale, Nr. Melton Mowbray, Leicestershire. Telephone: (066 475) 831/411. Contact: The Reservations Secretary. Duration: all year, 2, 3, 4 days or 1 week. Price: £30.43 per person for 2 days (until March 1981); from £95 (twin shar-
ing) for 3 days; from £125 (twin sharing) for 4 days; from £190 (twin sharing) per week. Includes accommodation, all meals and treatments as indicated in programme. VAT extra. Minimum age 16.

NORTHAMPTONSHIRE, Northampton

Healthy Holiday
Frimley's Health Farm

It's 'Health without tears' at Frimley's historic Thornby Hall. In keeping with their slogan 'No carrot juice at Frimley's', you can eat your way to health here in an elegantly relaxed atmosphere. First, it's breakfast in bed, then meals that feature such delicacies as grilled river trout and strawberry mousse – slimming with sophistication is the order of the day.

You'll also have ample opportunity to pamper yourself with saunas, massages and various beauty treatments. There's a well-equipped gymnasium, free use of bicycles for touring the picturesque villages and surrounding countryside, and facilities nearby for golf, swimming and riding (not included).

Thornby Hall is a 600-year-old mansion surrounded by fine English gardens. A special feature is the four-acre water garden with its own lake and wandering path. Inside, the Hall has the atmosphere of a stately home, complete with antiques and other works of art. You can choose the room where Cromwell slept, or one of the nine four-poster beds.

Frimley's Health Farm, The Hall, Thornby, Northampton. Telephone: (0604) 740001. Duration: all year, 3 days (Sunday to Wednesday) or 1 week. Price: doubles £94.50 for 3 days (1981); singles £214 for 1 week. Includes comprehensive treatment programme, accommodation and all meals. VAT extra.

SURREY, Hindhead

Health and Beauty
Grayshott Hall

Come to Grayshott Hall for a 'Positive Health' holiday. Shortly after arrival you'll have a personal consultation so that your individual diet and treatment can be prescribed by the next morning, when it all begins. Treatment usually includes a short period of fasting and rest which, with massage, steam and sauna baths and aquatherapy, help rid your body of accumulated toxins. It may also involve osteopathy and physiotherapy, under the direction of the matron and sisters. The hall is an attractively restored Victorian country house set in forty-seven acres of landscaped and wooded grounds. Activities on offer include yoga classes, golf on a 9 hole par three course, tennis on an all-weather court, and swimming in a heated indoor pool. The atmosphere is relaxed and informal, so bring only casual clothing. There's a boutique, resident beautician and hairdressing salon. Every room has a private bathroom, fine views, fitted carpets, central heating and, if you want, colour TV.

Grayshott Hall Health Centre, Grayshott, near Hindhead, Surrey GU26 6JJ. Telephone: (042873) 4331. Manager: Peter Craig. Duration: all year. Price: from £25–£42 (estimated average 1981) to £80 per person per day. Includes basic treatment, full board, supplementary treatments. Service and VAT extra. Initial consultation fee £5.

WEST YORKSHIRE, Otley

Health and Beauty
Chevin Hall Health and Beauty Hotel

You're sure of personal attention at Chevin Hall which is spectacularly situated overlooking the Wharfe Valley. Only eighteen clients at a time are admitted for five-day courses of rest, relaxation and weight reduction. No drastic fasting here – instead, a well-balanced high-protein diet and controlled fluid intake for safe, sensible slimming. Physical exercise isn't compulsory, but there's a full range of gymnastic equipment, and a 'slim and trim' class every afternoon. Treatments average five a day, and include Swedish massage, short-wave diathermy, steam baths, aqua massage and the invigorating Roman Spa bath, a hot, bubbling communal bath in seaweed-charged water. Facials, manicure, pedicure, hand and foot waxing, scalp massage and hairdressing are also covered by the basic fee. There is colour TV in every room, a covered heated pool, table tennis room, croquet lawn, tennis court and outdoor sauna, all for your enjoyment.

Chevin Hall Health and Beauty Hotel, Otley, West Yorkshire. Telephone: (0943) 462526. Manager: Mrs E. L. Atkinson. Duration: 5 days. Price: from £180 per person (1981). Includes course, treatment, full board and VAT.

HISTORY

BUCKINGHAMSHIRE,
Great Missenden

Historic Madness in High Places
Missenden Abbey

Some of the great rogues of 2,000 years of history come under scrutiny during this course, from the monster Caligula of the Roman Empire to the scourge of the 20th century, Adolf Hitler. You'll be fascinated by lectures on the madness of kings, the wit of Nietzsche, the quirks of the Marquis de Sade and much else, delivered by speakers who include a Fellow of St Hilda's College, Oxford, a Senior Fellow of Lincoln, a Harley Street psychiatrist and an army general. The abbey's an appropriate setting – one of its own abbots had to be locked up.

Missenden Abbey, Great Missenden, Buckinghamshire HP16 OBD. Telephone: (02 406) 2328. Contact the Warden. Duration: weekend in April. Price: £30 (1981) £26.50 for Buckinghamshire residents. Includes accommodation (usually double rooms, although some singles available), and all meals from Friday dinner to Sunday lunch. No VAT.

See also LACEMAKING, LITERATURE, PARANORMAL, WOODWORKING, YOGA.

KENT, Folkestone

Roman, Medieval and Local History
St Andrews Hotel

Textbook history springs vividly to life in the company of Duncan Harrington, Licentiate of the Institute of Heraldic and Genealogical Studies, and lecturer at the University of Kent. At St Andrews Hotel, Folkestone, Mr Harrington delivers illustrated lectures on medieval language, art and agriculture to make more meaningful your tours of castles, churches, ancient buildings, coal mines and water mills in the district. You'll visit the ancient towns of Rye and Dover and the fairy castle of Leeds, and be a guest at a medieval banquet thrown for you at Chilham Castle. Sixth form history was never like this. Back at the hotel, relax with a swim in the pool.

Galleon World Travel Association Ltd, Galleon House, King Street, Maidstone, Kent ME14 1EG. Telephone: (0622) 63411, or Hobby Holidays (01) 859 0111. Lecturer: Duncan Harrington. Duration: 1 week, 19–26 September. Price: £149 per week (est). Includes bed, breakfast and dinner, and VAT. Add £3.90 for seaview room, £11.90 for private bath.

See also ANTIQUES, CRUISING: INLAND WATERWAYS, GARDENS, PONY TREKKING, SURFING.

WALES, GWYNEDD, Bangor

Sources of Local History
University College of North Wales

Last year's course provided an in-depth look at the development of the Welsh landscape from 1200 to 1750. Eminent researchers such as Professor G. R. J. Jones lectured on topics like 'Welsh Edwardian Castles', 'Urban Expansion and Decay in North Wales 1200 to 1550', and 'Agriculture and the Welsh Land-scape'. There was an afternoon excursion to historic Rhuddlan Castle and town. The 1981 course will be along similar lines; write for details.

Department of Extra-Mural Studies, University College of North Wales, Bangor, Gwynedd LL57 2DG. Telephone: (0248) 51151 ext. 404. Duration: weekend, March. Price: £31 per person (est). Includes tuition, full board.

See also WELSH STUDIES.

HOME EXCHANGE

COUNTRYWIDE

Holiday Home Exchange Register

That expensive holiday you always wanted but knew you could never afford is possible with this home exchange programme. The idea is simple – you swap your house with someone else's at the same time and each of you lives rent free. As an added bonus plants are watered and pets fed. Your home doesn't have to be luxurious or in a tourist area – there are sure to be others with similar homes or people who want to visit relatives in your locality. Times are as flexible as people's various needs. Some participants want a summer holiday, others a weekend break, while still others plan a business trip or a second off-peak holiday and a swap. To make your exchange as smooth as possible Home Rooms Ltd have a number of sensible suggestions such as getting in touch with your partner well ahead of the exchange date to work out details and arranging for a neighbour to be on hand to welcome your guests.

To join the scheme apply between autumn and Christmas to be listed in the main exchange register which is distributed early in the new year. (You can also be included in the May supplement if you register before Easter.) Hundreds of homes are on offer all over the world as well as within the UK.

Home Rooms Ltd, 7 Provost Road, London NW3 4ST. Telephone: (01) 722 8973. Director: Joan Jarosy. Price: Weekend Exchange Club membership £7 (1981): Holiday Home Exchange register £14. Includes Weekend Exchange Club membership.

HONEYMOON

AVON, Bath

Royal Crescent Hotel

This, one of the world's most luxurious and historic hotels, is a Grade 1 Listed Building. Its at the centre of Bath's famous Royal Crescent yet the attentive service and open log fires epitomize the warming atmosphere of an English country house. You'll enjoy it as much as George III's son, the Duke of York did who tarried here in 1795 and 1796. The present Duke of York suite, like all the suites and rooms, boasts a private bathroom, central heating, colour TV, radio and direct-dial phone. There's full room service and twenty-four hour porterage. Some suites offer superb four poster beds. Architectural delights include fine 18th century stucco ceilings, a sweeping horseshoe staircase (one of the finest in Bath) and the formal central staircase with its classical Venetian window. The hotel has a fine art collection and each picture has historical links with Bath. The dining room's food is excellent and surroundings are elegant with an open fireplace and two particularly fine portraits by William Hoare, a founder member of the Royal Academy.

The Royal Crescent Hotel, Royal Crescent, Bath, Avon. Telephone: (0225) 319090. Duration: all year. Price: £36–£60 double, £80–£125 suites per day (1981). Includes accommodation service and VAT.

CUMBRIA, Carlisle

Honeymoon Special
Dalston Hotel

You're guaranteed privacy if you book the honeymoon suite in this elegant 16th century mansion – your room has its own special entrance through the 'Yatt Gate', and you've exclusive use of the original 15th century spiral stone staircase that leads to the six-foot six-inch four-poster bed. Alongside, modern amenities include a double sunken bath with twin showers and, more prosaically, colour TV and a telephone. A half bottle of wine and basket of fruit await you.

Dalston Hotel, Carlisle, Cumbria CA5 7JX. Telephone: (0228) 710271, or Best Western (01) 940 9766. Duration: any 2 nights. Price: £45 per person (est). Includes room, breakfast, a meal voucher of £4 per person per day, service and VAT.

CUMBRIA, Kendal

Honeymoon Weekend
Crooklands Hotel

Crooklands is a romantic, ivy-covered 16th century coaching inn, a perfect base for touring the Lake District. Chris Gabbott, your host, will make sure there's a welcoming bottle of champagne in your room and see that you're served breakfast in bed on your first morning there. The hotel's Swiss Chef guarantees a splendid candlelit dinner in the Olde Worlde restaurant, and on Saturday evening there's a dinner dance. To ensure that 'just marrieds' start with a clean slate, the management has your car washed gratis.

Crooklands Hotel, Kendal, Cumbria LA7 7NW. Telephone: (044 87) 432 or Best Western on (01) 940 9766. Duration: all year, 2 nights, any Friday to Sunday. Price: £40 per person (1981), 31 October–

30 March; £45, 1 April–29 October. Includes double room, all meals, 1 bottle champagne, service and VAT.

DEVON, Honiton

Honeymoon
Combe House Hotel

Delightfully secluded and dating from the 14th century, Combe House Hotel is an idyllic honeymoon retreat. The Great Hall and other reception rooms are gloriously grand and comfortable. Over the past ten years talented John Boswell and his French, cordon bleu trained wife Thérèse, have been gradually furnishing and opening more rooms. It's a labour of love, reflected in such touches as homemade butter biscuits in the bedrooms and fresh flowers everywhere. Thérèse personally supervises the kitchen and John, unusually for a proprietor, serves in the restaurant. The outstanding cuisine includes dishes such as crêpes des moines, filled with locally-caught seafood; gougère de canard (duck baked in mushrooms and cream), and home-baked milles feuilles.

Candlelit in the evenings, the two dining rooms both enjoy fine views of Combe's cedar trees and the park beyond. Honeymooners' best bets are the 'Tommy Wax Room', thirty feet square with a ten-foot ceiling, and the 'Putt Room', with its own little staircase running down to the lawns; both have *en suite* baths.

Combe House Hotel, Gittisham, Nr Honiton, Devon. Telephone: (0404) 2756. Proprietors: John and Thérèse Boswell. Duration: mid March to end December. Price: doubles £40–£52 (1981). Includes breakfast, service and VAT.

DEVON, Kingsbridge

Honeymoon
Buckland-Tout-Saints Hotel

This gracious Queen Anne mansion in its fine park holds the AA's coveted Red Star Award and is recommended by Egon Ronay. An elegant country house atmosphere mingles with quiet informality to ensure you a wonderful weekend. Rooms overlooking the South Hams each have a private bathroom. Guaranteed peace and quiet and a welcoming bottle of champagne are ingredients which can only enhance the situation.

Buckland-Tout-Saints Hotel, Kingsbridge, Devon TQ7 2DS. Telephone: (0548) 2586/3172 or Best Western on (01) 940 9766. Duration: end of April to end of October, 3 or 7 days. Price: £80–£89.75 per person for 3 days (est); £170–£182.50 per person for 7 days (est). Includes double bedroom with private bathroom, full English breakfast and dinner each day, flowers, 1 bottle champagne and VAT.

SOMERSET, Wells

Honeymoon Weekend
Swan Hotel

If you're planning a winter wedding, this is for you. Arrive to the welcoming warmth of log fires, and the comfortable splendour of a four-poster bed and private bathroom, in this famous 15th century timbered coaching inn. Right on its doorstep, you have a superb view of the West Front of Wells Cathedral. The Swan is a perfect centre from which to enjoy the surrounding West Country.

The Swan Hotel, Wells, Somerset. Telephone: (0749) 78877 or Best Western on (01) 940 9766. Duration: autumn/winter/spring weekends only. Price: £41.50 per couple (est). Includes bed, breakfast, dinner, service and VAT.

WALES, DYFED, Capel Isaac

Honeymoon
Maesteilo Mansion

Start married life in style at Maesteilo Mansion Country House Hotel. This superb small family mansion, run by resident owners, Mr and Mrs C. E. Roberts, is set in sixteen acres of fine timbered grounds, with panoramic views across valley and woodland, its own small lake and formal gardens. A very limited number of guests (no more than ten) have a choice of four luxury suites as well as other fine rooms. Amenities include a thirty-two foot heated, covered swimming pool, tennis court and games room, while good fishing and riding can be arranged locally (at extra cost). Their cordon bleu menu features home-grown fruit and vegetables, and their own poultry, all served in the elegant Country House dining room. It's just the right sort of peaceful atmosphere and personal attention for your honeymoon.

Maesteilo Mansion, Country House Hotel, Capel Isaac, Llandeilo, Dyfed, Wales. Telephone: (05584) 510. Proprietors: Mr and Mrs C. E. Roberts. Duration: all year. Price: from £40–£50 per couple (1981) 1 night full board, and from £250–£270 per couple 1 week full board (est). Service and VAT extra.

WILTSHIRE, Swindon

Happy Honeymooners
Blunsdon House Hotel

Set in twenty superb Cotswold acres, Blunsdon House has been tastefully modernized. Couples who rent their deluxe honeymoon suite with the four-poster are treated to champagne on arrival, dinner and wine for two (up to £20) in their cosy Ridge Restaurant, and as much breakfast as you can devour. If you plan to arrive late, you can transfer your meals to Sunday. The price then includes your room on Saturday night, breakfast, traditional Sunday lunch with roast beef, and table d'hote Sunday dinner.

Blunsdon House Hotel, Swindon, Wiltshire SN2 4AD. Telephone: (0793) 721701 or Best Western on (01) 940 9766. Duration: all year, any Friday to Sunday. Price: £56 (1981) per couple in autumn/winter; £60.50 in spring; £65 in summer. Includes room with private bath and colour TV, breakfast, 2 nights dinner, Sunday lunch, service and VAT. Honeymoon suite with 4 poster £10 extra.

HORSE-DRAWN CARAVANS

EIRE

Horse Drawn Caravans Holidays
Joe Walsh Tours

One of the most relaxing and colourful ways to explore the Emerald Isle is by horse-drawn caravan. This Joe Walsh holiday makes it easy – on arrival in Cork you're met and transferred by private car to the caravan base at Kilbrittain. There you'll receive full instructions on harnessing your horse and other necessary information. You'll also be provided with suggested routes and a list of overnight campsites (cost approximately £3 per night). Your caravan sleeps four comfortably and is fully equipped with cooking utensils and bedding. (Bring your own towels.) If you want to bring your own riding horse along this can be pre-arranged.

Joe Walsh Tours Ltd, Reservations Department, Ireland House, 150 New Bond Street, London W1Y 0AQ. Telephone (01) 493 3201. Duration: 1 week May to October. Price: from £107 (est) per person with sea ferry ticket, from £148.50 (est) per person with air ticket. Includes hire of fully equipped caravan for one week, transfer from sea or airport to caravan base. Reductions for children under 14.

See also FISHING: COARSE, GOLF.

NORFOLK, Wymondham

Breckland Holidays

These caravan holidays let you tour the heart of Norfolk with some of England's most unspoilt countryside at an old-fashioned pace. You'll travel in a fully-equipped luxury caravan (built in Breckland's own workshops), be given full details of suggested routes and stop-overs carefully selected for their peaceful atmosphere and scenic delights and be pro-

PICKERSGILL'S STAGE WAGGON.

vided with a specially-trained horse. You don't need any previous experience – Breckland's 'on the move' twenty-four hour a day service ensures constant help in animal management. (Each caravan has a special animal care locker which contains all the feed and equipment you're likely to require plus printed instructions.) A service vehicle visits recommended overnight stopping sites daily to check harness and cope with any problems. At the end of your holiday you're invited to a barbecue at Mill Farm which includes free wine and soft drinks. Apart from the use of the bath and shower facilities you'll be able to enjoy the outdoor pool, croquet lawn and tennis court.

Breckland Holidays, Mill Farm, Deopham, Wymondham, Norfolk NR18 9DQ. Telephone: (0953) 850380. Duration: 1 week April to September. Price: from £145 per week (1981). Includes 4 berth caravan, horse feeds, caravan parking, use of facilities, public liability insurance. VAT extra.

WALES, POWYS, Talgarth

Welsh Horse Drawn Holidays
Rhydybont Farm

Roam through Wales Romany-style. These caravan holidays give you a chance to explore unspoilt rural country at a properly leisurely pace. Previous experience with horses is unnecessary – these animals are docile and used to all kinds of handlers. They're also strong. During the winter they're liable to be ploughing champions. So wherever you want to go they'll lead.

When you set out with your four-berth caravan there are 500 square miles of National Park and Wye Valley countryside ahead of you. See the Black Mountains and the Brecon Beacons. Many of its summits exceed 2000 feet.

The centre provides you with maps which outline many great routes and mark the best overnight stopping places. There are toilets at or near all overnight stops. (You can paddock your horse at an adjacent farm – at £2–£3.) Oats are supplied free and gas for cooking is supplied at cost.

Insurance and all necessary cutlery and utensils are also supplied. Showers are available at base and there are adequate water provisions *en route*. You'll find miles of fishing and many lakes stocked with trout and salmon in the area. (For details of charges and local rights enquire with the hirers.) This is the ideal family holiday – you'll find that your horse soon becomes a member of the family.

Welsh Horse Drawn Holidays, Rhydybont Farm, Talgarth, Powys, Wales. Telephone: (087 481) 346. Proprietors: Glenys and Austin Gwillim. Duration: Wednesday to Wednesday, Saturday to Saturday, March to November. Price: From £130 to £190 per week according to season (1981). Includes 4 berth caravan, horse, horse feeds, harness, public liability insurance. Riding pony can be hired, £40 per week. VAT extra. Campsite charges £2 per night. Gas extra.

Horse Racing

COUNTRYWIDE

Racing Days and Weekends
Racegoers Club

Be a winner and join the Racegoers Club. For an annual £3.50 subscription fee you'll be entitled to reduced admission to fifty-four racecourses on over 300 racing days a year, free racecards at many courses, lectures and film shows on racing, conducted visits to stables, overseas tours to France, America and other countries, a quarterly Club Newsletter, discounts on selected racing publications, and an opportunity to join racehorse ownership syndicates. The club's distinguished patrons include The Marquess of Abergavenny (Her Majesty's Representative at Ascot) and the chairmen of Cheltenham, Goodwood, Devon and Exeter, and Wolverhampton racecourses.

The club arranges many special events. One example: a visit to the Royal Stud at Sandringham where members were shown around by the Queen's stud manager Michael Oswald. They also organize weekends such as a Cheltenham weekend which includes two days' racing, a racing celebrity dinner and a stable visit with accommodation near the race course.

The Racegoers Club, 42 Portman Square, London W1H 0JE. Telephone: (01) 486 4571. Price: membership £3.50 per year (1981) (plus £1.50 entrance fee). Details of weekends and outings provided in newsletter.

Hot Air Ballooning

AVON, Bristol

Ballooning Weekends
Grand Hotel

Prepare for lift-off, as a qualified pilot wafts you away on a carefully controlled balloon flight. Hovering hundreds of feet high in the sky, whole counties will be spread below you. You'll touch down at a preselected landing field, and be returned to the hotel by a Land Rover, which has followed the flight. You may have covered up to fifteen miles.

Safely home again, celebrate with your fellow travellers and champagne. (If the weather's unkind and you can't fly, come back on any Skysales weekend and have a free ride.) The weekend includes two nights in one of the historic city's finest luxury hotels.

The Grand Hotel, Broad Street, Bristol, Avon. Telephone: (0272) 291645 or Best Western on (01) 940 9766. Host: Denis Watkins. Duration: 2 nights, Friday and Saturday, late September to late November. Price: £96.50 (est). Includes balloon flight, champagne, accommodation, Friday and Saturday nights, breakfast, 3 main meals and VAT.

BERKSHIRE, Elcot Park

Weekend Ballooning
Country House Hotel

This is one holiday you won't want to go with a bang! Ballooning sessions with a qualified pilot whisk you aloft as high as 1000 feet. You'll arrive on Saturday in time for one o'clock luncheon, followed by discussions, slides, films and afternoon tea before taking off. Full English breakfast is available on Sunday morning, but a Continental breakfast is recommended if you're flying soon afterwards. Sessions will be arranged after Sunday lunch if the weather has prevented earlier flights and a Land Rover is on hand to retrieve you at your landing. If you're unable to leave the ground at all due to bad weather, there'll be a £15 reduction in your bill.

Elcot Park was built in 1678, and added to over the years. Its sixteen acres of parkland were planned in the 19th century by Sir William Paxton, a Royal Gardener.

Country House Hotel, Elcot Park, near Newbury, Berkshire (five miles from Newbury on the A4). Telephone: (04885) 276/421. Duration: weekends early April; early May; end of September; mid October. Price: £55 per person (est) April and May; £70 per person (est) September and October. Includes tuition, bed, all meals from Saturday lunch to Sunday tea and VAT.

See also NEEDLEWORK, THEATRE GOING.

INDUSTRIAL ARCHAEOLOGY

DERBYSHIRE, Castleton

Canals and Railways of the Peak
Peak National Park Study Centre

Backtrack your way to a bygone age. The rugged Peak District long provided a barrier to communication which was not fully overcome until the 18th century. These holidays give you a chance to explore the old systems of aqueducts and locks which linked the Cromford and Peak Forest Canals. Visit the Anderton Lift – the only working canal lift in Britain. See the Middleton Top Engine House, High Peak Wharf, and the Crich Tramway Museum, all fascinating remnants of the great industrial age in Britain. You can also trek over the Peaks, take boat trips, and walk along the old railway lines.

You'll stay at the Peak National Study Centre, a century-old mansion which stands in twenty-seven acres of parkland. It's now completely modernized, with central heating, social rooms, a large slide laboratory and a wide range of audio-visual equipment which can be used by guests. There's also a shop which sells everyday articles from sweets to pens. Guests are advised to bring warm clothing, waterproofs and walking shoes, since much of the holiday will be spent outdoors.

Peak National Park Study Centre, Lose-hill Hall, Castleton, Derbyshire S30 2WB. Telephone: (0443) 20373. Principal: Peter Townsend. Duration: 8–15 August. Price: £98 (1981) plus VAT. Includes accommodation, meals, tuition, various other facilities and occasional transport.

See ARCHAEOLOGY.

WALES, GWYNEDD, Betws-y-Coed

1 Practical Industrial Archaeology I and II
2 Quarries, Mines and Railways in North Wales
The Drapers' Field Centre

Increasingly we're becoming fascinated by our industrial past. In the first of these courses you'll be introduced to the photographic and other techniques used to record and assess industrial history. Later in the year you can study the extensive remains of a disused lead and zinc mine in a beautiful wood overlooking the Conwy Valley. The object of this course is to unravel little-known history and to publish the results.

John Horsley Denton, an expert in North Wales' industrial archaeology, runs the Quarries, Mines and Railways course. This examination of slate and stone quarries, mines and associated transport systems is strenuous, since many of the long abandoned sites are remote.

The Drapers' Field Centre, Rhyd-Creuau, Betws-y-Coed, Gwynedd, Wales LL24 0HB. Telephone: (06902) 494. Warden: Tony Scharer. Duration: dates on application. Price: £84 per person per week (est). Includes tuition, accommodation, all meals. £10 deposit required. Membership of Field Studies Council required, subscription £2 per year.

A wide variety of other courses also available, send for brochure.

See also RURAL SKILLS.

IRISH STUDIES

EIRE, Dublin

EIRE, Dublin

In Search of Ireland
University College, Dublin

Whether you're interested in Ireland's yesterdays or tomorrows, from Brian Boru to modern Belfast, University College has a course. These are given on the Belfield campus of University College, Dublin, just three miles from the centre of the city. Lecturers include distinguished members of the university itself, such as Donal McCartney, Professor of Modern Irish History, and Maurice Manning, Lecturer in Political Science, and outside experts such as William Shannon, US Ambassador to Ireland, and Hugh Gerrard, the well-known author.

Seminars are devoted to such topics as the arts in Ireland, the political and economic life of the country and its historic development. As part of the course, there are two day-long field tours to historic and archaeological sites such as Glendalaugh and the Boyne Valley. The college's programme attracts an international range of students and is renowned for the lively social atmosphere.

Accommodation is in private houses within a three mile radius of the campus. This is normally in twin-bedded rooms, though some singles are available.

Summer School Office, University College, Belfield, Dublin 4, Eire. Telephone: (01) (0001 from England) 693244. Contact: Nora Gallagher. Duration: 16 days, 1–17 July. Price: £166 Irish pounds (twin bedded room), £173 (single) per person (1981). Includes tuition, visits, field tours, entertainments, bed and breakfast. A few scholarships and fee remissions are available.

1 Wells of Irish Literature
2 Dubliners All
Trinity College

The Institute of Irish Studies is a small independent organization established in 1969 to meet an international demand for third level and adult education courses on Irish life and culture. The Advisory Committee includes James Carney, Professor at the Dublin Institute for Advanced Studies, and Basil Payne, noted Irish poet and writer. The 'Wells of Irish Literature' programme is an interdisciplinary lecture series which investigates the main sources of influence on Irish writers through the centuries. The fee includes lectures, excursions, theatre, other entertainment and city-centre campus accommodation. In 'Dubliners All' students are given seminars of one week each on three major writers – James Joyce, Sean O'Casey and Flann O'Brien. Each is preceded by a one-week interdisciplinary course of Irish studies. Again the fee includes campus accommodation and the above extras.

The Institute of Irish Studies, 5 Wilton Place, Dublin 2, Eire. Telephone: (01) (0001 from England) 763276. Director: Noelle Clery. Duration: 1 6–17 July, 2 27 July–21 August. Price: 1 (Irish pounds) £245, 2 £490 (1981). Includes tuition, accommodation, excursions and entertainment.

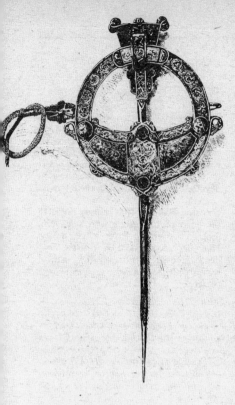

NORTHERN IRELAND, COUNTY LONDONDERRY, Coleraine

Talk Tour
New University of Ulster

The aptly-named New University is one of the youngest institutions of higher learning in the UK. It's set in the bustling market town of Coleraine which spans the River Bann, and has an excellent shopping centre, a bird sanctuary and a boating marina.

Every summer, the University offers a series of non-residential courses organized by leaders chosen for their specialized knowledge of the area. This one emphasizes the deep links between Ireland and America. You'll visit the famous Gray's Printing Works at Strabane, where the man who printed the American Declaration of Independence learned his trade, and where President Woodrow Wilson's grandfather worked. You'll also tour the ancestral home of American multi-millionaire Andrew Mellon, and the Ulster-American Folk Park with its 18th century Irish cottages and log-built replicas of early American settlements.

'Talks and Tours 81' office J 705, 7th Floor, Tower, New University of Ulster, Coleraine, County Londonderry, Northern Ireland. Telephone: (0265) 4141, ext 501. Duration: 1 day. Price: £4.50 adult (est), £2.50 child (est). Includes entrance fees. Accommodation list on application to Coleraine Borough Council, Cloonavin, Portstewart Road, Coleraine, Northern Ireland. Telephone: (0265) 52181. Example: Mrs Jean Brown, 174 Ballbogey Road, Coleraine. Telephone: (02657) 31627. Price: £5.25 (est). Includes room, breakfast and VAT.

JAZZ

BUCKINGHAMSHIRE, Milton Keynes

1 All Music Easter Course
2 Summer Jazz Course
Wavendon All Music Plan

Make it with the music at Milton Keynes. Here they run everything from courses for classicists to jamborees for jazz fanatics. The musical tutors are of the highest standards. Members of the Albineri String Quartet are among the classics tutors and there are improvisation demonstrations by Johnny Dankworth and Paul Hart.

The Summer Jazz Course is for musicians interested in jazz and participants should be able to read music and have a reasonable standard of instrumental ability. There will be personal tuition, talks and discussions and in the evening there'll be a jam session when you can play for the entertainment of your fellow students.

Wavendon All Music Plan, The Stables, Wavendon, Milton Keynes, Buckinghamshire MK17 8LT. Telephone: (0908) 582522. Contact: The Administrator. Duration: 1 18–25 April; 2 29 August–4 September. Price: 1 £90 per person per week (1981). Includes tuition, full board single; 2 £85 per person per week. Includes tuition, full board single.

LANCASHIRE, Preston

Jazz Courses
Alston Hall

The 'Play Jazz' course is designed for the keen amateur. You'll have sectional rehearsals under the capable direction of two tutors, followed by full band rehearsals of the standard big band repertoire. There'll also be talks and a session devoted to improvisation in the big band context.

Alston Hall is a 19th century house in the heart of Lancashire with a magnificent view over the River Ribble valley. Half the accommodation for the residential courses is in twin rooms, half in rooms with pleasant well-equipped single cubicles.

Alston Hall, Longridge, Preston, Lancashire PR3 3BP. Telephone: (077 478) 3589. The Principal: Mrs Anne Lightfoot. Duration: 16–18 January and 1 week August. Price: 1 week £80.50 per person (1981), Lancashire residents £66.50. Weekend £24 per person, Lancashire residents £20. Includes tuition and full board. No VAT.

See also LITERATURE, OPERA.

JEWELLERY

CORNWALL, Penzance

Jewellery Making
Ponsondane

Ponsondane is a spacious mansion on the outskirts of town, with a large modern wing and a sweeping view across to St Michael's Mount. This holiday is for beginners, although any talents you have in the use of tools will come in handy. Craftsman jewellery designer Peter Ball instructs you in the basic methods of handling silver and gemstones, so at the end of the week you'll be familiar with silver-soldering and cold forging, and will probably have designed and made at least one piece of jewellery. Silver and other materials can be bought on the premises.

For details of Holiday Fellowship see WALKING, *Loch Awe.*

Holiday Fellowship, 142/144 Great North Way, London NW4 1EG. Telephone: (01) 203 3381. Leader: Peter Ball. Duration: 1

DEVON, Tiverton

Lacemaking
The English Lace School

This residential school offers five-day lacemaking courses in one of England's best loved Devon holiday centres. Lacemaking is not particularly difficult – it takes time and patience but doesn't require expensive equipment. Moderate ability can, within a single course, produce a small but exquisite article such as a paperweight, hankie edge, brooch or pendant. Several of the skills on offer are in danger of being lost and forgotten – you can study Downton Lace making under the tutelage of the last Downton worker as well as Branscombe Point taught by one of the last two Branscombe lacemakers' nieces. Courses also cover care and preservation of lace, Dorset buttons, English quilting, identification of lace, smock-making, tatting and introduction to bobbin lace.

The English Lace School, 42 St Peter's Street, Tiverton, Devon. Telephone: (08842) 3918. Principal: Susan Cox. Duration: weekends and 4½ days February to December. Price: weekends from £18 (est); 4½ days from £32 (est). Includes tuition. Accommodation £21 per person (est). Includes 2 nights (twin) breakfast and dinner. £52 per person (est). Includes 5 nights (twin) breakfast and dinner. Send for brochure for further details of the programme.

YORKSHIRE, Ripon

Lacemaking
Grantley Hall

This is a practical course for beginners as well as those who want to improve their technique.

Grantley Hall Adult Residential College, Ripon, North Yorkshire. Telephone: (076 586) 259. Director: Mrs M. Scott. Duration: 4 days, 30 January–2 February. Price: £15 per day (1981) (£8 for residents of North Yorkshire and parts of surrounding area). Includes tuition, accommodation 3 or 4 per room and all meals. Students are expected to make their beds and help with evening tea making. Patterns and materials provided for beginners but bring your own if you have them. No VAT.

See also SENIOR CITIZENS.

LANGUAGES

BEDFORDSHIRE, Woburn

Language Follow-Up
1 Kontakte
2 Russian Language and People
3 Advanced German Weekend
Maryland College

These programmes set out to consolidate what's been taught to date of the courses on BBC 1 and Radio 4 language broadcasts.

'Kontakte' is specially designed for beginners in German who want to follow the rebroadcast of the successful BBC 'Kontakte' course. It'll also prepare you for some of the problems to come. Be sure to bring the course books with you.

The Russian course follows the BBC TV series, and the Advanced German weekend is for German speakers of 'O' Level standard who are following the BBC 'Keine Problem' series.

The Principal, Maryland College, Woburn, Milton Keynes MK17 9JD. Telephone: (052 525) 688. Duration: weekends; 1 and 2 dates on application; 3 13–15 February. Price: £27.24 (1981), Bedfordshire students £24.25. Includes tuition, accommodation (mainly single rooms, some twins), and all meals. Bring course books and own towel. No VAT.

See also GARDENING, LACEMAKING, PHOTOGRAPHY.

CHESHIRE, Burton

Intermediate French
Burton Manor College

The popular Intermediate French course is offered regularly at Burton Manor. In 1980 it was conducted, in French, by Mimi Brown, for students who had studied the language before. You're encouraged to speak *en français* whenever you can. For details of the 1981 programme, send SAE for brochure.

For details of Burton Manor, see CINEMA AND VIDEO.

Burton Manor College, Burton, Wirral, Cheshire L64 5SJ. Telephone: (051) 336 2262. Principal: Allan Kingsbury. Duration: weekend. Price: £17.70 per person per day (1981). Includes tuition, full board (twin room) and VAT.

See also ASTRONOMY, CINEMA AND VIDEO, DANCE, ECOLOGY, FURNITURE RESTORATION, GARDENING.

LANCASHIRE, Chorley

South East Asian Language and Culture
Lancashire College

These highly intensive courses are designed to make you fluent in the languages spoken by most Asians from India, Pakistan and Bangladesh. They'll provide a basic knowledge of practical conversational Punjabi, Urdu, Bengali and Gujurati, plus an insight into South-Eastern Asian culture. You'll be taught in groups of one to four by native speakers, and will speak the language concerned from breakfast at 8.30 a.m. until bedtime. There are generally about eight hours of formal teaching a day and an unlimited number of hours of informal tuition. When the course is over, your tutors will meet and tape a series of follow-up exercises to suit each student's individual requirements. Study facilities include modern lecture rooms, audio-visual aids (including closed circuit TV), reprographic services (offset litho, photocopying, duplication, OHP slide-makers etc.), display stands and screens. Other languages are taught by similar methods, including Chinese, Swahili, Russian, Romanian, Arabic, Farsi, Japanese and Serbo-Croat.

For details of Lancashire College, see WINE TASTING.

Lancashire College, Southport Road, Chorley, Lancashire PR7 1NB. Telephone: (025 72) 76719. Courses Secretary: Diane Gibney. Duration: weekend, weekly, January to December. Price: £72.50 per person per week (1981), Lancashire residents £67.50; £29 per person per weekend, Lancashire residents £27. Includes course, accommodation and full board.

See also DANCE, WINE TASTING.

SUSSEX, Chichester

Languages
The Earnley Concourse

A visit to Earnley is guaranteed to freshen up your French, get your German into good shape, increase your Italian or make your Spanish sparkle. Each language course is presented over a series of five weekends at a different level of proficiency.

For details of the Concourse see ANTIQUES.

The Earnley Concourse, near Chichester, Sussex PO20 7JL. Telephone: (0243) 670392/670326. Duration: 1 and 2 weekends, May to July. Price: 2 day course £40 (est). Includes tuition, accommodation in a twin room with private bath and all meals. VAT extra. Choose course carefully; contact 'Language Course Information' at above address. Minibus from Chichester Station 90p each day.

See also ANTIQUES, CREATIVE WRITING, FLOWER ARRANGING, FOLK AND JAZZ, MUSIC, PUPPETRY, SURVIVAL TRAINING, WINE TASTING.

WEST MIDLANDS, Wolverhampton

French for Holidaymakers
Pendrell Hall

Pendrell Hall is a mid 19th century building set in ten acres of landscaped gardens, not two miles from the village of Codsall. In the early 1900s, it was extensively renovated, and the fine wood panelling and carved pillars added. It's named after the Pendrell family, friends of the one-time owners the Giffords, who collaborated to spirit Charles II out of the country after his defeat at the Battle of Worcester. On his return at the Restoration, the Pendrells were granted a perpetual pension, which some descendents still receive.

The wide range of non-vocational and recreational subjects offered here includes one that's perfect if you're planning to holiday in France and speak little or no *français*. You'll learn enough to be able to book hotel rooms, order meals, ask directions and have simple chats with the locals. The course includes illustrated talks (in English) on the most popular tourist regions – Brittany, Côte d'Azur, Ardèche, Provence and Paris – to help you plan your route, choose your destination and make the most of your visit. Saturday is capped with a French-style evening meal and entertainment.

Pendrell Hall, College of Residential Adult Education, Codsall Wood, near Wolverhampton WV8 1QP. Telephone: (090 74) 2398. Secretary: Mrs Kathy Banks. Duration: 3 days, summer. Price: singles £30 (1981) (lower rates for residents of West Midlands area). Includes tuition and full board. Bring towel and soap.

See also FLOWER ARRANGING, WINE TASTING, YOGA.

LIFESTYLES

NORTH YORKSHIRE, Settle

Life and Creativity Course
High Trenhouse

Have you ever rock climbed, baked bread, milked a cow, built a wall? Or spun wool, navigated in the dark, cooked a feast for twenty? There's lots new to do and lots to learn at High Trenhouse. The aim here is to develop creativity and a positive approach to life through sharing a stimulating range of activities in beautiful countryside on a smallholding. You'll sleep in single and double bedrooms (with fitted bunks and continental quilts) in the farmhouse, and you'll eat a wholesome, generous diet, mainly from home produce. Specialist equipment is provided for all activities – which range from acting and bivouacing to woodwork and weaving – but visitors should bring warm, practical clothing, good boots and waterproofs. (Any course of five days minimum or three weekends combined qualifies for the Duke of Edinburgh Residential Project.)

High Trenhouse, Malham Moor, Settle, North Yorkshire BD24 9PR. Telephone: (072 93) 322. Duration: 5 or 7 nights all year round. Dates on application. Price: £40–£46 (est) per person for 5 nights, £76–£101 (est) for 7 nights, according to season. Includes tuition, specialist equipment, transport when necessary and full board. VAT extra. Some equipment can be hired. Group courses can be specially arranged. 1981 dates and prices not final at press time, send for brochure.

WALES, POWYS, Machynlleth

Lifestyles and Ideas
Centre for Alternative Technology

The Centre for Alternative Technology is living proof of the exciting possibilities of self-sufficiency in a world of rapidly dwindling resources. In this marvellously sited old slate quarry overlooking Snowdonia National Park, thirty resident enthusiasts contribute a wide range of skills, and run an alternative technology experiment which is sponsored by the Society for Environmental Improvement (a registered charity). You can visit it every day except Christmas, from 10.00 a.m. to 5.00 p.m. (dusk in winter), or choose from a wide range of two-day residential courses, such as the 'Philosophy of Alternatives', an examination of alternative approaches to energy, food, shelter, work, politics and lifestyle. 'The Future of Work', on the other hand is a thought-provoking look at the social implications of modern technology which examines issues such as rising unemployment, co-operative work schemes and educating for leisure. Other courses examine solar energy, vegetarian wholefood cookery, blacksmithing, beginner's beekeeping and small-scale fish farming. (If you are unemployed there's a £10 reduction in the normal course fee.)

Centre for Alternative Technology, Machynlleth, Powys, Wales. Telephone: (0654) 2400. Secretary: Jill Whitehead. Duration: 2 and 5 days. Price: 2 days from £35.25 per person (est); 5 days from £69.50 per person (est). Includes tuition, full board and VAT.

LITERATURE

BERKSHIRE, Eton

Literary Summer Courses
1 *Creative Approach to Literature*
2 *English Writers*
3 *The Art of the Book*
4 *The Victorian Novel*
Eton College

Eton's more recent illustrious graduates include such literary figures as Aldous Huxley, George Orwell and Ian Fleming. In the English Writers course you'll trace the history of English literature by examining manuscripts, letters and books from Eton library's own priceless collection, including first editions and original manuscripts from Tudor plays to James Bond novels.

Creative Approach covers the basics of literature through discussion, and gives you the opportunity to do some creative writing of your own under the guidance of Eton tutor Christopher J. Woodland.

The Art of the Book deals with the practical side of things – production, decorating, binding, plus a special look at pre-17th century techniques, and the aesthetics of book collection.

The Victorian Novel will focus on three or four major works; you'll be notified in advance of the course outline.

For details of Eton College see ARCHITECTURE.

Independent Summer Schools, Southfield, Bath Road, Marlborough, Wiltshire SN8 1PA. Telephone: (0672) 54222. Duration: 1 5 half days (afternoons) August; 2, 3 and 4 10 half days (mornings) in August. Price: £150 (est) for full course; 1 must be combined with another half course. Includes tuition, accommodation in single study bedrooms and all meals.

See also ARCHITECTURE, DRAMA.

BUCKINGHAMSHIRE, Great Missenden

Leading Ladies in English Letters
Missenden Abbey

Attention all women – the course you've been waiting for has arrived. Two gentlemen tutors combine their comprehensive scholarship in two delightfully literate days which celebrate centuries of female literary achievements, including medieval mystic Julian of Norwich, Aphra Behn (a lady spy for King Charles II), the Brontës, Jane Austen, Virginia Woolf and Iris Murdoch – to name but a few. In the first session you're invited to share your own favourite female writers.

Missenden Abbey, Great Missenden, Buckinghamshire HP16 0BD. Telephone: (024 06) 2328. Duration: weekend, end of November. Price: £30 (1981), Buckinghamshire residents £26.50. Includes tuition, accommodation (mainly twin rooms) and all meals from Friday dinner to Sunday lunch.

See also HISTORY, LACEMAKING, PARANORMAL, WOODWORKING, YOGA.

DORSET, Dorchester

Thomas Hardy Holidays
The Old Rectory

See where it all happened – visit Thomas Hardy country in deepest Dorset and stay at the Old Rectory, which is just two miles from Dorchester (Hardy's Casterbridge) and one and a half miles from Hardy's Buttflow and Stensford (Melstock) Church, where Hardy's heart is buried. The Old Rectory itself dates from before Hardy's time (it was built in 1767, though there's been a house on this site since 1292). It used to be the home of the local rector, and Thomas Hardy visited the house regularly to dine with the rector and his friends. There are three large double rooms with bed and breakfast provided. Guests are free to stay for as long as they wish and these holidays are not according to any rigid timetable. Jane Davis is a member of the Thomas Hardy Society and provides printed pamphlets (price 10p) of special tours to areas described in Hardy's greatest books. (For example, Tour No 1 covers the country of 'Tess of the D'Urbervilles', giving a detailed map with the real names and Hardy's names for main sites.) This is your chance to 'live' some of English literature's finest works for yourself. The Old Rectory is just seven miles from the coast.

The Old Rectory, West Stafford, Dorchester, Dorset DT2 8AB. Telephone: (0305) 4643. Proprietor: Jane Davis. Duration: all year. Price: £6 per person per night, for bed and breakfast (1981). Tour guide 10p. Includes VAT.

EIRE, Sligo, Douglas High Bridge

The Twenty-Second Yeats International Summer School

In 1973 the riverside Royal Bank, Sligo was presented to the Yeats Society. It's now the home of the International Summer School which has been drawing students and admirers of the artist's work for twenty-two years. Lectures and seminars are given by an internationally distinguished group of academics, including Dr John Kelly, Oxford; Prof. Helen Vendler, Boston University; Prof. Francis J. Byrne, University of Toronto. The course of more than fifty hours is worth the equivalent of most unit or three credit courses. Upon its successful completion certificates are issued on request. There's also provision for graduate credits through special seminar exercises and specialist consultations.

On the first day you'll be the guest of the Mayor of Sligo at a reception for students and lecturers in the Town Hall and that evening you can attend a Yeats play presented by the Sligo Drama Circle. Other highlights in addition to the lectures and seminars include a song and harp recital, an informal Irish concert, a film show that features 'Yeats and the Coming Times' and 'Yeats Country', an all day bus tour to Coole and Thoor Ballylee, plays, poetry readings and a farewell party.

Yeats Society, Douglas Hyde Bridge, Sligo, Eire. Telephone: Sligo 2693. Secretary: Kathleen Moran. Duration: 8–22 August. Price: £105 (est), includes course fee. Accommodation arranged, prices from £12 per person per day (est) for hotel accommodation, bed and breakfast, £7 (est) for guest house accommodation.

HEREFORD AND WORCESTER, Stoke Heath

The Heart of England – Its Literature and Art
Avoncroft College

A. E. Housman spent much of his boyhood in rural Worcestershire so Avoncroft College, two miles from Bromsgrove, makes an ideal centre for a study of some of the great names in the arts who hail from the Midlands. The course is built around a programme of daily visits to local places of interest such as Wenlock Edge and Stratford-upon-Avon. Treats such as an evening performance at the Royal Shakespeare Theatre and visits to Wightwick Manor and Birmingham Cathedral to see the work of pre-Raphaelite painter Burne-Jones are also included. Coach excursions will be preceded by lectures at the college and there's plenty of informal discussion. The 1980 programme included lectures such as a slide presentation 'The Enigma of the Shropshire Lad', 'Sons and Lovers: Growing up in Eastwood'; and 'Elgar – The Man and his music'. Course members on a visit to the Birmingham City Art Gallery's pre-Raphaelite collection were guided by the Gallery's Keeper of the Department of Fine Art. They also took a guided tour of D. H. Lawrence's birthplace as well as other excursions. The fee includes one week's board and accommodation, tuition, theatre tickets and excursions.

City of Birmingham, Personnel Department, Avoncroft College, Stoke Heath, Nr Bromsgrove, Worcestershire B60 4JS. Telephone: (0527) 31331. Head of College: Mr Bertram Foord. Duration: 1 week, July. Price: £77 per person (1981). Includes tuition, theatre tickets, visits and full board. Single room supplement £4. VAT extra.

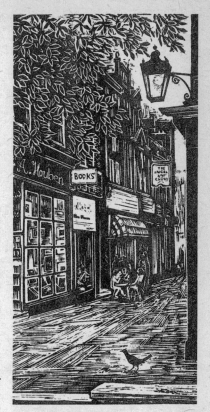

LANCASHIRE, Preston

The Fiction of Henry James
Alston Hall

Peter Cushing and David Evans will lead this look at Henry James' work. You'll focus on two novels, *The Europeans* and *What Maisie Knew*, with a showing of the recent film version of the former.

For details of Alston Hall see JAZZ.

Alston Hall, Longridge, Preston, Lancashire PR3 3BP. Telephone: (077 478) 3589. The Principal: Mrs Anne Lightfoot. Duration: 6–8 February. Price: £24 per person (1981), Lancashire residents £20. Includes tuition and full board. No VAT.

See also JAZZ, OPERA.

YORKSHIRE, Bingley

Yorkshire and the Brontës
Bankfield Hotel

The West Riding and its moors and dales feature strongly in many of the works of the prolific Brontës. Chris Summers, a specialist on this fascinating family and their books, leads discussions and visits to the Brontë Parsonage, Haworth itself, Hartshed Church, Roe Head School, Mirfield Moor, Clough House, Hightown, Oakwell Hall, the Red House and Shears Inn – all places of pilgrimage for enthusiastic Brontë admirers.

Leisure Learning Weekends, Embassy Hotels Ltd, Station Street, Burton-upon-Trent, Staffordshire DE14 1BZ. Telephone: (0283) 66587. Leader: Chris Summers. Duration: weekends, 25–27 September. Price: £48 per person (1981). Includes lectures, excursions, accommodation in rooms with private bath, all meals (from Friday dinner to Sunday lunch), service and VAT. Bring waterproof clothes and strong footwear.

See also CASTLES AND HISTORIC HOUSES, CHURCHES AND CATHEDRALS, PHOTOGRAPHY, POTTERY, WINE TASTING.

MOUNTAIN SKILLS

CUMBRIA, Keswick

1 Three Day Fellcraft
2 Five Day Fellcraft
Blencathra Centre

The centre is superbly situated on the flanks of the northern fells with a panoramic view of Borrowdale, St John's in the Vale and the loftiest peaks of the Central fells. You'll stay in one of the self-contained group hostels with two, three and four bedded rooms, central heating, common rooms, showers and modern facilities.

Both courses are organized and staffed by the Lake District Park Ranger Service assisted by visiting speakers and field lecturers. Study facilities include a library and reference room, teaching/lecture rooms and a comprehensive range of audio-visual equipment.

The three-day adult course is particularly valuable for party leaders. You're given instruction on basic mountain craft skills: accurate use of map and compass, route choice, equipment choice, safe movement in difficult terrain, mountain hazards, weather, emergency procedure and bad weather alternatives. You'll also consider the problems of access to open country, leadership responsibility and be briefed on the local farmer's point of view.

The five-day course covers the same ground but gives you more opportunity to practise relevant skills.

Blencathra Centre, Threlkeld, Keswick, Cumbria CA12 4SG. Telephone: (059 683) 601. The Courses Secretary. Duration: 1 20–23 March. 2 2–8 May. Price: 1 £44 per person (1981). 2 £66 per person. Includes tuition and full board. A kit list will be forwarded with booking confirmation.

TAYSIDE, Pitlochry

Scotland above the Snowline
Bunrannoch Hotel

The school was founded in 1975 to provide expert tuition in such strenuous outdoor activities as rock climbing, cross-country skiing and general mountaineering. This combined ski-mountaineering and winter mountaineering course is designed for those who want to combine the challenges of exploring the rugged Scottish winter landscape with learning how to ski-tour in wild snow-covered country.

This intensive course has been compiled from the first-hand experiences of the school's winter clients. This is a physically demanding course so make sure you're fit before applying. The syllabus covers navigation, ice-axe and crampon techniques, belaying on snow and ice, survival, mountain first aid, rudiments of piste skiing, waxing and introductory snow and ice-climbing.

You'll stay in the Bunrannoch Hotel on the edge of Kinloch Rannoch village. The school is equipped with top modern equipment for outdoor activities such as canoeing, sailing, rock climbing and ski-mountaineering. You're entitled to a 10 per cent discount on any equipment sold in the school's outdoor equipment retail outlet.

Loch Rannoch Scottish School of Adventure, Bunrannoch Hotel, Kinloch Rannoch, Pitlochry, Tayside, Scotland. Telephone: (08822) 325. The Administrator: Peter Robins. Duration: 7–14 and 21–28 February, 7–14 and 21–28 March, 11–18 and 18–25 April. Price: £110 per person per week (1981). Includes tuition, full board, course transport and equipment. VAT extra. Bring 6 pairs of woollen socks, ex-service trousers, thermos, pen and note-paper.

WALES, GWYNEDD, Capel Curig

Mountain Craft and Hill Walking
Plas y Brenin

Plas y Brenin Centre is set in some of the world's best rock climbing country. There's a wide range of outdoor activities on offer, and all training is supervised by a well-qualified staff of seven, backed by other specialists and sometimes assisted by coaches from bodies such as the British Mountaineering Council.

This course is ideal if you're a hill walker or general mountaineer looking for new challenges. You'll be instructed in navigation with map and compass, basic rescue techniques, rock climbing, ridge scrambling and, if conditions are right, snowcraft and how to camp in winter. Evening lectures and films complement the day's instruction.

Centre facilities include a belay practice machine, artificial floodlit ski slope with tow, outdoor heated pool for canoe practice, lecture rooms with cine, slide, sound and video facilities, comprehensive library, bar and common room, four minibuses, and a lake and river only yards away.

The centre accommodates up to sixty in comfortable two and three bedded rooms, and bunk house accommodation will be available soon.

Booking Department, Plas y Brenin, Capel Curig, Betws-y-Coed, Gwynedd, Wales LL24 0ET. Telephone: (06904) 214. Administrator: Roger Orgill. Duration: weekly, March to December. Price: £95 per person (1981). Includes tuition, full board and VAT. Equipment issued free. Minimum age 16 years. Special weeks 14–16 year-olds. Duration: 1 week August, September, October. Price: £85 per person.

Multi-activity

CHANNEL ISLANDS, GUERNSEY
St Peter Port

Leisure Centre
Beau Séjour

It's all happening at Beau Séjour. Guernsey is justly proud of its modern leisure centre, one of the finest around with activities for everyone – discos, badminton, table tennis, trampolining and roller skating to name just a few. Add to that a fabulous heated indoor pool, tennis and squash, a fully-equipped gymnasium and a wide range of other indoor amusements (including dodgems, astroglide, a giant air castle and nightly first run movies), and refreshments are available at the cafeteria while the White Elephant Bar is open from 11.00 a.m. to 11.00 p.m. (bar snacks and lunches). Daily admission to the lot is 20p and you pay for other amenities as you use them. Charges vary. Swimming, for instance, is 35p (children 25p), and tennis is £1 per court per hour. Racquets and balls for tennis and squash, and a wide range of equipment for other sports, are available for hire. Accommodation is available at nearby hotels. This is your chance to see Guernsey on a holiday the whole family can enjoy, even the most bored and recalcitrant member!

Beau Séjour Leisure Centre, Guernsey,
Channel Islands. Telephone: (0481) 27211. Director: Mrs J. Morrison. Duration: seasonal. Pay as you go. Accommodation: Duke of Richmond Hotel, St Peter Port, Guernsey. Telephone: (0481) 26221. Price: £27 per person daily (est). Includes accommodation and all meals. Children under 14 years stay free in parents' room. La Retraite Hotel, Rue des Frères, St Peter Port, Guernsey. Telephone: (0481) 24791. Price: £11 (est) per person bed, breakfast and dinner.

CORNWALL, Falmouth

Multi-Activity Holiday
Melville Hotel

The Melville is a family-run hotel just 5 minutes walk from the nearest beach and only one hundred yards from the Falmouth Club. Guests have free use of this licensed club's seven tennis courts, squash court, table tennis, snooker, billiards and bridge facilities. What's more you're only one mile away from an 18 hole golf course.

The hotel's tiered garden is beautifully landscaped and boasts palm trees and sea views. There are two lounges, one with colour TV, a cocktail bar and patio where, weather permitting, your friendly hosts, the Butchers, throw a weekly barbeque. Children are extra-welcome, and cots, high chairs, laundry facilities and early teas are provided.

Melville Hotel, Seaview Road, Falmouth, Cornwall. Telephone: (0326) 312134. Proprietors: Maureen and Stanley Butcher. 100 yards from the Melville is the Falmouth Club, all facilities of which are free to guests. Duration: all year. Price: £87 per person per week (est). Includes dinner, bed and breakfast. Seasonal reductions at off-peak periods.

See also PAINTING.

CUMBRIA, Eskdale
WALES, GWYNEDD, Aberdovey

The Executive Course
Outward Bound Trust

Outward Bound offers this special executive course for businessmen and women who want to tackle a challenging new experience. You can attend independently or be sponsored by your company. Middle managers and senior executives will find the course particularly valuable since it presents difficulties which can only be overcome by team work – a vital factor in most successful organizations. Activities include white water canoeing, wilderness expeditions, orienteering races, rapelling, rock climbing, tree-top rope courses, search and rescue on cliffs and water, sailing in dinghies and cutters and a solo expedition. You spend a day and a night alone in wild surroundings. The wardens and instructors are careful not to permit any course member to exceed their physical limitations. Activities vary somewhat according to the school's location (there are centres in Wales, the Lake District and Scotland); write for details.

Outward Bound Trust, Avon House, 360 Oxford Street, London W1N 9HA. Telephone: (01) 491 1355. Duration: Wales 28 February–7 March. Cumbria 20–28 February. Other dates on application. Price: *£100 per person per week until 31 March (1981); £112 per person per week from 1 April. Includes tuition, use of boats, canoes, loan of waterproofs, accommodation and all meals. Minimum age 25.*

DERBYSHIRE, Edale

Edale Adventure Holidays

How about the high life? These holidays are designed for the discerning adult who enjoys good food and has a taste for adventure. The holiday includes a well-organized introduction to a number of active pursuits in an intimate house party atmosphere deep in the Derbyshire Hills. Swimming (in a heated open air pool), pony trekking over the Peak countryside, sailing in a racing dinghy on a nearby lake, rock climbing, hill walking, orienteering and caving are just some of the activities organized for you – with all specialized equipment and transport included in the price of your holiday. Though you'll need to bring your own suitable clothing (advice is forwarded to you when you book).

Guests are accommodated at The Warren in Edale, a picturesque village set in a valley in the heart of the Peak District. The great 2000 ft summit of Kinder Scout soars above the village, and you're right next door to the Old Nag's Head, a 16th century pub. There's also a small intimate bar in The Warren, and a well-stocked cellar. You'll need to be fairly fit (though there's no need to go in for any drastic training programme beforehand) and there's a minimum age limit of 20.

Edale Adventure Holidays, The Warren, Edale via Sheffield, Derbyshire S30 2ZD. Telephone: (0433) 70256. Duration: 1 week, May to October. Price: from £110 per person per week (est). Includes tuition, accommodation, all meals, service and VAT. Minimum age 20.

DEVON, Thurlestone

Torture and Pleasure Break
Thurlestone Hotel

This five-day break offers you the delights of luxurious accommodation in a first-class hotel and ample opportunity for strenuous physical activity. Thurlestone is one of the most picturesque little villages in this scenic part of Devon. The hotel is set in fourteen acres and offers a 9 hole par three golf course (with a resident professional), a heated outdoor swimming pool, squash, badminton, saunas, snooker and table tennis; and there's a 16th century pub. All rooms have baths, showers, radio, TV and telephone.

This holiday operates in conjunction with the nearby Courtlands Activity Centre. A typical programme welcomes you with a cocktail party and introductory talk. Next day you'll be woken early to work up an appetite for breakfast with a 7.45 a.m. run, followed by squash and badminton before a pub lunch and then a ramble along the cliffs, before a hotel cream tea. Play squash or badminton until dinner at 7.30 p.m. then – if you're still able – play snooker or table tennis. Some days you'll go to the Courtlands Centre for coaching on the outdoor assault course, or in the fully-equipped gym. Highlights of the programme include a competition in the centre's grounds where you can test skills learned during the week in the orienteering course, a Tor scramble and a pony trek. On the final evening there's a darts match – less strenuous but just as much fun.

Thurlestone Hotel, Thurlestone, near Kingsbridge, Devon TQ7 3NN. Telephone: (054 857) 382. Resident Director: Graham Gross. Duration: go for any five days between early November and early March, except Christmas, New Year or Bank Holiday periods, phone for details. Price: £115 per person for 5 days (1981). Includes accommodation, all meals, activities, transport from the hotel to Courtlands Centre, VAT. Partners who do not join in the programme pay £25 less.

EIRE, COUNTY CORK, Kanturk

Multi-Activity Hotel
Assolas Country House

This charming 17th century riverside country house offers you free Blackwater salmon, trout and coarse fishing, tennis, croquet and boating. All are right on the grounds. You can ride one of the seven hunters in the house's stables for £3 per hour (est). (The hotel is normally closed from November to March, but you can make a special arrangement, for small parties only, to follow the local Dunhallow Foxhounds and Stonehill Harriers in the off-season.) Fresh fruit and vegetables from the gardens help the cuisine maintain its high standard.

Assolas Country House, Kanturk, County Cork, Eire. Telephone: Kanturk 15. Proprietor: Mrs C. Bourke. Duration: April to September/October to March. Price: £11.50 per person per night (est), bed and breakfast; bed, breakfast and dinner £19.50 per day (est) (min. of 3 days); £108 per week (est). Private bath supplement of £3.50 per night (est). Light or packed lunches available. Children under 12 sharing adult accommodation 33% reduction, otherwise 25% reduction. Service charge 10%.

See also FISHING, GOLF, RIDING.

EIRE, COUNTY DONEGAL, Letterkenny

Multi-Activity Hotel Holiday
Fort Royal Hotel

All-rounders will find plenty to keep them busy here. The hotel's eighteen acres of lawn and woodland include a 9 hole par three golf course; Ireland's oldest 18 hole course, the Otway, is only a mile-and-a-half away. There's an all-weather tennis court in the garden, and table tennis and squash courts are available free to residents. The hotel's own stables provide mounts for riding on the beaches or for trekking, at about £2.50 per hour. You can hire dinghies to explore the loch, which is also popular with water skiers.

The Fletcher family has run the Fort Royal for thirty years, and the friendly local staff make you feel instantly at home. The excellent cuisine uses produce grown in the hotel's own kitchen garden. It has earned high praise from various French gastronomic guides, and a coveted AA rating of two red stars.

Fort Royal Hotel, Rathmullan, Letterkenny, County Donegal, Eire. Telephone: Rathmullen 11. Prices: £21.25 (est) per day full board for a front room with private bath overlooking the loch, or £18.50 (est) half board (minimum 3 days) including VAT, plus 10% service.

EIRE, COUNTY KERRY, Parknasilla

Multi-Activity Holidays
Parknasilla Great Southern Hotel

Picnic among the palm trees of County Kerry, South West Ireland, where the Gulf Stream first washes the shores of Europe. The Parknasilla Great Southern Hotel is situated on the picturesque shore of Kenmore Bay, with its rocks, islets and pine-dotted headlands – everything but leprechauns.

George Bernard Shaw wrote much of his celebrated 'St Joan' here, and his stay is commemorated by the charming Dolittle Bar and elegant Pygmalion Restaurant which, despite the fact that GBS was a strict vegetarian, serves the finest French cuisine. The hotel's private 18 hole golf course is free for guests, and there's a superb indoor heated swimming pool. A list of optional activities includes salmon and trout fishing on nearby rivers (£16 per day), pony trekking (£3.50 per hour), deep sea fishing (£8 per day), sea fishing (free), and water skiing (£8 for tow). Prices are approximate. Use of all facilities in the indoor sports complex is free, including hard court tennis, billiards, sauna and table tennis. Day tours into the nearby countryside are also organized by the hotel, at various prices – this is your chance to kiss the Blarney Stone!

Parknasilla Great Southern Hotel, Parknasilla, County Kerry, Eire. Telephone: Sneem 45122. Manager: Brendan Maher. Duration: April to November. Price: £205–£268 (est) per person per week (est). Includes bed, breakfast, dinner, service and VAT.

EIRE, COUNTY WEXFORD, Wexford

Multi-Activity Hotel Holiday
Talbot Hotel

The modern, friendly Talbot Hotel overlooks the sea in the ancient town of Wexford. Of the one hundred and sixteen rooms, ninety-two have a private bath, while all have radio and telephone. The hotel incorporates a Leisure Centre with an indoor heated pool, squash, saunas, solariums, children's and adult's games rooms, a resident beautician and a hairdressing salon all free to guests. You are also taken on a free guided walking tour of Wexford. Riding can be arranged at nearby stables (see RIDING – Horetown House) at £3 per hour, £4 with tuition. There are several all-weather tennis courts close to the hotel, and Wexford has its own 9 hole golf course. You can swim from the hotel beach or at many other fine sandy beaches that dot this coast.

The Talbot Hotel, Wexford, County Wexford, Eire. Telephone: (00053) 22566. Price: Accommodation with private bath, dinner and breakfast costs £23.50 (est) per night in a twin room, plus 10% service. Half board costs £149.50 per person per week (est). Rates are higher in the autumn during the Wexford Opera Festival. The Leisure Centre is open all year round.

HIGHLAND, Aviemore

Cairngorm Holiday Ticket
Highland Guides

The scheme offers five 'holiday tickets'. Group 1 is the most expensive, Group 5 the least. Activities at the Spey Valley centre include canoeing, sailing, windsurfing, skiing, pony trekking, walking and cycling. You can also join an estate ranger on a walk into Lairig Ghru (Britain's highest pass), tour a highland estate and take an evening wildlife excursion. Individuals, families and unaccompanied children (daytime only) are welcome and instruction is available at both intermediate and advanced levels. You can make up your own programme if the ones on offer aren't suitable; indicate your preferences on the booking form and the centre will price your ticket and return it. If you find a new activity you like while on the holiday you can add it to your programme. Non-residential but you'll be sent a list of nearby accommodation. Average weekly cost of bed and breakfast £35.

Highland Guides, Inverdruie, Aviemore, Highland. Telephone (0479) 810729. Director: Ian Hudson. Duration: May to October up to two weeks. Price: from £12–£32.00 (est) low season, from £13.50–£38.50 (est) high season. Reductions for children under 16.

See also CROSS COUNTRY SKIING.

HIGHLAND, Kincraig

Sport-a-day Holiday
Insh Hall

If you're interested in taking up a new sport, or just want to brush up old skills, this is for you. You can be coached in canoeing, sailing, hill walking and cycling, with each day devoted to a different activity from 10.00 to 12.00 a.m. and 1.30 to 3.30 p.m. The course fee includes five days instruction, use of equipment and accommodation with full board.

Cairngorm Canoeing and Sailing School Ltd, Insh Hall, Kincraig by Kingussie, Highland PH21 1NU. Telephone: (05404) 272. Manageress: Sally Freshwater. Price: £90 per person per week (June and September), £96 (July and August) (1981). Includes course and accommodation, from

4.00 p.m. Sunday to 10.00 a.m. Saturday. Accommodation in centrally heated double and 4-bunked rooms. Price also includes dinner, bed, breakfast, packed lunch from Sunday dinner to Saturday breakfast and VAT. Unaccompanied children should be over 14. Transport from the main line station at Aviemore is available on request at time of booking.

See also CANOEING, SAILING, SKIING.

KENT, Folkestone

Multi-Activity Holidays
Folkestone Activity Holiday Centre

Since the FAHC was founded in 1973 over 5000 young people have taken advantage of the variety of sporting courses offered. There are ten in all and these cover most outdoor pursuits. Popular demand has led to the inclusion of a new 'Special Multi-Activity Course'. Centre coordinator Ed Mackenzie is a trained youth and community worker, experienced sailor and senior instructor for the British Canoe Union. He and his team of equally qualified instructors believe in making the courses enjoyable as well as educational.

On the multi-activity course you're asked to select four of the centre's eight sports: sea fishing, tennis, canoeing, sailing, powerboating, water-skiing, riding and windsurfing. You'll be involved in the course every morning and afternoon save for Sunday afternoon and one other morning or afternoon during the week. Saturday is reserved for arrivals and departures.

The FAHC's special accommodation centres provide hotel quality living in two, three or four bedded rooms. The weekly charge includes full English breakfast, a snack lunch and a three course evening meal. Lounges have colour TVs and table games.

Folkestone Activity Holiday Centre, 235 Canterbury Road, Folkestone, Kent CT19 5QH. Telephone: (0303) 55651. Coor-

dinator: Ed Mackenzie. Duration: 1 week, all year. Price: £47 per person (1981). Includes tuition and use of equipment. Accommodation £59 per person per week. Includes dinner, bed, breakfast and snack lunch.

KENT, Tunbridge Wells

Multi-Activities
Bowles Outdoor Pursuits Centre

The centre is situated in six acres of countryside. This encloses a long sandstone outcrop (ideal for introductory climbing), an open air floodlit ski slope and a sheltered swimming pool at the foot of a rocky slope (used for canoe practice and recreational swimming). The surrounding countryside provides plenty of scope for other activities: introductory canoeing is taught on the River Medway; the sea is easily accessible for surfing and expedition canoeing; nearby Bewl Bridge Reservoir is ideal for sailing; and Ashdown Forest provides a good setting for hiking, camping, map reading and orienteering.

Courses vary in length from one day to two weeks and may be residential or non-residential. All you need to bring is appropriate clothing (you'll be sent a suggested list) since all specialist equipment is provided. You can specialize in one activity on your holiday or take a multi-activity course and try your hand at everything. Bowles is a registered charity. As a non-profit making organization fees are reasonable. Most tuition is given by full-time professional staff. The centre suggests that you telephone first to establish whether there are vacancies on the course you've selected.

Bowles Outdoor Pursuits Centre, Eridge Green, Tunbridge Wells, Kent TN3 9LW. Telephone: (08926) 4127. Duration: March to October. Price: from £32 per person per weekend (est), £85 per person per week (est). Includes tuition, use of equipment and full board. VAT extra.

NORTHUMBERLAND, Belford

Windy Gyle Parachute and Outdoor Centre

The activity holidays at Windy Gyle Outdoor Centre offer you a chance at a full week's participation in several activities. The aim isn't to produce experts, but to give you a memorable and enjoyable holiday with a difference. Here's your chance to have a go at many activities, including rock climbing on the famous Northumberland Outcrops; a day's hiking in the Cheviot Hills; a day at the Centre's watersport headquarters at Newton by the Sea, where you can canoe, sail and windsurf; and riding, including tuition for novices and trekking across the coastal moors.

For details of accommodation see PARACHUTING.

Windy Gyle Parachute and Outdoor Centre, Belford, Northumberland NE70 7QE. Telephone: (06683) 289. Duration: one week June to September. Dates on application. Price: £90 per person per week (est). Includes tuition, dormitory accommodation, full board, all activities and excursions, use of equipment and VAT. Family units also available. Bring thermos flask, training shoes, swim suit, warm clothes.

TAYSIDE, Kenmore

Try-A-Sport Holidays
Loch Tay Sailing School

Kenmore Village, on the shores of Loch Tay, is a renowned beauty spot. It's also the location of the Loch Tay Sailing School and Water Sports Centre, located at the head of the lake overlooking the village. The school offers a lively five-day 'Try-A-Sport' course, which gives you an introduction to seven sports. You'll water ski and sail on Loch Tay, canoe on both the lake and the River Tay and try your hand at wet and dry fly fishing and trawling (mainly for brown trout). On land you can go hill walking in the magnificent surrounding countryside, pony trekking along forest trails, and play golf at Taymouth Castle Golf course, a first class private 18 hole golf course in the grounds of Kenmore Castle.

The school provides accommodation in three architect-designed log chalets (each with a barbeque installed on its patio) on a three acre site ten minutes walk from the village, which boasts trees, shrubs and an attractive water garden. You can also choose to stay in the village at the Loch Tay Guest House, run by the school; all rooms have sweeping views.

Loch Tay Sailing School, Kenmore, Tayside, Scotland. Telephone: (088 73) 236. Principals: Alison and Stanley Hampton. Duration: 5 days, March to October. Price: £55 per person (1981) includes tuition. Accommodation arranged at Loch Tay Guest House. Price: £6.50 per person per day, £45 per week, bed and breakfast. £11.25 per day, £75 per week, dinner, bed and breakfast. Price includes VAT. Self-catering accommodation also available.

WALES, SOUTH GLAMORGAN, Cardiff

Weekend Getaway Breaks
St Mellans Hotel and Country Club

There's something for all the family here. St Mellans Hotel sits in the middle of St Mellans Golf Course, which residents may use by arrangement. There are squash courts, a heated indoor pool, saunas, games room, bar billiards, table tennis, solarium and darts – all included in the price. All rooms have private baths, refrigerators, Teasmades and colour TV.

St Mellans Hotel and Country Club, Cardiff, South Glamorgan, Wales CF3 8XR. Telephone: (0633) 680355 or Best Western Getaway Breaks (01) 940 9766. Write to the manager. Duration: weekends all year, closed 25 and 26 December. Price: £50 per person (est) for 2 nights. Includes accommodation, dinner and VAT.

WEST YORKSHIRE, Leeds

Family Holiday Week 1981
Leeds Polytechnic

These international family holidays at Leeds Polytechnic offer an exceptionally wide variety of sporting, art and craft activities, ranging from archery to yoga, and badminton to volley ball. The scheme requires each member of the family to choose two activities, one to do in the morning and the other in the afternoon. (Participants should indicate whether they are beginners, intermediate, or advanced at each activity.) In most cases, equipment is supplied at no extra cost, though a few activities such as racquet games and photography, require you to bring your own. For full details, send for their brochure.

Accommodation is in the halls of residence at the Polytechnic. Each course member is allocated a bedroom with washing facilities; bathroom, showers, and kitchen facilities are available. Parents are normally allocated rooms which can accommodate two extra single beds. For the evenings, there's a bar, disco, TV rooms, films and talks.

West Yorkshire Metropolitan County Council, Recreation and Arts Division, Department of Administration, County Hall, Wakefield, West Yorkshire WF1 2QW. Telephone: (0924) 67111. Head of Division: D. E. Hogan. Duration: 1–8 August. Price: £110 per person per week (est). Includes tuition and full board, VAT extra.

MUSIC

CUMBRIA, Bassenthwaite Lake

Art of Song
Higham Hall

An eminent team of experts will lead this summer school course for singers and accompanists. Conductor, composer and arranger Dr Havelock Nelson is one of Ireland's most distinguished musicians. He'll lecture on repertoire, the art of song and on piano accompaniment techniques. Freelance singer of recitals, oratorio and opera Christopher Underwood divides his time between performances throughout Europe and teaching at the Royal Northern College of Music. He specializes in French *melodie* and aims in this course 'to bring to all members the interest and joy that singing can give'. David Parkinson, Music Adviser to the Cumbria Education Authority, will direct the choir and small ensembles. The course is open to singers over fifteen years who have reached a reasonable technical standard. Friends can be invited to Friday's informal concert.

For details of Higham Hall, see ART APPRECIATION.

Higham Hall, Bassenthwaite Lake, Cockermouth, Cumbria CA13 9SH. Telephone: (059 681) 276. Warden: Peter Hadkins. Duration: 1 week July. Price: £85 per person (est). Cumbrian residents £79 (est). Includes course and full board. Minimum age 15.

See also ART APPRECIATION, DRESSMAKING, WAR GAMES.

DEVON, Torquay

Saturday Night is Music Night
Imperial Hotel

Once a month the enterprising Imperial Hotel organizes a concert to delight music lovers. It could be anything from an evening with Ian Wallace of 'My Music' and Glyndebourne fame, to Gilbert and Sullivan opera, or piano recitals by Malcolm Binns and Howard Shelley. Why not make a weekend of it at the special £29 per day 'wisely and warmly' winter demi-pension rate? The Imperial has other good ideas too – gastronomic weekends (see GOURMET) and weekends geared to antique buffs (see ANTIQUES) are two examples.

Imperial Hotel, Torquay, Devon. Telephone: (0803) 24301. Contact: General Manager. Duration: 1 Saturday a month, October to March. Price: £29 per day (1981). Includes evening meal, bed and breakfast. Prices include VAT.

See also ANTIQUES, GARDENING, GOURMET.

COUNTY DURHAM, Stanley

Dinner Recitals
Beamish Hall

Beamish Hall is attractively placed in a wooded valley two miles from Stanley, the nearest town. A residential adult education college, it often plays host to professional musicians. Dinner at 7.30 p.m. in the wood-panelled dining room is followed by a 9.00 p.m. recital. (Sometimes the order is reversed, with a 7.30 p.m. recital followed by a buffet supper at 8.30 p.m.) Without a car, you can arrange transport to the college from Stanley and stay overnight in either a twin-bedded or single study-bedroom with central heating and washing facilities. There are only five twin rooms, so book early. The college also has a theatre, library, music room and bar.

Beamish Hall Residential College for Adult Education, Stanley, County Durham DH9 0RG. (2 miles from Stanley off A6076.) Telephone: (0207) 33147. Contact: The Principal. Duration: 1 evening mid May, June, July. Price: dinner £4 (wine extra); 1 night bed and breakfast £7.55 per person (single or twin) (1981). Prices include VAT.

See also ARCHAEOLOGY, ASTRONOMY, GARDENING, JEWELLERY.

HEREFORD AND WORCESTER, Broadway

Musical Weekends
1 John Lill – Piano
2 Pro Arte String Quartet ·
Lygon Arms

For over 400 years the Lygon Arms has offered shelter to travellers, while its 20th-century extension has been lauded as a perfect example of the architect's marriage of new with old. In the agreeable barrel-ceilinged, oak-panelled Great Hall you can enjoy concerts by John Lill, a brilliant pianist who regularly plays with the world's great orchestras. He gave his first public recital at the age of nine and won the 1970 Moscow International Tchaikovsky Competition. Your first weekend features his interpretations of four Beethoven sonatas.

During the February weekend you can hear works by Haydn, Ravel, and Schumann performed by the Pro Arte String Quartet. Formed in 1973 by students of the Salzburg Music Academy, the 'Mozarteum's' distinguished mentors and teachers include Professors Otto Strasser, Jurgen Creise and Sandor Vegh.

For your accommodation, choose between ancient chambers dating from 1530 (one has a four-poster), and the modern comforts of a room with private bathroom and shower. All enjoy central heating and attentive service.

The Lygon Arms, Broadway, Hereford and Worcester, WR12 7DU. Telephone: (0386) 852255. Duration: 1 17–18 January; 2 14–15 February (Saturdays and Sundays). Price: £55 single, £95 double (1981). Both with private bathroom. Prices include VAT.

LINCOLNSHIRE, Lincoln

Musical Weekends
White Hart Hotel

This dignified hostelry has occupied the spot between the castle and the cathedral for seven centuries. The antique-filled lounges and dining room are well-appointed in traditional style, and the sixty-eight bedrooms range from luxury to simple modern and functional. Amenities include central heating, telephone, radio, colour TV and Saturday dinner dances once a fortnight in winter. In 1980 the November weekend featured the Krenzberger String Quartet. Contact the White Hart for further details.

White Hart Hotel, Bailgate, Lincoln LN1 3AR. Telephone: (0522) 26222. Duration: weekends, 23–25 January, 20–22 November (tentative). Price: singles with bath/shower £51 per night (est), without bath £46 (est); doubles with bath/shower £86 (est), without £83 (est). Includes service and VAT.

LOTHIAN, Dalkeith

String Quartet
Newbattle Abbey College

If you're already a member of a practising string quartet, you and your fellow players are eligible for this course. (The school asks for groups already formed, to ensure that players will be familiar with one another's style and temperament.) With the tutorial staff, your group will play and study works of your own choice, and will participate, either as players or listeners, in several pieces that present technical and interpretative difficulties, such as Haydn's Op. 77 No. 2 and Beethoven's Op. 59 No. 3. Members will be asked to bring their own scores of the works to be performed, as well as some pieces of your own choice. If you don't want to perform the listed works, the following repertoire is suggested: Beethoven Op. 18, any version, and Haydn Op. 33, any version. Your tutors and demonstrators are members of the Edinburgh Quartet: Miles Baster, Peter Markham, Michael Beeston and Christopher Gough. Last year's visiting lecturers were Hans Keller, internationally famous musicologist and critic, and Denis Matthews, distinguished concert pianist and the first Professor of Music at the University of Newcastle-upon-Tyne. Morning and afternoon sessions may be varied by visits to the Edinburgh Festival, lectures from the visiting speakers, or excursions. Generally, evenings are free.

For details of accommodation see ANTIQUES.

Newbattle Abbey College, Dalkeith, Lothian EH22 2LL. Telephone: (031 663) 1921/2. Duration: 15–22 August. Price: £172 per person (est). Includes tuition, excursions, concert tickets, accommodation and all meals. No VAT.

See also ANTIQUES, CASTLES AND HISTORIC HOUSES, FESTIVALS, PAINTING.

SHROPSHIRE, Shrewsbury

Music at Leisure
Lion Hotel

Wine, dine and enjoy good music in the comfort of selected hotels. These Trusthouse Forte concerts offer the best of the classics, jazz, musical comedy and more – for example the Cambridge Buskers and leading American mime Bob Berkey. The brochure gives full details of accommodation and the musical programmes. One example: the Lion Hotel, Shrewsbury, a picturesque posting inn whose elegant Adam Ballroom provides the perfect setting for the Endellion String Quartet. This award winning ensemble will perform pieces by Haydn, Mendelssohn and Dvořák.

Lion Hotel, Wyle Cop, Shrewsbury, Shropshire SY1 1UY. Telephone: (0743) 53107. Manager: Mr Nicholas Axon. Duration: 29 January, 12 March and first Thursday October and November. Price: £21 per person (until April 1981). Includes concert, accommodation for 1 night, breakfast, dinner and VAT.

SOMERSET, Taunton

Weekend Festival
Castle Hotel

You'll be welcomed with cocktails on Friday at 6.30 p.m., and then entertained by the Franz Schubert String Quartet. This young Austrian ensemble has quickly established an international reputation, and garnered high praise for its virtuosity and technical assurance. They perform pieces by Mozart, Ravel and Brahms, which is followed by dinner presided over by Maitre d'Hotel, Didier Pinguenet. Choose your accompanying wines from a cellar stocked with 220 vintages (the fifty-eight clarets include all the Premiers Crus). Highlights of the morning and evening performances include a Haydn Quartet in D Opus 64/5, and works by Schubert, Beethoven, Bartók and Mozart. At 9.00 p.m. there's a gala dinner. On Sunday you'll be treated to Mozart and Schumann quartets then farewell with luncheon at 1.00 p.m.

For details of accommodation see THEATRE GOING.

The Castle Hotel, Castle Green, Taunton, Somerset, TA1 1NF. Telephone: (0823) 2671. Managing Director: Christopher Chapman. Duration: 16–18 January, 13–15 March. Price: £98 (1981). Includes accommodation with private bath, all meals. VAT extra.

STAFFORDSHIRE, Rugeley

Music Week
Spode Conference Centre

This imaginative course combines liturgical and secular music to attract amateur and professional musicians, composers and performers. The emphasis is on practical music-making under such noted conductors as George Malcolm, John Sloboda and Robert Sherlaw Johnson. You'll hear music ranging from medieval masses and Gregorian chants to classical jazz, Bruckner motets or Messiaen. Active participation is encouraged, and you're urged to bring any scores which interest you, and either sing in the choir or bring a musical instrument. There are three rehearsals a day and much informal music-making in the intervals.

The Spode Centre is run by Dominican friars who welcome guests of all denominations, feed them well and even provide two bars. Choose your accommodation from singles, doubles, family rooms or curtained dormitories.

For details of the Conference Centre see RELIGIOUS RETREATS.

Spode Conference Centre, Hawkesyard Priory, Rugeley, Staffordshire WS15 1PT. Telephone: (0543) 490112. Contact: the Warden. Duration: 1 week, 20–27 April. Price: from £53 (est) (dormitory), £69 (est) (single) plus VAT. Course fees extra.

See also CALLIGRAPHY, RELIGIOUS RETREATS.

SUSSEX, Chichester

Music: Appreciation and Practical Hi-fi
The Earnley Concourse

Music lovers can choose from a symphony of courses here. Some take a close look at the work of particular composers, while others give you a chance to practise and improve your own vocal or instrumental talents. Write for details.

If the only instrument you play is the stereo, the unusual hi-fi weekend is for you. You'll learn how to get the best possible quality of sound reproduction within your budget; and along the way you'll examine a wide range of hi-fi equipment and find out how to care for records and tapes.

For details of the Concourse see ANTIQUES.

The Earnley Concourse, near Chichester (7 miles south), Sussex PO20 7JL. Telephone: (0243) 670392. Duration: all year, weekend and midweek. Prices: from £35 per person double, £38 single (est). Includes 2 nights accommodation, all meals,

course fees and use of facilities. VAT
extra. Minibus from Chichester station 90p
each way.

See also ANTIQUES, CREATIVE WRITING,
FLOWER ARRANGING, FOLK AND JAZZ,
LANGUAGE, PUPPETRY, SURVIVAL TRAIN-
ING, WINE TASTING.

SUSSEX, Fittleworth

Keyboard Cavalcade
The Old Rectory

'Singing for Fun' classes offer solo training in a relaxed atmosphere guaranteed to
give you new confidence and ability. In
'Keyboard Cavalcade', Janet Canelly-
Clarke takes you on a tour of musical history as expressed through the keyboard,
with practical demonstrations. The course
is timed to coincide with the nearby
Arundel Festival (theatre tickets are not
included in the course fees).

For details of accommodation see SENIOR
CITIZENS.

The Old Rectory, Fittleworth, Pulborough,
Sussex RH20 1HU. Telephone: (079882)
306. Proprietors: Brenda and Graham
Salmon. Course: midsummer. Prices: from
£85 per person (twin room), £95 (single)
for the week (1981). This price includes all
meals and tuition. VAT extra. The fee does
not include course materials or entry to
places visited.

See also CASTLES AND HISTORIC HOUSES,
CLOCKS, GENEALOGY, ORNITHOLOGY, QUILT-
ING AND PATCHWORK, SENIOR CITIZENS.

WILTSHIRE, Marlborough

Summer Music School
Marlborough College

This historic public school offers a range
of weekly summer courses guaranteed to
delight music lovers. One of the most
unusual is the 'Children's Opera' course.
Participants are expected to be able to
sing, but needn't necessarily be able to
read music as long as they're able to concentrate and work hard. Highlight of the
week is the production of their own performance.

For intellectual stimulation try the
'Music and Literature' course, an examination of the influence of such literary
'greats' as Dante, Goethe and Shakespeare on 18th-century music. You'll also
consider the treatment of poetry in songs
and lieder from Schubert to Britten.

'Music in the 20th Century' is a
thoughtful introduction to contemporary
music which examines the work of important modern figures and places them
in historical perspective.

Brass band and orchestral players will
enjoy 'Sounding Brass', which gives individual lessons, tutorials in composing,
arranging and conducting, and a chance
to show your mettle in band performances. The emphasis here is on modern
repertoire.

For details of accommodation see ARCH-
AEOLOGY.

Marlborough Summer School, Marlborough, Wiltshire SN8 1PA. Telephone:
(0672) 53888. Secretary: Mrs Glynis
Lewis. Duration: 1 week, 20 July–9
August. Price: £155.25 (single) per person
(est), £126.50 (dormitory) per person (est),
£103.50 per child under 14 in dormitory
(est). Includes tuition, full board, service
and VAT.

See also ARCHAEOLOGY, FISHING, SCULP-
TURE.

NATURIST

HAMPSHIRE, Fareham

Naturist Holidays
South Hants Sun Club

The good weather records enjoyed by this part of Hampshire help to make this one of Britain's most popular naturist holiday centres. This carefully tended ten-acre woodland site includes large sheltered sunbathing areas, a heated pool, four mini-tennis courts, a volleyball court, a badminton court and a children's paddling pool and play area. There's a large hotel bar and dance floor, a restaurant overlooking the pool and a discothèque. Snacks and meals are available. Accommodation in the hotel is for up to six on demi-pension basis or you can choose a self catering holiday in four and six bunk caravans. If you chose to camp there's a large sunny area for tents with adjacent bathrooms and toilets. Alternatively you can bring your own caravan.

South Hants Sun Club, 'Stockers', North Boarhunt, Fareham, Hampshire. Telephone: (0329) 832919/832147. Director: Michael Wilson. Duration: April to September. Price: £45–£66 per person per week (est). Includes hotel accommodation, bed and breakfast. From £35–£49 (est) per week for four berth self catering caravan. Camp site also available.

NEEDLEWORK

BERKSHIRE, Elcot Park

Needlepoint Weekend
Country House Hotel

First you'll be welcomed by blazing log fires in this magnificent country house hotel, parts of which date from the 17th century. The surrounding park and gardens are full of rare and splendid shrubs, creating a truly tranquil atmosphere in which to study the delicate art of needlework under the guidance of Mrs E. M. Scaramanga, internationally known in the embroidery world, and a first class designer. Both beginners and advanced students will be surprised at how fast they learn. Designs for all levels are available for purchase in kit form, together with needlepoint frames, canvas, wool etc.

The weekend cost includes a generous buffet lunch and four course dinner, plus morning coffee, afternoon tea and pre-lunch and dinner sherry.

Country House Hotel, Elcot Park, near Newbury, Berkshire RG16 8NJ. Telephone: (04885) 276/421. Duration: Friday and Saturday, mid March, late March, end of October. Price: £60 per person (est) in twin or double room with bath. Includes tuition, full board (from Friday morning to Sunday breakfast) and VAT. Equipment and materials extra.

See also HOT AIR BALLOONING, THEATRE GOING.

ESSEX, Colchester

Machine Embroidery

Joy Lucas has exhibited at the Victoria and Albert Museum, is a visiting lecturer at the Royal College of Needlework in Kensington, and has lectured in the USA. She does all her work on an ordinary domestic machine, and is delighted to share her expertise and show you how to make machine embroidery an exciting creative adventure. Her course is geared to all levels of experience or none.

Two bedrooms are set aside for guest students in the modern Colchester home she shares with her chartered accountant husband and student daughter. Once you've booked your course (through ABC) you'll be sent full details as to how to get there and when to arrive.

Avocations (Bristol Crafts) Ltd, 37 Coombe Bridge Avenue, Bristol, Avon BS9 2LT. Telephone: (0272) 686417. Director: Gerald Richardson. Duration: 1 week, all year. Price: £117 per person per week (1981). Includes tuition, full board (twin). Single supplement 15% extra. No VAT.

See also BATIK, DRESSMAKING, ENAMELLING, TAPESTRY, WOODWORKING.

LEICESTERSHIRE, Loughborough

Creative Embroidery
Loughborough University

If you have basic sewing skills, here's a chance to investigate more exciting techniques, including patchwork, machine embroidery, fabric manipulation and cutwork. Your tutor, Mrs Andrea Stratham, will encourage you to spend one day exploring each technique, and to experiment with colour and texture, rather than completing just one piece. Some materials and equipment, including machines for embroidery, will be provided, but you'll be asked to bring along some basic tools and materials. A list will be provided upon acceptance.

For details of accommodation see SCULPTURE

Centre for Extension Studies (BR), University of Technology, Loughborough, Leicestershire LE11 3TU. Telephone: (0509) 631711 ext 249/213. Duration: 1 week, August. Price: £98 per person per week (est). Includes tuition, full board and VAT.

See also CAR MAINTENANCE, CREATIVE WRITING, SCULPTURE.

NORFOLK, Blakeney

Needlepoint Holiday
Blakeney Hotel

Anna Pearson has travelled and lectured extensively in America and Europe and runs a school of needlepoint in London. Some of her work has been exhibited at New York's Metropolitan Museum of Art, and in England there's a permanent exhibition of her work at the Whitbread Museum and the London Museum. On this course she'll give instruction each morning and evening in the attractive hotel lounge overlooking the harbour, and will be available for advice every afternoon. The Blakeney Hotel, built in 1925 using the traditional Norfolk materials of flint and pantiles, offers a high standard of accommodation. It's one of the most painted and photographed hotels in Britain.

The Blakeney Hotel, Blakeney, Nr Holt, Norfolk NR25 7NE. Telephone: (0263) 740797. Duration: 23–26 March. Price:

£98 per person (1981) (twin room). Includes tuition, 3 nights accommodation with bath, dinner, bed and breakfast, materials. £10 single supplement. Includes VAT and service. Golf and ornithology holidays also available. Send for brochure.

OPERA

LANCASHIRE, Preston

Appreciation of opera:
Mozart's *Magic Flute*
Alston Hall

This weekend course is an opportunity to examine one of Mozart's most delightful works. *The Magic Flute*, first produced in Vienna in 1791, is the story of the search for the high places of Wisdom and the trials suffered on the way. Your lecturer will be Peter Gellhorn.

For details of Alston Hall see JAZZ.

Alston Hall, Longridge, Preston, Lancashire PR3 3BP. Telephone: (077 478) 3589. Principal: Mrs Anne Lightfoot. Duration: 2–4 January. Price: £24 per person (1981), Lancashire residents £20. Includes tuition and full board. No VAT.

See also JAZZ, LITERATURE

GWYNEDD, WALES, Llandudno

Llandudno Opera Holiday
Welsh National Opera

The Welsh National Opera has collaborated with nine hotels in Llandudno to produce an opera lover's dream holiday. Six nights room, breakfast and dinner, plus three opera performances of your choice, is standard fare from all the hotels. The weekend includes room, breakfast and dinner for two nights, plus

two opera performances. This year's performances include three very well known operas, The Barber of Seville, The Marriage of Figaro, and Rigoletto, plus one newish opera called the Greek Passion which should be a smash hit when it opens in Cardiff in April. Cost, including opera tickets, service and VAT, ranges from £147 (est) for the week, £55 (est) for the weekend, at Llandudno's three-star St George's Hotel on the Promenade, to £61 (est) for the week (£26 weekend) at the small, select St Moritz Hotel, only two minutes from the theatre. Prices in the other ten hotels vary between these two extremes.

Contact Welsh National Opera Publicity Officer, Carole Strachan, John Street, Cardiff. Telephone: (0222) 40541 for performance details. Hotel list from Mrs Barbara Jones, Sea Court, Golddaeth Avenue, Llandudno, Gwynedd, Wales. Telephone: (0492) 79876. Duration: 6 days 19–27 June (operas on 19 and 20, and 23–27) or 2 days 19–21 and 25–27 June. Price: 2 nights from £26 to £55 (est); 6 nights from £61 to £147 (est). 2 nights includes 2 operas, bed, breakfast, dinner and VAT. Same deal for 6 nights, but 3 operas. Discount on extra seats booked.

ORIENTEERING

CUMBRIA, Coniston

Orienteering
Monk Coniston

Orienteering involves maps, map reading and navigation across unfamiliar terrain. You'll study how a map is made and, after some basic exercises, how to estimate distance, set a map and use a Silva compass. The week is devoted to specially designed exercises over this, the best orienteering countryside in the British Isles – Tarn Hows, Parkamoor, Broughton Moor, Loughrigg Fell and High Dam. Bring strong walking boots and adequate outdoor clothes, including rainwear, and a Silva compass.

Monk Coniston stands in an azalea-filled garden which is at its most beautiful in May. A wide variety of accommodation with full board is available.

For details of Holiday Fellowship see WALKING, *Loch Awe.*

Holiday Fellowship Ltd, 142–144 Great North Way, London NW4 1EG. Telephone: (01) 203 3381. Price: £82–£94 (1981). Includes accommodation, all meals and tuition. VAT extra.

See also BOWLS, BRASS RUBBING, CREATIVE WRITING, ECOLOGY, FOLK MUSIC, GENEALOGY, JEWELLERY, THEATRE GOING, WALKING, YOGA.

EIRE, COUNTY WICKLOW, Ashford

Orienteering
Tiglin Adventure Centre

The centre runs occasional weekend courses and a popular one-week summer course in the scenic Devil's Glen Forest. There are two modern 'O' maps and some permanently marked short courses from basics to Controller Course. Setter and map-making sessions are offered throughout the year in cooperation with the International Orienteering Association. You're expected to be reasonably fit and between sixteen and sixty years old. However, if you're particularly experienced or exceptionally fit, the age limit may be waived.

For details of accommodation see CANOEING.

Tiglin Adventure Centre, Ashford, County Wicklow, Eire. Telephone: (0404) 4169. Secretary: Yvonne Christian. Duration: weekends all year and 1 week in summer. Price: £16 (est) weekend (Friday to Sunday); £80 (est) week (Saturday to Saturday). Includes dormitory accommodation, all meals. A minibus can be arranged to meet the local bus from Dublin. Walking boots may be hired at 25p per day.

See also CANOEING, WALKING.

ORNITHOLOGY

CHANNEL ISLANDS, Guernsey

Birdwatching Holidays
Holiday Pak

Holiday Pak will send you superb illustrated ornithologist's field guides, along with the brochure which details their range of specialist holidays. They organize small, informal groups of up to ten which are led by experienced guide and programme director Tim Earl. These holidays take advantage of Guernsey's role as both a migrating way station and a great holiday centre. The itineraries are flexible and allow you to plan each day according to the weather and the available birds. Guernsey holidays include three days of birdwatching on Guernsey itself with added excursions to Herm and Sark. One day is left free or you can fly to Alderney. (The latter trip includes a boat trip to see Burhou's puffins and the gannet colonies.)

Holiday Pak Ltd, the Travel Bureau, St Pierre du Bois, Guernsey, Channel Islands. Telephone: (0481) 64475. Director: Tim Earl. Duration: 1 week, April, May, September. Price: variety of accommodation available. Sample price: from £150 per person (est) at Ashdown Guest House. Includes accommodation, dinner, bed and breakfast, birdwatching, return air fare from London. Packages using boat service also available. Other activity holidays also available, send for brochure.

DEVON, Bideford

Come and See the Birds
Yeldon House Hotel

Although the hotel doesn't organize expeditions, it's an ideal centre for birdwatchers – as you'll see when you examine the sightings book, a valuable aid to visiting enthusiasts. The best places to find interesting birds are the estuary at low tide, Fremington Flats, Braunton Burrows, Windbury Point, and of course Exmoor and Dartmoor. You can also arrange day trips via steamer from Ilfracombe to remote Lundy Island off the North Devon coast, famed for its bird life.

Yeldon House Hotel, Durrant Lane, Nr Bideford, Devon EX39 2RL. (Off the Bideford–Westward Ho! road.) Telephone: (02372) 4400. Proprietors: Judi and Chris Fulford. Duration: weekends. Price: £46 per person (est). Includes accommodation, all meals (Friday dinner to Sunday lunch), service and VAT. Regular bus service from Bideford.

See also GOLF, GOURMET.

DEVON, Bovey Tracey

Birdwatching Weekends
Coombe Cross Hotel

Go birdwatching in Devon with experienced ornithologist Brian Baker, a man with a wealth of local knowledge. You'll go off for the day by minibus to moorland and estuary sites. Packed lunches are provided, but you'll need to bring wellingtons. In the evening Mr Baker shows slides and talks on British birds and local habitats.

Coombe Cross Hotel, Bovey Tracey, Devon TQ13 9EY. Telephone (0626) 832476. Proprietors: The Misses Anne and Elizabeth Hebditch. Duration: weekends March and September. Price: £52 per person (est) March. £63 per person (est) September. Includes guide, visits, 3 nights full board, transport, service and VAT. Single room supplement £5 (est). Bring heavy shoes, waterproofs and binoculars.

See also BRIDGE, CASTLES AND HISTORIC HOUSES, GARDENS, ECOLOGY.

EDINBURGH

Birds for All Seasons
Forth Bridges Lodge

Ken Shaw, the Development Officer for Scotland of the Royal Society for the Protection of Birds, organizes and leads this weekend where you'll study the teeming birdlife of the Forth Estuary and surrounding lochs, and pay a visit to Vane Farm, which is a wildlife reserve and nature centre on Loch Leven. Species include the velvet scoter, longtailed duck, golden eye, four types of grebes and numerous waders. It's an outstanding area for grey geese, especially the rare pink feet. Your modern hotel overlooks the famous Forth road and rail bridges.

'Birds for All Seasons', 7 Stratford Place, London W1A 4YU. Telephone: (01) 629 6618, ext. 220. Accommodation at Forth Bridges Lodge, South Queensferry, Edinburgh. Duration: weekend 20–22 February.

Price: £49.23 per person (1981) (twin with bath), £53.23 (single with bath). Includes 2 nights accommodation, breakfast, dinner and packed lunch for the 2 days, coach transport to birdwatching sites, a local guide, film shows, illustrated talks, service and VAT. Sunday night bed and breakfast £9 per person (single or twin).

See also DO-IT-YOURSELF.

NORFOLK, Swaffham

Birds for All Seasons
George Hotel

The stretch of North Norfolk coast near this hotel has long been a mecca for ornithologists. During the weekend you'll visit Cley and Salthouse Marshes, accompanied by an expert local guide. This area's renowned for its variety of waders, wildfowl, snow bunting and shore larks. Another excursion takes you to Holkham Park Lake wildfowl sanctuary to see large flocks of Canada and Egyptian geese. Just across the road, the woods around Holkham Gap harbour crossbills, woodpeckers and red squirrels.

Your headquarters is a carefully pre-served, lovingly modernized Georgian coaching inn. Cost of the weekend includes breakfast, two dinners, two substantial packed lunches, coach transport to birdwatching areas, guides, film shows, illustrated lectures and service.

'Birds for All Seasons', 7 Stratford Place, London W1A 4YU. Telephone: (01) 629 6618, ext. 220. Contact: Lydia Bielak. Accommodation at George Hotel, Swaffham, Norfolk. Duration: weekend 13–15 February. Price £49.23 per person (1981) (twin with bath), £53.23 (single with bath). Includes 2 nights accommodation, breakfast, dinner and packed lunch for the 2 days, service and VAT. Sunday night bed and breakfast £9 per person (single or twin).

See also DO-IT-YOURSELF, YOGA.

SUSSEX, Fittleworth

Bird Watching
The Old Rectory

There's far more to bird watching than picking up a pair of binoculars and this course is an excellent introduction to a fascinating hobby. Informal discussion

periods with slides and exhibits are interspersed with field trips to woods, commons, marshes, lake and sea shores. On evening walks you'll find out how to do some sharp-eyed tracking of nocturnal species.

For details of accommodation see SENIOR CITIZENS.

The Old Rectory, Fittleworth, Pulborough, Sussex RH20 1HU. (Off A283 Pulborough–Petworth road.) Telephone: (079882) 306. Proprietors: Brenda and Graham Salmon. Duration: 1 week 3–10 June. Price: £81.70 (twin) (est), £104 (single) (est): VAT extra. Includes accommodation, meals and course. Local bus from Pulborough Station.

See also CASTLES AND HISTORIC HOUSES, CLOCKS, GENEALOGY, MUSIC, QUILTING AND PATCHWORK, SENIOR CITIZENS.

WALES, DYFED, Devil's Bridge

Bird Watching Break
Devil's Bridge Hotel

This special two-day break is offered at one of Britain's most renowned centres for elusive birds of prey; the last stronghold of the red kite. The manor house style hotel overlooks the Mynach Falls and is justly well known for its traditional Welsh cooking. Guests have the use of its private stretches of river for trout fishing.

Devil's Bridge Hotel, Devil's Bridge, Dyfed, Wales. Telephone: (097 085) 232. Duration: 2 day breaks March to late May. Price: £35 per person (1981). Includes any two nights accommodation, dinner, breakfast and packed lunch, VAT.

See also FISHING.

PAINTING

BUCKINGHAMSHIRE, Winslow

Painting and Drawing Courses
The Barn Studio

Spend anything from a weekend to a fortnight as a guest of painter Paul Millichip and his wife Shirley, at Barn Studio in the midst of Buckinghamshire, near Aylesbury. Converted from an old tithe barn, the studio forms part of a group of 16th century buildings around a quiet walled garden. Courses are run for painters at various stages of development, including absolute beginners. Besides studio sessions and landscape excursions to nearby villages, there are talks and practical demonstrations. Groups are small and friendly with lots of scope for individual tuition.

The Barn is known for its good food and easy-going atmosphere. If required, guests can be met at Bletchley Station.

Easels, drawing boards and folding seats are available for use (free), but you should bring your own paints, brushes, canvasses, sketchbooks, etc. (Basic art materials may be purchased at The Barn Studio.)

The Barn Studio, Horn Street, Winslow, Buckinghamshire MK18 3AL. Telephone: (029671) 3232. Proprietor: Paul Millichip. Duration: weekends, 1 and 2 weeks 13 March–23 October. Price: £49.50 per person (1981) (Friday to Sunday), £98.50 per person (Friday to Friday.) Includes accommodation (single or double), all meals, easels, seats, drawing boards. Bring sketchbook, pencils, canvasses, brushes, paints. Art shop on premises. Local bus from station.

CORNWALL, Falmouth

A Painter's Dream Holiday
Melville Hotel

Well-known artist Juliet Pannet PS, FRSA, and her sister Phoebe Somers, also an accomplished painter, run this relaxed painting course with the help of a teacher friend. Each tutor specializes in a particular aspect of watercolour painting. The maximum number is thirty in a group, so you'll get lots of individual attention, and every day your best work is mounted and put on exhibit. Tuition (from 10.00 a.m.–12.00 noon and 2.00–4.00 p.m.) is in the secluded hotel grounds with its fine sea views, or at a picturesque site near a good pub where you can lunch well.

For details of the Melville Hotel see MULTI-ACTIVITY.

Melville Hotel, Seaview Road, Falmouth, Cornwall TR11 4NL. Telephone: (0326) 312134. Contact: The Manager. Duration: 2–9 and 9–16 May. Price: £94 per person per week (1981). Includes 6 days tuition, 7 nights accommodation, breakfast and dinner. VAT extra. Bring materials.

ESSEX, Colchester

Painting
Flatford Mill Field Centre

What better place to learn to paint than in the mill immortalized by John Constable's paintings? He was born in East Bergholt, and the surrounding countryside inspired him and earlier, Thomas Gainsborough. Both created some of the world's best-known paintings right here. The 18th century Flatford Mill and equally famous Willy Lott's Cottage across the Mill Pool have been converted to accommodate fifty students in two to four bedded rooms. Some single accommodation can be arranged. Breakfast, tea and dinner are served in the refectory and you'll be given a packed lunch so you can spend as much time as possible in the field.

Flatford Mill Field Centre, East Bergholt, Colchester, Essex CO7 6UL. Telephone: (0206) 298283. Warden: John Bingley. Duration: Wednesday to Wednesday, February to August. Price: £84 per person (1981). Includes full board, tuition, use of library. Membership £2. Bring sleeping bag or bed linen, towels and soap. No VAT.

See also CHURCHES AND CATHEDRALS.

HEREFORD AND WORCESTER, Malvern

Painting
Malvern Hills College

The college, nestled in the scenic Malvern Hills, is surrounded by some of the country's finest views. A wide range of summer courses is available. All are taught by highly qualified instructors. Classes are held in well-equipped studios and you'll take field trips to local beauty spots. The life painting atelier and portrait modelling atelier run in close association. Thus you can paint or model in clay using several different subjects. Both courses include two illustrated lectures and a special studio session where you'll work to live background music provided by the Beacon Wind Ensemble. Instruction, largely by demonstration, is often outdoors and individual advice is based on your work in progress. Each course ends with a group showing of all students' work.

The college is non-residential but will supply a list of local hotels and guest houses. Most are within walking distance.

Malvern Hills College, Albert Road North, Malvern, Hereford and Worcester WR14 2TW. Telephone: (06845) 65351. Principal: Mr Arthur Hayens. Duration: 2 and 5 days July and August. Price: from £4–£8 (est). Includes tuition and easels. Bring notebooks, pastels, paints, paper and brushes if you have them but they can also be purchased locally. For accommodation list send SAE. For example, Cotford Hotel. Telephone: (06845) 2427. Price:

single £9 (1981), double with private bath £10.25 per person. Includes bed, breakfast and VAT.

KENT, Shoreham

Drawing and Painting Summer School
Samuel Palmer School of Fine Art

Famous 19th century painter Samuel Palmer lived in this peaceful Kent village for eight years and that period inspired his most visionary work. The late Franklin White, his keen admirer, ran residential art courses from a beautifully preserved 15th century building. Now his widow Gertrude, a Slade-trained artist herself, continues her husband's methods, teaching small groups of amateurs. Students work mainly in oils or watercolours in the large bright garden studio or the informal garden and orchard. Subjects include landscape, simple still lifes, draped figure and composition, and a wide variety of slides are used to demonstrate various techniques. Vacancies are limited, so apply early.

You'll stay in single or double rooms in the main building in the centre of Shoreham. There are extra rooms in the village. Painting materials are on sale at the studio, but you're urged to bring your own paints, easel and folding stool if possible, although there are a few easels and stools for hire.

Samuel Palmer School of Fine Art, Reedbeds, Shoreham, Sevenoaks, Kent. Telephone: (830) 2035. Proprietor: Gertrude White. Duration: August, 1 to 3 weeks, Saturday to Saturday. Price: £75 per person per week (est). Includes tuition, accommodation (single or double), breakfast and dinner. No VAT. Transport from station arranged.

LOTHIAN, Dalkeith

Painting
Newbattle Abbey College

Newbattle Abbey and its magnificent surroundings make perfect subject matter for eager artists. In this practical course you're encouraged to use a variety of media, with the number of members limited to ensure that students get plenty of individual attention. You also visit an exhibition in Edinburgh.

For details of accommodation see ANTIQUES.

Newbattle Abbey College, Dalkeith, Lothian EH22 2LL. Telephone: (031) 663 1921/2. Duration: 1 week, July. Costs £97.75 (est). Includes full board, tuition. No VAT.

See also ANTIQUES, CASTLES AND HISTORIC HOUSES, FESTIVALS, MUSIC.

NORTHERN IRELAND,
COUNTY DOWN, Newcastle

Mourne Holiday School of Art
Newcastle

The legendary beauty of the Mountains of Mourne gives plenty of inspiration to beginners and more experienced art students alike. Newcastle stands on a vast stretch of scenic, sandy coastline where the fishing harbours are also a long-time favourite with artists. Weather permitting, you'll work out of doors, while classroom instruction covers basic drawing techniques, composition, colour, tone and figure work. Classes meet on Monday, Tuesday, Wednesday and Friday from 10.00 a.m. to 12.30 p.m. and 2.00 to 4.30 p.m. and on Thursday from 10.00 a.m. to 12.30 p.m. Your tutor J. H. M. Savage, a visiting lecturer to the Belfast College of Art for twenty-five years, has exhibited widely and illustrated numerous technical and children's books.

The course runs from 3–14 August, but a limited number of students will be accepted for one of the two weeks only.

Newcastle Technical College, Donard Street, Newcastle, Co. Down BT33 0AP. Telephone: (039 67) 22451. Principal: J. E. Ellis (non-residential). Duration: 1 or 2 weeks, August. Price: £12 for 2 weeks, £7 for 1 week (est). Accommodation list on request. For example, the Slieve Donard Hotel (Grade A). Telephone: (039 67) 23681. Price: £18.50 (single) (est). Includes bed, breakfast, service and VAT. Fountain-ville Guest House, Central Promenade. Telephone: (039 67) 22317. Price £7.15 (single) (est). Includes bed, breakfast, dinner.

the Hereford Centre will supply a list of addresses for accommodation.

Malvern Hills College, Albert Road North, Malvern, Hereford and Worcester WR14 2TW. Telephone: (06845) 65351. Principal: Mr W. A. Hayens (non-residential). Duration: 5 days August. Price: £25 (est). Send SAE for list of accommodation. For example, Wheatsheaf Inn. Telephone: (0584) 2980. Price: £13 (double) (est), £18.50 (family room for 4) (est), £7 (single) (est). Includes bed and breakfast. VAT extra.

SHROPSHIRE, Ludlow

Painting at Ludlow
Hereford Diocesan Education Centre

Malvern College operates this course from the Hereford Diocesan Education Centre, Lower Galdeford, Ludlow, Salop. You work mainly in Ludlow, one of the most attractive old towns in England. Its ancient castle and the old stone bridges across the River Teme make ideal subject matter. Field trips take you to other Shropshire beauty spots.

You can make drinks and light snacks in the school's well-equipped kitchen, and there's plenty of free parking space. It's non-residential, but Malvern College or

STRATHCLYDE, Isle of Mull

Painting Holiday
Inniemore Lodge

Paint amidst the mountains of Mull. Artist Julia Wroughton runs a summer painting school at her house, Inniemore Lodge, amidst the remote splendour of Western Scotland. It has attracted amateur painters from all over the world, and all types of painter (beginners too) will enjoy the informal atmosphere here. There are good sandy beaches nearby for children.

The emphasis is on landscape painting in all mediums. Julia Wroughton conducts most of the tuition herself, supported by other qualified artists. Painting classes normally consist of about a dozen

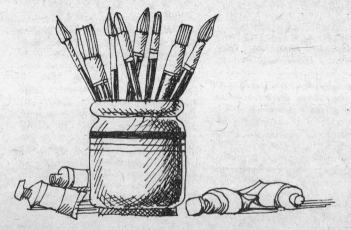

pupils, so there's great room for individual tuition.

Oil and water-colour materials may be purchased on the premises and easels may be borrowed. As part of the course, expeditions are arranged to other parts of the island and to Iona.

There are lots of other amenities nearby, including fishing, pony-trekking, boating and golf at Tobermory.

Inniemore Lodge was originally built as a shooting lodge. Its superb situation at Carsaig, 300 feet above sea level, on the south coast of Mull, commands a magnificent view across the Firth of Lorne to Jura and other isles – an ideal spot for painters.

The Inniemore Summer School of Painting, Pennyghael, Isle of Mull, Strathclyde. Telephone: (06814) 201. Proprietor: Julia Wroughton. Duration: May–September. Price: singles, £165 per week (est). Doubles £110 per person per week (est). Tower rooms, £85 per week (est). Includes tuition, all meals, transport, all extras. VAT extra.

TAYSIDE, Aberfeldy

Painting Holidays in Scotland
Russell House

Surrounded by rivers, lochs, wooded hills and spectacular mountains, Aberfeldy is the perfect spot for a painting holiday. Your host and experienced tutor, Peter Bourne DA, helps you develop your painting skills by way of demonstrations, discussions, and plenty of individual advice (there are never more than eight guests). Russell House is the fine period home of the Bournes; thoroughly modernized to provide comfortable accommodation. Your meals will include home-baked bread and home-grown vegetables from the attractive garden. Breakfast, picnic lunches, afternoon teas and dinners are lovingly prepared, and aperitifs and wine are included. Non-painting friends and spouses are also welcome.

There are twelve weeks to choose from, and both singles and twins are available. Bring your own materials – write for a brief list of basics.

Russell House, Tay Bridge Road, Aberfeldy, Tayside, Scotland. Telephone: (088 72) 363. Proprietors: Marjorie and Peter Bourne. Duration: weekly, May to September, Saturday to Saturday. Price: £85 per person (est). Includes tuition, accommodation (single or twin), all meals, use of easels and drawing boards. Bring painting materials and thermos. Transport can be arranged from Pitlochry Station.

WALES, GWENT, Tintern

Holiday Painting Courses
1 Painting Spring Flowers
2 Summer Painting School
3 Painting Fruits, Foliage & Fungi
The Nurtons

Artist Elsa Wood leads the spring weekend, just after Easter, in the picturesque Wye Valley, when the mass of flowering plants provides an endless variety of subject matter. Both beginners and the more experienced are welcome. The summer course, under the direction of Claire Spencer, is a painting and drawing course, again for artists of all ages and abilities. Elsa Wood also takes the last weekend, a course in colourful botanical illustration.

The Nurtons, Tintern, Nr Chepstow, Gwent, Wales NP6 7NX. Telephone: (02918) 253. Directors: Elsa and Adrian Wood. Duration: 2 and 6 day courses, dates on application. Prices: £28.80 per person (est) (Friday evening to Sunday 4.00 p.m.), £90 (est) (Saturday to Saturday). Includes accommodation in double and family rooms (single 15% extra), breakfast, dinner and packed lunch (vegetarian) and tuition. VAT extra. Reduced rates for children under 12 sharing parents' room. Local bus from Chepstow.

See also YOGA.

YORKSHIRE, Ruswarp

Holiday Painting Course
Old Hall Hotel

Yorkshire artist Harry Beadnell runs these courses for amateur painters and beginners in the olde worlde atmosphere of the Old Hall Hotel. Courses concentrate on outdoor painting at a variety of local venues. You could find yourself painting by river, moor or sea. Harry's an expert in oils, watercolour, pastels and acrylic, and he's renowned as a sympathetic critic and accomplished demonstrator. He'll advise on colour-mixing and composition, while encouraging you to discuss and develop your own style.

The fee includes bed and full board at the Old Hall Hotel, Robin Hood's Bay. Relax in the separate TV lounge, cosy licensed bar and secluded grounds. Dinner is à la carte, and substantial packed lunches are provided for painters on location; bring your own thermos flask. Bring an easel too, if you have one – otherwise hire one here.

Other materials are available, but be sure to write for details of what you'll need.

The Old Hall Hotel, Ruswarp, Whitley, North Yorkshire. Telephone: (0947) 2801. Proprietors: John and Liz Rankin. Duration: 30 May–6 June, 4–11 July, 5–12 September. Price: £150 per person (1981). Includes tuition, accommodation, breakfast, dinner, packed lunch and VAT. Bring paper, paints, brushes and canvasses. Art materials may be purchased. Hire an easel at £1 per week, a stool at 50p.

YORKSHIRE, Whitley

Drawing and Painting Course
Moorlands Hotel

Artist Frank Slater's residential weekends for drawing and painting are relaxed and friendly. Beginners are encouraged and the spectacular views of the nearby moors provide ideal landscape subjects. The course includes outdoor instruction and an illustrated talk.

Accommodation and full board (including packed lunches) are provided at the Moorlands, a small (licensed) family-run hotel at the head of the village within easy reach of Castleton Moor Station. Your fee does not include equipment, which is available for hire if required.

Moorlands Hotel, Castleton, Whitley, North Yorkshire YO21 2DB. Telephone: (02876) 206. Proprietor: John Aubertin. Duration: Friday to Sunday, May and October. Price £35 per person (est). Includes tuition, accommodation, breakfast, dinner, and packed lunch.

PARA ASCENDING

DEVON, Dawlish

Para Ascending Courses
Rosemount Hotel

Rosemount is a small private hotel in a peaceful area only a few minutes' walk from the sea. The resident proprietors have made a special arrangement at a nearby private airfield so you can include an introduction to the exciting sport of para ascending with your stay at the hotel. You can choose a one-day introduction or a two-day residential course.

The beginner is attached to a tow line and can go to any altitude above ten feet, then (still attached) descend at a slow rate. The more advanced student can release from the tow line and parachute to a target on the ground. The school has been operating since 1965 and instructors are all BAPC licensed. You'll cover such facets of the sport as landing techniques; launching signals; canopy control; and airfield procedure. Transport to and from the airfield from Rosemount will be provided if required. Hotel amenities include two lounges, one with colour TV and one a sun lounge, a car park and a restaurant.

Rosemount Hotel, 8 Barton Terrace, Dawlish, Devon EX7 9QH. Telephone: (0626) 863368. Proprietors: Betty and John Birkett. Duration: 2 days. Price: £18 per person (est). Includes tuition, hire of equipment, one nights accommodation, bed and breakfast. Minimum age 14 years.

KENT, Lympne

Para Ascending
Eagle Sports

Para ascending is one of the simplest and cheapest ways of getting into the air. You're launched much the same way as a glider – by means of a tow line attached to a Land Rover with your parachute held open behind you by two wing tip holders. You're airborne after a few steps, then gently ascend to about 800 feet where you release from the tow line to make a normal parachute descent. After some experience you should find it easy to make a stand-up landing; then it's back to the launch point for another go. The club's detailed training programme takes a novice through a basic training which covers landing roll practice, control of the canopy and the first flight. You'll start with low ascents (to only fifty or one hundred feet), remaining on the tow line without the need for a landing roll. When your instructor thinks you're ready, you'll make your first self-release from the line.

One-day courses are held most weekends. The club house at Ashford Airport includes a licensed bar where snack meals are available.

Eagle Sports, Ashford Airport, Lympne, Nr Hythe, Kent. Telephone: (0303) 60816. Proprietor: George Sugden. Duration: 2 days, all year. Price: £15 per person per day (1981). Includes instruction, equipment, 3 ascents, insurance and VAT. Minimum age 14 years. Minimum body weight 96 lbs. Bring rubber soled boots. Accommodation arranged (e.g. bed & breakfast from £4.50 per person). Campsite facilities available.

See also PARACHUTING.

PARACHUTING

HUMBERSIDE, Bridlington

Parachuting
British Skysports

British Skysports Centre, Britain's first such centre, has introduced over 4,000 people to parachuting and skydiving. Facilities include inexpensive bunk bed accommodation, a dining room, a day room, a bar/disco, showers, a sauna, lecture rooms, three aircraft, modern training aids such as tripod-mounted binoculars or 'telemeters'. Every parachute descent is closely observed both from the aircraft and the ground and is followed up with a detailed critique by qualified instructors. Two types of courses are offered: Courses A and B provide a minimum six and a half hours' training which concentrates on an explanation of equipment, the theory of stability and free fall, practice in suspended harness, exit and emergency drills, canopy control and landing falls. The fee includes one descent, kit hire, aircraft hire, insurance for three descents and provisional membership of British Skysports. Courses C and D are combined holiday and training courses, one lasts five days, the other twelve. On both full accommodation is included in the fee. The former offers thirteen, the latter twenty hours of training. All courses begin at 9 a.m.

British Skysports, Bridlington Aerodrome, Bridlington, Humberside YO16 4YB. Telephone: (0262) 77367. Duration: 1 day, 1 week and two weeks, January to October. Price: 1 day from £40 per person (1981). 1 week from £115 per person (1981). Two weeks from £220 per person. Includes descents, kit hire, aircraft hire and insurance and VAT. Bring boots, tracksuit, gloves and helmet.

See also FLYING.

KENT, Lympne

Parachuting
Eagle Sports

The basic course involves approximately six hours of on-ground tuition which covers how a parachute works, how to leave the aircraft, how to control an open parachute, what to do in an emergency, and how to land (despite any qualms you have, it's the equivalent of jumping from a height of about four feet and forward four feet). On your first six descents (minimum) the parachute will be automatically opened for you from the aircraft. After each jump your instructor will give you a critique of your performance and any further instruction you need. You'll be using the most modern parachutes available and one of the largest hazard-free drop zones in the country. The Centre has an impressive record – it's safely trained 3500 people in the past four years.

Eagle Sports, Ashford Airport, Lympne, Nr Hythe, Kent. Telephone: (0303) 60816. Proprietor: George Sugden. Duration: 2 days, all year. Price: £45 per person (1981). Includes 2 day course tuition, equipment, first descent, insurance and VAT. Further jumps £5.50 per descent. Bring rubber soled boots. Accommodation arranged e.g. bed and breakfast from £4.50 per person. Campsite facilities available.

See also PARA ASCENDING.

NORTHUMBERLAND, Belford

Sports Parachuting Courses
Windy Gyle Parachute and Outdoor Centre

Why is parachuting one of the fastest-growing sports in the country? Because your first jump is probably the most exciting thing you'll ever do. It's a young sport, but safety standards have risen rapidly. If you stick to the rules it's actually safer than more conventional sports – the Windy Gyle centre points with pride to a record of only two fractures in five years. The training courses are of the full thirteen hours recommended by the British Parachute Association (to which the centre is affiliated). Your instructors have all been active in the sport for at least eleven years, most of that time as qualified instructors. Your first jump will be from an aircraft at 2500 feet on a 'static line' (automatically opened) parachute. On the seven-day courses you'll be trained to make your first 'free fall', usually after about eight static line jumps. All jumps are made over the centre's 'drop zone' at Brunton, with its superb views of the Northumbria coast. On a weekend course training begins on Friday evening and lasts till Saturday night, which leaves all Sunday for the first jump. If the weather's bad you can return to complete the jump on any subsequent course. Accommodation is in small comfortable dormitories for between three and twelve, in a converted country house. All bedding is provided, and facilities include a lounge with colour TV, games room, residents' bar and garden.

Windy Gyle Parachute and Outdoor Centre, Belford, Northumberland, NE70 7QE. Telephone: (066 83) 289. Duration: Weekends and weeks all year. Price: £50 per person per weekend (est), £100 per person per week (est). Includes tuition, equipment, first descent, third party insurance, dormitory accommodation, all meals and VAT. Additional jumps after the first are extra. Bring overall or track suit and *rubber soled lace-up boots. Minimum age 16 – bring medical certificate if over 40.*

See also MULTI-ACTIVITY.

WILTSHIRE, Savernake

Parachuting
Savernake Forest Hotel

Stay comfortably at this fine red brick country house which specializes in traditional English cooking. Most unexpectedly, it's your base for a two-day course where you can experience the thrills of parachuting under the guidance of experienced instructors at the RSA Parachute Club in Thruxton. The package includes equipment and aircraft hire, your first jump and two days' dinner, bed and breakfast. What a way to see the area's marvellous scenery!

The Savernake Forest Hotel, Burbage, Nr Marlborough, Wiltshire SN8 2AY. Telephone: (0672) 810206 or Best Western on (01) 940 9766. Proprietor: Kingsley Morris. Duration: all year, 2 day (Thursday to Sunday) courses. Price: £70.50 winter, £73 spring, £76 summer per person (1981). Includes room, breakfast and dinner, instruction, equipment, aircraft hire, first jump and VAT.

Paranormal

BUCKINGHAMSHIRE, Great Missenden

Paranormal Phenomena
Missenden Abbey

If you're partial to the paranormal or extraterrestrial, this serious investigation into as yet scientifically unexplained phenomena should prove fascinating. The rare assemblage of the foremost British experts in the field includes the President of the Psychical Research Society, the Rt Hon. Earl of Clancarty, the country's foremost champion of 'UFOlogy' and a specialist in science fiction. They and other experts will conduct discussions on subjects such as faith healing, possession and exorcism, dowsing, UFOs and paranormal communications.

The abbey is a marvellous setting for this course. Founded in 1133, it was largely rebuilt in neo-Gothic style in the 19th century. In 1964 it became an adult education centre run by the Buckinghamshire County Council. Appropriately, it's haunted.

The Warden, Missenden Abbey, Great Missenden, Buckinghamshire HP16 0BD.

Telephone: (02 406) 2328. Duration: weekend, 3–5 April. Price: £30 (1981), £26.50 for Buckinghamshire residents. Includes tuition, accommodation (mainly twin rooms) and all meals from Friday dinner to Sunday lunch.

See also HISTORY, LACEMAKING, LITERATURE, WOODWORKING, YOGA.

Just the Thing for a Holiday Present.

DAESTU

THE WONDROUS WRITING POWER

WALES, CLWYD, Ruthin

Stay in a Haunted Castle
Ruthin

Meet the ghost of Ruthin Castle, an ethereal lady said to have taken shelter in the

castle when it was under siege in medieval times. She met her death under mysterious circumstances and wanders the battlements to this day, looking for her lover.

You get the best of both worlds at Ruthin Castle. It stands in thirty acres of parkland, and is a mere three minutes walk from the town centre. This gem in the crown of the Principality of Wales sits amid the rolling countryside of the Vale of Clwyd in North Wales, twenty miles from Snowdonia. It's equally close to the sea, and only minutes away from Pullglas' 9 hole golf course. There's also good trout fishing on the River Clwyd.

Your accommodation reflects the middle ages, without those ancient discomforts. Prepare for medieval banquets with jesters, minstrels and buxom serving wenches as part of the scene. Prices vary according to season and entertainment, though the ghost is always free.

Ruthin Castle, Ruthin, Clwyd, North Wales, LL15 2NU. Telephone: (082 42) 2664. Manager: Derek Evans. Duration: all year. Price: £20 single, £18 double, per person for bed and breakfast (est). Full board £27.50 (est) (minimum stay of 3 days). 50% reduction for children under 5, 25% reduction children under 12. Prices include VAT, not service.

YORKSHIRE, York

Ghosts
Haunted and Historic York

If you're feeling fearless, take the two-hour evening walking tour of the favourite haunts of York's best-known ghosts. You'll set out at 8 p.m. with your intrepid guide. The more adventurous may want to take the weekend tour, led by John Mitchell, author of 'Ghosts of an Ancient City'. He'll take you to sites not normally accessible to the public, such as the Treasures House cellar where the shades of Roman soldiers have been seen. Backstage at the Theatre Royal you may encounter the mysterious Grey Lady. If you wish you can meet eye-witnesses who'll describe their hair-raising encounters.

To really get into the spirit of the thing stay at Cromwell House. Although it's new the hotel was built on the site of the dungeons of a medieval castle. Former residents seem to have been disturbed by the construction, as visitors in rooms 33, 34 and 35 have testified to nightly knockings on their doors.

Enrichment Travel Ltd., 7a St Sampsons Square, York YO2 4BB. Telephone: (0904) 52232. Contact: Angie Broadhead. Duration: Friday evening to Sunday afternoon, dates on application; or nightly tours Monday to Friday, May to October. Price: Weekends from £45 per person per week-

end (1981), includes 2 nights bed, breakfast and dinner, price varies according to accommodation. Nightly tours, adults £1 children 60p (1981).
Cromwell House, Annexe of Lady Anne Middleton Hotel, Cromwell Road, York. Telephone: (0904) 32257. Duration: all year. Price: single £8 (1981). Includes continental breakfast. VAT extra.

PHOTOGRAPHY

BEDFORDSHIRE, Woburn

Photography
Maryland College

For experienced photographers, this weekend will give valuable help and practice in the art of composition and the technical quality of your work. You'll deal with still life, while models and students provide the subject matter for portraiture. Chemicals and a dark room are provided for you to develop your film.

Maryland runs other week and weekend photographic courses; including one on techniques of print developing.

Maryland College, Woburn, Milton Keynes, MK17 9JD. Telephone: (052 525) 688. Contact: the Principal. Duration: 24–26 April. Cost: £32.25 (1981). Includes room (single or twin), meals from Friday dinner to Sunday lunch, tuition, chemicals for colour transparencies. Bring own towel. Facilities for disabled. Prices include VAT.

See also GARDENING, LACEMAKING, LANGUAGES.

GREATER MANCHESTER, Stockport

Country Photography
Alma Lodge Hotel

Leisure Learning Weekends have organized a series of landscape photography sessions in areas carefully chosen for their completely different mood and atmosphere. Derek Watkins, author of 'SLR Photography', guides your use of the camera in the High Peak district, where subject matter includes fast-flowing rivers, brilliantly coloured cave formations and picturesque canals and viaducts.

Leisure Learning Weekends, Embassy Hotels Ltd, Station Street, Burton-upon-Trent, Staffordshire DE14 1BZ. Contact: Gordon Hopper. Telephone: (0283) 66587. Duration: 4–6 September. Price: £48 per person (1981). Includes 2 nights accommodation (with bath), all meals (Friday dinner to Sunday lunch), lecture, slide shows, service and VAT.

See also CASTLES AND HISTORIC HOUSES, CHURCHES AND CATHEDRALS, LITERATURE, POTTERY, WINE TASTING.

LEICESTERSHIRE, Loughborough

Country Photography

Derek Watkins, author of 'SLR Photography', is full of helpful tips on your first day here, as you choose from subjects such as timbered Tudor houses, Puritan churches and local canals and woodlands. On the second day, a demonstration darkroom is set up in the hotel, where the

Chief Colour Demonstrator of Eumig (UK) will provide and demonstrate Durst equipment for developing, enlarging and printing. Photo Technology Ltd will provide all necessary materials.

Leisure Learning Weekends, Embassy Hotels Ltd, Station Street, Burton-upon-Trent, Staffordshire DE14 1BZ. Telephone: (0283) 66587. Contact: Gordon Hopper. Duration: 1–3 May. Price: £48 per person (1981). Includes 2 nights accommodation (with bath), all meals (Friday dinner to Sunday lunch), lectures, photocolour materials, service and VAT.

See also CANALS, CHURCHES, HISTORIC HOUSES, POTTERY, WINE TASTING.

POLO

EIRE, COUNTY WATERFORD,
Waterford

Polo
Whitfield Court Polo School

Learn the sport of princes for nothing like the cost of a king's ransom. At Whitfield Court, Major Hugh Dawnay offers sportsmen the chance to play polo without the expense of owning a string of polo ponies; and inexperienced players can take this chance to improve their game. Major Dawnay learnt to play polo with the 10th Hussars, played regularly for his regiment in international competitions and is now one of the country's most experienced instructors.

The polo school has excellent facilities – a full-sized ground, a second all-weather ground and a practice ground. There are twenty-four ponies, and the emphasis is on expert instruction covering tactics and the basic equine skills necessary for the game. In addition, there's a swimming pool and tennis court (balls and racquets provided) for the use of guests.

Your quarters are in the annexe at Whitfield Court, one of Ireland's fine Palladian mansions, set in open countryside just a few miles from Waterford. There's a sitting room with bar facilities and meals of a high standard are served in a convivial family atmosphere.

Whitfield Court Polo School, Waterford, Eire. Telephone: (0005) 84216. Chief Instructor: Major Hugh Dawnay. Duration: April to September, Monday noon to Friday evening. Price: from £350 to £500 (est) according to participation. Accommodation at Whitfield Court £35 per day (est) including all meals and VAT. Reduction for course participants.

PONY TREKKING

CUMBRIA, Troutbeck

Pony Trekking
Troutbeck Hotel

Spend your summer in the saddle, pony trekking through the Lake District. The Robinsons keep a wide variety of mounts: Fell, Highland, Welsh Mountain and Icelandic ponies, all well-suited to long distance trekking over rough terrain. All the ponies are reliable and well-behaved. The sturdy Icelandic ponies are particularly suitable for beginners on account of their easy ride and even temperament, while the Fell and Highland breeds give the more experienced a good ride. Instruction is given before you leave and each trek is escorted by an experienced leader who knows the local country.

Inexperienced riders under ten are not usually accepted. Accommodation is at the Troutbeck Hotel, a small country inn (with a residents' TV lounge) next door to the stables. Be sure to bring suitable riding clothes (hard hats provided).

Troutbeck Hotel, Troutbeck, Cumbria CA11 0SJ. Telephone: (085 33) 243. Manager: Peter Robinson. Duration: daily, Easter to October. Price: half-day treks from £4 (1981). Bed and breakfast £5 + VAT; with evening meal £7.50 per day + VAT.

EIRE, COUNTY DONEGAL, Dunfanaghy

Pony Trekking
Arnold's Hotel

Arnold's is a fully licensed one-star hotel which accommodates up to seventy-four. You can choose from the hotel's stable of six sure-footed ponies for hacking and trekking. Donegal's marvellously varied terrain means you can ride in the nearby mountains and forests, and on beaches and cliff trails.

Dunfanaghy Stables, Arnold's Hotel, Dunfanaghy, Donegal, Eire. Telephone: (0007) 36208. Manager: Derek Arnold. Duration: Monday to Saturday, April to September. Price: £107 (est) April to June and September, £130 (est) July and August per person per week. Includes 10 hours riding and full board. Bring riding hat.

WALES, CLWYD, Vale of Llangollen

Pony Trekking

This is a flexible package, first because you can choose any week between April and mid-September and secondly because the accommodation (either in a farm-house or one of two hotels) gives you a choice of price. If you stay at the farm six miles from the centre, you'll need a car.

You meet your pony after arrival on Saturday afternoon, so you've got plenty of time to get acquainted before the first trek on Monday. An instructor/guide will accompany you on four full day treks, and Wednesday is a free day. The minimum age for accompanied children is eleven and they're expected to have had at least a few previous lessons. Hats are provided free, but there's a mandatory £2.50 surcharge for insurance.

Galleon World Travel Association Ltd., Galleon House, King Street, Maidstone,

Kent ME14 1EG. Telephone: (0622) 63411 or (01) 859 0111. Duration: April to September. Price: £120 per person (est) Saturday to Saturday. Includes farmhouse accommodation, breakfast, dinner, packed

lunch, guide, trekking and VAT. Insurance £2.50 extra.

See also ANTIQUES, CRUISING: INLAND WATERWAYS, GARDENS, HISTORY, SURFING.

POTTERY

DUMFRIES AND GALLOWAY, Moniaive

Pottery
Crossford Craft Studio

The studios, formerly the two classrooms of a small rural school, are equipped with a potter's wheel and kiln. Many other facilities are available (for details, see ENAMELLING), and you can receive tuition in all the other crafts as well as pottery.

Crossford Craft Studios, Schoolhouse, Crossford, Moniaive, Dumfries and Galloway, Scotland. Telephone: (038 782) 410. Proprietor: Duncan Devlin. Duration: weekly, July and August. Price: £45 per person (est) (20% student reduction). Includes use of studios and tuition; materials extra. Varied accommodation from £45 per week (est), all meals included. No VAT.

See also ENAMELLING.

OXFORDSHIRE, Ipsden

Pottery for beginners
Braziers Adult College

The wide variety of courses at this experimental community ranges from writing and guitar playing to weaving and pottery. Tutors Glynn Faithful, Pat Sentinella, Ora Pray and a dozen others, all specialists in their chosen fields, give courses for beginners as well as for practised amateurs and professionals.

Accommodation is in a castellated Gothic mansion set in fifty acres of gardens, woodland and a farm run by the staff on a community basis. There are single, double and treble rooms and a small cottage. Children under seventeen must be accompanied. The community atmosphere is encouraged and students are expected to help with minor chores – hence the economical price of £80 (est) for six-day courses (with pottery approximately £1 per day extra). Visitors should bring their own materials for the spinning and weaving courses – though there is a nearby art shop and you can buy natural wool from Braziers' own shop.

Swimming, riding and tennis can be arranged nearby.

Braziers Adult College, Ipsden, Oxfordshire OX9 6AN. Telephone: (0491) 680221. Convener of Studies: Dr Robert Faithfull. Duration: 6 days July to August. Price: £80 per person (est). Includes double accommodation (single room supplement £2 per night) all meals and tuition. Small charge for clay. No VAT.

SOMERSET, Butleigh

Pottery
Dove Workshops

This full and busy workshop programme provides opportunities for throwing, slab-building, pinching and, most exciting, raku pottery. This ancient Japanese firing technique means pots can be glazed, fired and drawn from the kiln in less than an hour. It's an exciting technique which produces some wonderful copper lustres and brilliant blues and greens. You'll mix clays and glazes and build a woodfired kiln. If you're especially interested in one particular technique you're welcome to specialize.

Dove Workshops Courses, Dove Workshops, Barton Road, Butleigh, Nr Glastonbury, Somerset. Telephone: (0458 50) 682. Proprietor: Barbara Stubbs. Duration: 5 days, August. Price: from £35–£44 per person for 5 day course (est). Materials £3 extra. Bed and breakfast accommodation £4 per person per night (est).

See also STAINED GLASS.

STAFFORDSHIRE,
Newcastle-under-Lyme

History and Tradition of Pottery
Clayton Lodge Hotel

These weekends at Clayton Lodge Hotel are set up by David Seekers, one-time director of the Gladstone Pottery Museum. Together you'll trace the development of the pottery and ceramics industry and visit the Minton and Wedgewood works and the new City Museum and Art Gallery to see some of the world's most outstanding pottery and porcelain. You'll see potters at work at the Gladstone Museum and visit the Cheddleton Flint Mill where raw materials for china-making originate.

Any one of these weekends is an excellent introduction to the practical courses offered.

Leisure Learning Weekends, Embassy Hotels Ltd, Station Street, Burton-upon-Trent, Staffordshire DE14 1BZ. Telephone: (0283) 66587. Contact: Gordon Hopper. Duration: 27–29 March, 22–24 May, 17–19 July. Price: £48 per person (1981). Includes lectures, visits, 2 nights accommodation (with bath), all meals (Friday dinner to Sunday lunch), service and VAT.

See also CASTLES AND HISTORIC HOUSES, CHURCHES AND CATHEDRALS, LITERATURE, PHOTOGRAPHY, WINE TASTING.

PRINTING

CUMBRIA, Lowick Green

Printmaking
Lowick House

Learn to make prints at Lowick House in the wilds of Cumbria. Courses run by John Sutcliffe and Mark Wilson (both active artist/printmakers) aim to provide an ideal working situation for artists, printmakers and non-artists alike, allowing great personal expression through lithography, intaglio, screen printing, relief printing and photo-related techniques. Lowick House prides itself on its fine equipment (the use of which is included in the course fee). If you wish to use more than two printmaking media during your stay, John Sutcliffe recommends a minimum stay of two weeks (unless you already have a full working knowledge of one of the media chosen).

Lowick House is situated in the village of Lowick Green, in the beautiful unspoilt Crate Valley near the foot of Coniston Water. The house itself is a traditional Lakeland farmhouse, completely modernized, and standing in its own wooded grounds with pools and a running stream. Accommodation is either in the house, caravans or nearby guest houses. (You are welcome to bring your own tent or caravan.) Breakfast and evening meal (and lunchtime sandwiches on request) are provided by the house. They have a large kitchen garden and rear their own sheep, geese and free range chickens.

Lowick House Printmaking, Lowick Green, Nr Ulverston, Cumbria LA12 8DX. Telephone: (022985) 698. Director: John Sutcliffe. Duration: weekly, March to October. Price: £110 per person per week (1981). Includes tuition, materials, room, breakfast, dinner and VAT. Self-catering caravans and campsite also available.

PUPPETRY

SUSSEX, Chichester

Making Glove Puppets
Earnley Concourse

This course will show you various ways of making glove puppets, using materials such as papier mâché, plastic, wood, felt and foam rubber. By the end of the weekend you'll have made your own puppet. You'll also study staging and suitable plays, so you can put on your own shows.

For details of the Concourse and fees, see ANTIQUES.

The Earnley Concourse, Nr Chichester, Sussex PO20 7JL. Telephone: (0243) 670392. Duration: Friday to Sunday, October to November. Price: from £20 per person (double), £22 (single) (est). Includes tuition, accommodation and all meals Friday dinner to Sunday lunch. VAT extra. Minibus from Chichester Station £1 each way.

See also ANTIQUES, CREATIVE WRITING, FLOWER ARRANGING, FOLK AND JAZZ, LANGUAGES, MUSIC, SURVIVAL TRAINING, WINE TASTING.

QUILTING AND PATCHWORK

DEVON, Beaworthy

Patchwork
Lower Forda

Your resident hostess on this cottage-based course is Mrs Nina Skinner. She's a qualified long-time crafts instructor at the North Devon Community Centre and is ably assisted by other qualified tutors when necessary. The patchwork course is one of the most popular (and doesn't require any special equipment). You can also study soft toy making, rag dolls, crochet, gingham embroidery and cane work.

For details of Lower Forda, see DRESSMAKING.

Lower Forda, Shebbear, Beaworthy, North Devon. Telephone: (040 928) 218. Principal: Nina Skinner. Duration: 6 days, April, September. Price: from £75 per person (1981). Includes 4 days tuition, full board. Materials and outings extra. Transport from coach stop 25p per person.

SUSSEX, Fittleworth

Patchwork
The Old Rectory

Bring your prettiest cotton fabrics, plain and printed, and learn how to make colourful use of them with the time-honoured skill of patchwork.

For details of accommodation see SENIOR CITIZENS.

The Old Rectory, Fittleworth, Pulborough, Sussex RH20 1HU (off A283 to Pulborough). Telephone: (079882) 306. Proprietors: Brenda and Graham Salmon. Duration: Tuesday to Friday, September to October. Price: from £36 per person, twin room; £51 single (until April 1981). Includes tuition and full board. Bring cotton fabrics.

See also CASTLES AND HISTORIC HOUSES, CLOCKS, GENEALOGY, MUSIC, ORNITHOLOGY, SENIOR CITIZENS.

WALES, DYFED, Llanwrda

Welsh Quilting and Needlecraft
Gwaith Llaw y Werin

Craft school courses here are designed to enable a complete novice to practise a skill, unsupervised, after only a week's tuition. This particular course concentrates on traditional Welsh quilting as a technique for making bed covers and clothing. Patchwork was traditionally used on one side of the work. You'll learn to work small samplers, how to prepare the fleece and choose fabrics and something of the symbolism of stitchery patterns, so you'll emerge with a piece of quilting as well as samplers. The course includes a visit to a collection of antique quilts displayed in a local museum. Groups of six receive three hours' daily tuition and a farmhouse lunch.

Gwaith Llaw y Werin, Cottage Industries Crafts School, Wernfeudwy, Ffarmers, Llanwrda, Dyfed, Wales SA19 8PJ. Telephone: (055 85) 434. Proprietor: Judith Hoad. Duration: Monday to Friday, April to October. Price: £39 per person per week (est). Includes tuition and lunch. Accommodation list on request (e.g. £52 per person per week (est). Includes room, breakfast and dinner.) Bring 2 yards of lightweight plain fabric and 2 yards patterned fabric. Minimum unaccompanied age 16 years. No VAT.

See also CALLIGRAPHY.

RAILWAYS

NORTH YORKSHIRE, Pickering

Railway Interest Holiday
Freedom of Ryedale Holidays

What better way to explore Yorkshire's railway history than by train. The day after you arrive in Pickering, a small town on the edge of the North York Moors,

you visit Pickering Station where railway buffs will find plenty to interest them: display boards, an audio visual documentary of the area and the history of the line, a good bookshop and a Tourist Information Centre. Then you travel to Goathland, an isolated moorland village, by steam or diesel engined train. The line passes under the ancient ramparts of Pickering Castle and rises into spectacular Newton Dale and the National Park. From Goathland you travel on to Grosmont where you'll see engines and rolling stock. There's a viewing gallery in the locomotive shed so you can see how day-to-day engine maintenance is done. Additional displays give further information on the railway. You then take the early evening train back to Pickering. Next day you bus eight miles to Malton, then it's on by British Rail to York, and the National Railway Museum: a magnificent collection of engines and exhibits which covers the whole history of railway development. With over a mile of track the nearby Model Railway Exhibition is well worth a sidetrip. In the evening you can either return to Pickering or stay at a York hotel.

Freedom of Ryedale Activity Holidays, 23a Market Place, Helmsley, York YO6

5BJ. Telephone: (0439) 70775. Director: John Garry. Duration: 3 days, April to end of September. Price: £36 per person (est). Includes 3 nights hotel accommodation, breakfast and dinner. £22.50–£25 (est) for youth hostel accommodation. Return rail tickets to Grosmont and York and VAT. YHA membership and Model Railway Exhibition entrance fee extra.

See also CYCLING, WALKING.

REAL TENNIS

STRATHCLYDE, Troon

Real Tennis
Sun Court Hotel

This game – usually known to its followers simply as 'tennis' – is the ancestor of present-day lawn tennis, but really has more in common with squash. The unusual shape of the court derives from the courtyard of a typical French monastery; there were an estimated four hundred courts in Paris alone during the 13th and 14th centuries. The original asymmetrical racquet is still used today. The game became popular in Britain, although James I and VI decreed that only the nobility should be allowed to play – no wonder that the game became known as 'Royal' (now corrupted to 'Real').

The hotel maintains one of the few real tennis courts in the world; as a guest you enjoy automatic membership of the club. The Sun Court, built as a private luxury residence at the turn of the century, has twenty rooms (eighteen with bath). Most offer views of the Old Troon Golf Course and the Firth of Clyde. The high standard of service and comfort made this hotel one of the first winners of a British Tourist Authority's award for value for money establishments.

Sun Court Hotel, Crosbie Road, Troon, Strathclyde, Scotland. Telephone: (0292) 312727. Proprietors: Jill and Alastair Breckenridge. Duration: all year. Price: £14.50 per person (twin shared) per day (1981). Includes bed and breakfast, service and VAT. Use of real tennis court £3.40 per hour, includes tuition. Winter weekend breaks available October to March. Squash and tennis courts also available.

Religious Retreats

COUNTRYWIDE

Retreats
Association for Promoting Retreats

The retreat movement aims to provide settings for quiet contemplation, sometimes with guided study and prayer. An ecumenical journal, the *Vision*, is jointly produced by the Association for Promoting Retreats (APR) and the National Council for Retreats and Pastoral Centres (NCRPC). It provides detailed listings of a wide variety of retreat houses. For example, Bishop Woodford House in Ely, a purpose-built modern house which accommodates up to thirty-three in single rooms, is available for retreats, quiet days and conferences. At Trelowarren Fellowship, Helston up to thirty can be accommodated in a 17th century stately home with its own chapel. It's set in beautiful grounds near the Helford River. Prices vary; sample charges are £5 to £10 per day for full board (est). Details supplied upon application.

Association for Promoting Retreats, Church House, Newton Road, London W2 5LS. Telephone: (01) 727 7924. Secretary: Sister Joanna Baldwin. Duration: all year. Price: minimum subscription £2.50 per person.

CUMBRIA, Ulverston

Buddhist Retreats
Manjushri Institute

Manjushri Institute, unique in Britain, is a member of the Foundation for the Preservation of the Mahayana Tradition, a Nepal-based organization dedicated to transmitting and preserving the teachings of Buddha. The Institute's spiritual directors are Lama Thalsten Yeshe and Lama Thubten Zopa Rinpoche, who have been teaching Buddhist psychology and medi-

tation to Westerners since 1969. This religious and educational trust has its main centre at Conishead Priory, where there's a resident community of seventy composed of monks, nuns, lay people and children. The priory is set in seventy acres of wooded grounds on the shores of Morecambe Bay; it's been a seat of religious learning and contemplation since the 12th century, when Augustinian monks lived and worked here for over three centuries.

The retreats offered consist of four to six meditations and recitation sessions daily, led by senior students. The 1980 ten-day retreat, only open to those who had received prior initiation, gave students an opportunity to practice the teachings of Manjushri Yoga. The two two-week retreats were offered to students who had received Cittamani Tara initiation. Participation in any of the retreats fulfills the commitment for the Summer Festival initiation.

Manjushri Institute, College of Tibetan Buddhist Studies, Conishead Priory, Ulverston, Cumbria LA12 9QQ. Telephone: (0229) 54019. Secretary: Emily Strang. Duration: from 2 weeks, dates on application. Price: £4 per person per week (1981). Includes registration fee. Accommodation: £4 per day for those who work 3 hours per day, £4.70 for non-workers (1981). Price includes dormitory accommodation and all meals. Single and double rooms also available. Bring sleeping bag. Retreat only for the initiated courses, including meditation, psychology and oriental medicine also available, send SAE for brochure.

See also WORKING HOLIDAYS.

STAFFORDSHIRE, Rugeley

Religious Courses and Retreats
Spode Conference Centre

The Spode Centre provides interdenominational and secular retreats for those interested in spiritual enlightenment and also retreat courses for alcoholics. The centre is run by Dominican friars, who welcome all denominations. Accommodation is in the priory, or adjoining Spode House, in single, double or family rooms or curtained dormitories. The fee includes talks, optional services and full board –

and the friars believe in providing good hearty fare. The priory is half-way between Birmingham and the Potteries (twenty-five miles from each) and can be easily reached by rail or road. It has a chapel and is set in its own wooded grounds in a secluded peaceful atmosphere.

The Spiritual Quist-Hindu retreat is a weekday inter-religious course conducted by Swami Bhavyananda and Father Adam Michels. There is also a Dominical Secular Institute Retreat Day for Alcoholics Anonymous and a special Retreat for Alcoholics – all with talks, discussions and forums.

The Spode Conference Centre, Hawkesyard Priory, and Spode House, Rugeley, Staffordshire WS15 1PT. Telephone: (0543) 490112; ask for the Warden. Duration: 1, 3 and 7 days, all year. Price: £7.15 per night (£9.35 single) (est), accommodation only. VAT extra.

See also CALLIGRAPHY, MUSIC.

R IDING

DUMFRIES AND GALLOWAY, Corrybracken

Riding and Trekking
Corrybracken Riding Centre

The scenery of Galloway is magnificent and unspoilt. Come and stay on a 3000-acre estate and ride through the area's moors and woodland. The Corrybracken Riding Centre has eighteen mounts, from Shetland ponies to 16.2 hand hunters, to suit all ages and degrees of experience. Trekking can be arranged on an hourly, two hourly or half-day basis. Accommodation is in self-catering cottages on the McNeill Estate, where you'll have free use of a tennis court, table tennis and a private trout loch. An added bonus is the fun of farm life. Children are welcome to help out with haying and harvesting, and guests have been known to end up with a pet lamb in their garden.

McNeill Estates, Corrybracken, Kirkcowan, Newton Stewart, Dumfries and Galloway. Telephone: (067 183) 266. Proprietor: Pamela McNeill. Duration: Saturday to Saturday, March to October. Price: from £50 per week (1981). £70 per week June, July and August (1981), accommodation only. Trekking £2.50 per hour. Lessons £3.50 per hour. VAT extra. Bring linen.

EIRE, COUNTY GALWAY, Clifden

Riding
Errislannan Riding Centre

The Manor, four miles southwest of Clifden, stables fifteen ponies and is equipped with an outdoor riding enclosure, changing rooms and a hacking equipment shop.

Mrs Brooks and Miss Mead specialize in teaching children to ride and with competitions and games make learning a joy. Accompanied hacking jaunts, trekking on the moors and mountains, and tackling natural cross-country obstacles all help kids improve their horsemanship. If you're staying in the area you may be interested in their daily programme for youngsters which offers riding tuition plus tips on grooming, feeding and other aspects of pony care.

Errislannan Riding Centre, Errislannan Manor, Clifden, County Galway, Eire. Telephone: (Clifden) 27; to obtain this number contact operator. Manager: Mrs Stephanie Brooks. Duration: Monday to Saturday, April to September. Price: £120 (est) per week (8–15 year olds only). Includes tuition and full board. Daily ponycraft course £12 (est). 1 hour riding lesson £5 (est). Bring riding hat.

EIRE, COUNTY KERRY, Killarney

Dromquinna Riding Stables

The stables are open year-round for hacking and trekking on roads, beaches, forest trails and in the mountains. There are ten horses and six ponies available, a jumping paddock and a changing room where you can also get refreshments. Lessons cost £4.50 per hour, riding £3.50.

You'll stay further west along the coast at the family-run Butler Arms Hotel. It's a large white building, modern inside, with a sun room, cocktail bar and TV room. Guests have free use of the hard tennis court in the grounds, plus free salmon and sea trout fishing on Lough Currane from 17 January to 12 October. Deep sea fishing and tackle hire can be arranged at the hotel, and you're only one mile from an 18 hole championship golf course.

Dromquinna Riding Stables, Dromquinna Stud, Greenacre, Killarney, County Kerry, Eire. Telephone: Killarney 41043 (non-residential). Lessons £4.50 per hour (est). Riding £3.50 per hour (est). Accommodation Butler Arms Hotel, Waterville, County Kerry, Eire. Telephone: Waterville 5. Managers: Mary and Peter Huggard. Price: £17.75–£19.80 (1981). Includes room, dinner, breakfast and VAT. Packed lunch £2. Bed and breakfast costs £9.75–£11, or weekly demi-pension at £110–£130. Includes service and VAT. Private bath £1.50 a day extra.

EIRE, COUNTY WEXFORD, Foulksmills

Residential Riding Holidays
Horetown House

Horetown House offers accommodation for up to thirty-five and is registered for instruction in riding to competition standard. The stables house eight horses and seven ponies and tuition is available in basic riding, dressage, cross-country and show jumping. Facilities include an enclosed paddock (66 feet × 132 feet), a jumping paddock, prepared cross-country fences and changing rooms.

Horetown House, Foulksmills, Wexford, Eire. Telephone: (051) 63633. Manager: David Young. Duration: weekly, all year. Price: from £160 per person (est). Includes 7 days accommodation, all meals, tuition and 18 hours riding. 1 hour riding £3.75. 1 hour lesson £4–£5. Bring riding hat.

HAMPSHIRE, Brockenhurst

Trekking and Riding
New Park Manor

New Park Manor combines luxurious accommodation with first class riding facilities in a delightful woodland setting. The manor has always been the New Forest's principal residence, and can trace its origins back to the time of William the Conqueror who used it as a hunting base. In 1666 King Charles II made New Park his favourite hunting lodge (and also used it to rendezvous with Nell Gwynn) – you can see his Royal Coat of Arms carved in the panelling of the lounge. In 1970 the manor was lovingly adapted for use as a modern country hotel, losing none of its charm in the process. There's central heating throughout and all rooms have TV, radio, intercom and babylistening; most have private bathrooms and there's a tennis court and heated outdoor pool in the garden.

Weekday riding holidays include ten hours' riding divided into groups of similar experience with instruction in riding and stablework. You can bring your own mount for no extra charge.

The Rhinefield (New Forest) Polo Club lies behind New Park's stables, and welcomes visitors who are enjoying one of the hotel's riding holidays. The game is played every Saturday from the end of April to the end of September.

New Park Manor, Lyndhurst Road, Brockenhurst, New Forest, Hampshire SO4 7QH. Telephone: (059 02) 3467. Duration: all year. Price: £32 (until April 1981). Includes 10 hours riding (Monday to Friday) with instruction in riding and stablework. Or riding £3.50 per hour. Accommodation £15–£16 (until April 1981) per person per day (bargain break rate, minimum stay 2 days, not available mid June to end September). Includes bed and breakfast and one main meal, service and VAT.

HEREFORD AND WORCESTER,
Evesham

Riding
Moyfield Riding School

Set in 300 wooded acres, Moyfield is heaven for keen riders. Instructors will accompany you on all rides, including moonlit evening rides along the banks of the Avon, picnic rides and regular casual hacking through the lush Cotswold countryside. There will also be visits to local horse shows and gymkhanas and you can make arrangements for hunting and jumping. Guests are accommodated as family (blankets provided, but bring sleeping bags) and are guaranteed at least three hours' riding a day if under fifteen, six hours if older. Non-residential adults can join the school for £5, and ride with or without instruction from £2 per hour.

Moyfield Riding School, South Littleton, Nr Evesham, Hereford and Worcester. Telephone: (0386) 830207. Proprietor: Mrs Joan Bomford. Duration: all year, weekly. Price: £90 per week (1981). Includes dormitory accommodation, breakfast, lunch and tea, 22 hours riding. Parents accommodation: Parkview Hotel, Waterside, Evesham, Worcestershire. Telephone: (0386) 2639. Manager: Mike Spires. Price: from £7.95–£9.50 per person (est). Includes room, breakfast and VAT; dinner from £4 (est).

LEICESTERSHIRE, Leicester

Equestrian Weekender
Holiday Inns

Ride through the rural East Midlands. Based at the Holiday Inn Leicester, this programme caters for the adventurous spirit by including horse riding for the whole family. Horses are hired for you at nearby riding stables (free transport), giving you the opportunity to explore the gently rolling countryside of the 'Shires'. Arrangements (at extra cost) can also be made for golf, squash, tennis or cricket. The hotel has its own heated indoor pool, fully equipped gymnasium and sauna. Free tickets are provided for Leicester's Donington Collection (the world's largest) of single-seater racing cars, plus over eighty vintage cars, buses and lorries. Leicester boasts no less than thirteen museums, two just outside your hotel. Then there's an open air market – the largest in England – ideal for buying a locally produced Stilton cheese or Melton Mowbray pie.

For further details of facilities (especially for children) see Grampian Weekender, SPECIALLY FOR KIDS.

Holiday Inn, St Nicholas' Circle, Leicester. Telephone: (0533) 51161. Duration: weekends, May to October. Price: doubles £39 (until April 1981) for 2 adults per night with breakfast. Accommodation free to under 20s sharing room with parent. Meals extra. Price includes excursions and varied activities for children and adults, and VAT.

NORTHERN IRELAND,
COUNTY DOWN, Castlewellan

Riding Holidays
The Newcastle Riding Centre

The centre, in the village of Maghera, is ideally situated for the nearby varied and picturesque countryside with forest parks, fine sandy beaches, bridlepaths and, of course, the famous Mourne Mountains. Facilities include cross-country and show jumping fences for the accomplished rider, a small indoor school, and enclosed all-weather paddocks specially designed for novices. You can choose your mount from the centre's stable or children can bring their own ponies. Riding includes hourly, half-day and day treks (with packed lunches). Tuition by a qualified instructress is available. For absolute beginners lessons start in the ring with later treks as your skills and confidence increase.

Accommodation is in nearby farmhouses, hotels or the centre's caravans. In the latter case you can either have your own cooking facilities or meals can be prepared for you.

The Newcastle Riding Centre, The Lodge, 35 Carnacaville Road, Castlewellan, County Down, Northern Ireland BT31 9HD. Telephone: (039 67) 22694. Proprietors: R. K. and G. S. Martin. Duration: Monday to Saturday or riding by the hour. Price: £75 (est). Includes caravan accommodation, all meals and 16 hours riding. Farmhouse accommodation also available. Riding from £3 per hour.

NOTTINGHAMSHIRE, Wellow

Riding Holidays
Wellow Park Stables

Wellow, a charming village in the heart of Sherwood Forest, boasts a rare distinction. It's one of just three British towns with a permanent maypole on the green. Keen equestrians who take tuition from Mrs Willet in dressage, show jumping and side saddle riding live as her guests in three brick cottages which have been joined together and modernized. Your hostess can also arrange foxhunting weekends between November and February.

Wellow Park Stables, Potter Lane, Wellow, Nr Newark, Nottinghamshire NG22 0GB. Telephone: (0623) 861040. Proprietor: Mrs M. Willet. Duration: all year. Price: £90 per person per week (1981). Includes accommodation, dinner, bed and breakfast. Riding £4.50 per hour.

Hunting weekends £60–£70 per person. Includes accommodation, dinner, bed and breakfast and hunting. (November to February.)

SOMERSET, Churchill

Riding Holidays
Lyncombe Lodge

The lodge caters to riders of all ages and levels of experience and to families as well as individuals. In all cases the aim is the same – to combine sound individual instruction with trekking over some of Britain's most beautiful country. During the weekly holidays there are three half-day rides, two day rides, and, if required, several with tuition. You're encouraged to help with the horses and on the farm. Guests can bring their own mounts or choose from twenty-five horses and ponies. These vary from thoroughbreds to Welsh cobs. Courses in dressage, jumping and a complete beginners' course are available on a year-round basis. Instruction is led by John Lee, BHSI (ex-Assistant National Instructor), Mrs Sally Lee BHSAI, IMA and other qualified staff. Unaccompanied children over seven are welcome – they'll live as family and be kept amused in the evenings with activities such as barbecues, rounders matches, discos and swimming.

Lyncombe Lodge, in the middle of Lyncombe Woods, is a former hunting lodge which now boasts large lounges with stone-built log-burning fireplaces, central heating, colour TV, a Games Room, a Residents' Bar, a Junior Bar, a sun roof, and fine country fare which makes imaginative use of the farm's produce. Bread is home-baked.

Lyncombe Lodge, The Mendip Riding Centre and Farm Guest House, Churchill, Somerset. Telephone: (0934) 852335. Proprietors: Sally and John Lee. Duration: Tuesday to Friday, Sunday to Saturday, September to June. Price: from £92 adults, from £82 children (1981). Includes 1 week riding, room, breakfast and dinner. VAT extra. Bring riding gear and waterproofs.

ROCK HUNTING

CORNWALL, Newquay

Rock Gem and Mineral Hunting
Yonder Towan (Field Holiday) Centre

Thanks to an exceptionally wide range of rocks, minerals and semi-precious stones Cornwall is a geologist's paradise. This course is the ideal introduction to Britain's fastest growing hobby. At 9.30 a.m. a minibus takes you to a suitable site and you're briefed on what to look for with examples. The area yields quartz, amethyst, citrine, jasper, agate, tin, slate and granite among other minerals. Field trips are supplemented by evening lectures by qualified visiting tutors as well as by museum visits. The centre has a useful library, a special lecture/projection area and a comprehensive collection of rocks and minerals.

Accommodation is in Yonder Towan, a licensed hotel. All rooms are centrally heated, special facilities for families.

Yonder Towan (Field Holiday) Centre, Beachfield Avenue, Newquay, Cornwall Telephone: (06373) 2756. Course Organizer: J. G. Smith. Duration: 16–23 May, 26 September–3 October. Price: £72.50 per person (1981). Includes course and full board, VAT extra. Bring a geological hammer, chisel, hand lens and collecting bags.

SHROPSHIRE, Minsterley

Geological Holiday Courses
Phillips Tutorials

South Shropshire has been a favourite with geologists since the pioneer work of Lapworth and Murchison. You'll find Lower Palaeozoic rocks, early fossils and, at Snailbeach and The Bog, the spoil heaps provide a wealth of minerals. Phillips Tutorials set up extensive, but not exhausting, field studies to examine the history of rocks and their relationship to the landscape; to collect fossils, rocks and minerals; and to visit some of the country's and the world's most famous geological sites. In addition to the usual indoor introductory and concluding sessions, in extremely bad weather you'll study indoors. The course is suitable for both enthusiastic amateurs and the experienced, and tutors combine long expertise with deep personal knowledge of the local geology. Bed and breakfast accommodation is included in the fee but if you wish, the organization will make arrangements for you to park a caravan, rent a cottage or stay at the nearby youth hostel. Evening meals can be provided, at a surcharge. While most participants lunch at a local pub, packed lunches can be provided.

A barbeque is usually held on one evening and a visit to the Three Tuns pub, renowned for its home-brewed beer, on another (both included in the price). Enquire for details about the luxury week course. This includes a gala dinner, and is planned for the first week in November 1981.

Phillips Tutorials, Frogs Gutter, Minsterley, Salop SY5 0NL. Telephone: (058 861) 335. Principal: P. F. Phillips. Duration: 5–10 April, 19–24 July, 30 August–4 September. Price: £76 per person in a guest house (1981). From £89 per person in a hotel. Includes tuition, room, breakfast, evening meal. Reductions for children under 16 years. Bring walking shoes, rucksack, geological hammer, cold chisel and hand lens. Excursion transport £4 per person per week.

TAYSIDE, Montrose

Lapidary Tours
Park Hotel

Join other treasure seekers on a week-long exploration of the Forfar coastline.

A lapidary expert will lead your daily search for agates, corals and fossils, and in the evenings there'll be illustrated lectures and demonstrations to help novices and old hands alike make the most of their searches. A coach will meet you in Edinburgh on Saturday afternoon, and return you from Montrose the following Saturday after lunch.

Ghillie Personal Travel, 64, Silverknowes Road East, Edinburgh EH4 5NY. Telephone: (031) 336 3120. Contact: Marjorie Dewar. Duration: 11–18 April, 23–30 May, 12–19 September. Price: £184 per person (1981). Includes instruction, full board, twin room with bathroom, return transport from Edinburgh, and VAT.

See also GOLD PANNING.

RURAL SKILLS

WALES, DYFED, Whitland

Goat Keeping for Beginners
The Colinsdown Herd of Dairy Goats

Mrs Staniland has been giving invaluable tips to goat keepers for over a decade. These lectures are conducted in the best possible setting – her small Pembrokeshire farm where she keeps her own outstanding Colinsdown herd of dairy goats. Two-hour talks are given Monday to Friday from 10.30 a.m.; each session includes a practical demonstration supplemented by slides. Subjects covered in-

clude general management (housing, fencing, handling, hoof trimming), feeding, crops to grow, the various breeds, kid rearing for milk and meat, milking, dairy hygiene, simple practical remedies for accident and illness plus helpful information such as relevant books and helpful addresses to contact. Daily duplicate drafts of the lectures are handed out for you to keep. You can bring your own goats as long as you provide their accommodation in the form of trailer, horsebox or van.

The Colinsdown Herd of Dairy Goats, Pengawsai Fach, Lampeter Velfrey, Whitland, Dyfed, Wales SA34 0RB. Telephone: (099 44) 659. Proprietor: Mrs I. D. Staniland. Duration: 5 days, Monday to Friday, Easter to mid-October. Price: £8 (1981). Includes tuition. Deposit of £2 required. Accommodation list provided, sample price £5.50 (est) bed and breakfast.

WALES, GWYNEDD, Betws-y-Coed

1 Tools from Wood and Hedgerow
2 Keeping Livestock
3 Saddlery and Leather Repair
The Drapers' Field Centre

This centre, in the picturesque Conwy Valley, is perfectly sited for you to acquire rural skills. On the first course Dave Marshall will teach you how to select the right wood for the job, then how to work it with hand tools to make simple wooden implements, handles, stakes, hurdles and containers. You'll also learn about woodland management.

On the second course Arthur Clarke gives students a practical introduction to the problems and pleasures of keeping a variety of useful animals. You'll gain knowledge in how to raise poultry, geese, sheep, goats and bees.

Dave Marshall leads the introduction to saddlery and leather repair. The course includes practical tuition in simple leatherwork and repairs. These basic skills are easily learnt and can be practised at home. They're especially useful to anyone working with horses and ponies.

The Drapers' Field Centre, Rhyd-y-Creuau, Betws-y-Coed, Gwynedd, Wales LL24 0HB. Telephone: (069 02) 494. Warden: Tony Scharer. Duration: one week, August. Price: £84 per person per week (est). Includes tuition, accommodation, all meals. £10 deposit required. Membership of Field Studies Council required, subscription £2 per year.

A wide variety of other courses available, send for brochure.

See also INDUSTRIAL ARCHAEOLOGY.

SAILING

CENTRAL, Lochearnhead

Sailing
Mansewood Country House Hotel

This is a husband-and-wife venture, where Gloria Stuart runs the small first-class hotel, an old stone house tastefully modernized to include hot and cold water in all bedrooms, central heating and some private bathrooms and showers in the main house. Other rooms are available in a picturesque and cosy log cabin annexe. There's a log fire in the lounge, a sun room with magnificent views of Loch Earn and the wooded hills and a Snug Bar. All food is homemade, from the soups to the wholemeal bread.

At the Watersports Centre, which is under the direction of Jon Stuart, you can tackle an intensive course of twenty-four hours' total sailing accompanied by twelve hours of lectures. This programme leads to a Royal Yachting Association certificate at the appropriate level. A less rigorous course gives you more time on the water, less in the lecture room – or you can take half-day courses, keeping the other half of each day free. Lunch and hot snacks are available at the pavilion, where you'll find changing rooms, hot showers and a lounge.

Lochearnhead Water Sports Centre, Lochearnhead Watersports Ltd, Lochearnhead, Central. Telephone: (05673) 330. Principal: Jon Stuart. Duration: weekly March to October. Price: from £135–£165 per person according to season (1981). Includes 7 nights accommodation, breakfast, dinner, instruction, boat hire and VAT.

See also WATERSPORTS.

CHANNEL ISLANDS, GUERNSEY, St Peter Port

Sailing

Guernsey Yacht Chartering Ltd.

Charter yourself a yacht and sail around the Channel Islands and along the Normandy Coast – one of Europe's finest cruising areas. Yachts from 7.6 metre Fisher 25s to 10.7 metre Nab 35s are available. Most have four to six shipboard berths and cooking facilities. Price of hire includes a marina berth of your own in the Old Harbour, beside the shopping and commercial centre of St Peter Port. Restaurants and chandlery firms are all within 100 yards, and each harbour has fresh water, with shower facilities and toilet available free on the quay. Shoreside accommodation is available in any of the many nearby hotels and guest houses (list available from Guernsey Tourist Department). High season rates range from £275 to £390 per week (est). The strength and range of local tides requires sailing experience and knowledge of local conditions.

Guernsey Yacht Chartering Ltd, Alderney House, Grand Bouet, St Peter Port, Guernsey, Channel Islands. Telephone: (0481) 2235. Price: from £275 (est) per week July to August. £255 (est) per week

April, May, June and September for 5 berth, 7.6 metres sailing yacht. Accommodation list from States of Guernsey Tourist Department, PO Box 23, States Office, St Peter Port, Guernsey, Channel Islands. Telephone: (0481) 24411.

CHANNEL ISLANDS, JERSEY, St Aubin

Dinghy Sailing Courses

Channel Islands Sailing School

Since 1973 the school has been turning landlubbers into confident sailors. It caters to pupils who've had some previous experience as well as complete novices. By the end of the ten-lesson Elementary Course you should be able to take command of a sailing boat with someone of the same level of experience, in reasonable weather conditions. There's one instructor to every two students; yours would be following in the safety boat to come aboard if needed. You have a minimum of two hours' daily sailing instruction and a half day's sailing on six Wayfarer dinghies. Three squibs (open keel boats) are also used, especially for more advanced sailing as they have spinnaker gear, compasses and adjustable standing rigging. A twenty-five foot cruiser is equipped for offshore sailing, mostly carried out at weekends, and trips are made to other Channel Islands or France.

The school issues Royal Yachting Association certificates for Elementary, Intermediary and Advanced Standards. Students must be over thirteen.

The Channel Islands Sailing School, High Street, St Aubin, Jersey, Channel Islands. Telephone: (0534) 63286. Duration: April to October. Price: £50 per person (1981) for 10 elementary lessons. Student accommodation arranged, £50 per person per week (est). Includes dinner, bed, breakfast and packed lunch. Adults arrange own accommodation; sample £12 per person per day (est). Includes dinner, bed and breakfast at St Magloire Private Hotel, High Street, St Aubin. Telephone: (0534) 41302.

CORNWALL, Helston

Sailing
Tregildry Hotel

Naturalists, artists, sportsmen and just plain holiday makers all use this one star hotel set high above the serenity of the Helford River. A private footpath leads down to Gillan Creek, an ideal spot for messing about in boats, where you can hire and launch a craft. You can also arrange great value-for-money sailing lessons from only £10 per two hours for two people. A limited number of moorings are available. Brian Rigg will be glad to personally arrange your boat hire and lessons.

Tregildry Hotel, Gillan, Mannaclan, Helston, Cornwall. Telephone: (032 623) 378. Proprietor: Brian Rigg. Duration: all year. Price: from £96 per person (Friday to Friday) (1981). Includes room, breakfast, dinner, service and VAT. Sailing boat hire £15 per day. Tuition £10 for 2 hours for 2 people.

HIGHLAND, Aviemore

Try-a-Sport Sail Away
Post House Hotel

Come try this great four-day introductory package to water sports, with tuition by Royal Yachting Association qualified instructors in sailing, canoeing and windsurfing.

Post House Hotel, Aviemore, Highland PH22 1PJ. Telephone: (0479) 810771. Duration: Sunday to Thursday, May to October. Price: £122 per person (est). Includes 5 nights accommodation, breakfast, dinner, 4 days instruction, service and VAT.

See also FISHING: GAME, GOLF, WINDSURFING.

HIGHLAND, Kincraig

Sailing Holidays
Insh Hall

Sailors of all standards, from rank beginners to the well advanced, get expert tuition, sailing in Wayfarer, Enterprise and Mirror dinghies. Daily instruction from 10.00 a.m. to 3.00 p.m. includes lectures, films and practical work during an average of four hours a day afloat. The syllabus covered is recommended by The Royal Yachting Association, and supervised by an instructor whose aim is to have you handling a boat as quickly as possible. If the winds are reasonably good during the week, most people can learn to crew and to helm alone by their last day.

Day 1: Covers handling boats ashore, rowing, rigging, reefing. Sailing a simple course. Capsize drill theory.

Day 2: Safety afloat, how to select and make sail, getting underway from a beach, rules of the road.

Day 3: Righting a capsized dinghy, recovery of man overboard, practical ropework.

Day 4: Simple racing rules.

Day 5: Solo sailing under supervision from an accompanying rescue boat, simple triangular races.

Insh Hall, Kincraig, Highland, Scotland. Telephone: (05404) 272. Director: Clive Freshwater. Duration: weekly, June to September. Price: from £110 (est). Includes double bunk accommodation, all meals (Sunday dinner to Saturday breakfast) tuition, equipment and VAT.

See also CANOEING, MULTI-ACTIVITY, SKIING.

SUSSEX, Chichester

1 Dinghy Sailing
2 Cruising Courses
Bosham Sea School

Bosham (pronounced Bozzam) has been a sailing centre since King Harold set sail on his voyage to Normandy. The sea school, founded in 1952, offers dinghy sailing courses of various lengths for beginners, more experienced sailors and all others interested in dinghy sailing as opposed to yachting. At the end of the six-day course you will be able to handle a boat with complete confidence. Instruction, which covers the RYA Dinghy Certificates, is mainly practical with a forty-five minute morning lecture before setting out for a day on the water. Crews are three to a dinghy (four on a junior course) and each is assigned to an onshore instructor. Sailing begins at 9.30 a.m. and finishes around 5.30 p.m. with a two-hour lunch break at one of the harbour's beaches or at another waterside village.

Most of the cruising courses are taken by those who want to buy a yacht, gain experience for a charter or qualify under the RYA/DTI Coastal and Yachtsmaster Certificate Schemes. Five, twelve-day and weekend courses are on offer. You live and work on board your yacht and dock at a new port each night. You'll be relieved of most galley duties but are encouraged to take a full share in handling and navigating under the guidance of your professional skipper.

Bosham Sea School Ltd, Bosham, Chichester, Sussex PO18 8HN. Telephone: (0243) 572112. Duration: March to October 1 6 days, 12 days and weekends; 2 5 days, 12 days and weekends. Price: 1 5 days from £70 per person, 12 days from £135 per person (1981); 2 5 days from £140 per person, 12 days from £330 per person (1981). Weekends from £65 per person (1981). VAT extra. Private and single lessons and 6 day Junior Course also available. Bring rubber-soled shoes, oilskins and life-jacket. Sailing shop on premises. Accommodation with local families £7.50 per person for room, breakfast and dinner. Packed lunch 90p.

TAYSIDE, Kenmore

Sailing Courses
Loch Tay Sailing School

This course is perfect if you've had no, or very little, sailing experience. You'll do lots of practical work with qualified instructors. Aspects of the sport covered include how to select and make sail according to conditions, handling boats ashore and under oars, sailing a course solo and how to right a capsized dinghy. Onshore you'll be given lectures in the school's purpose-built log cabin style lakeshore office on subjects such as how to tie bends and hitches, recovery of a man overboard, elementary first aid and lifesaving, winds, tides and currents and their effect on sailing dinghies. You'll have the use of five new Wayfarer dinghies and an assortment of others.

For details of accommodation see MULTI-ACTIVITY.

Loch Tay Sailing School, Kenmore, Tayside, Scotland. Telephone: (088 73) 236. Principals: Alison and Stanley Hampton. Duration: 2 or 5 days, March to October. Price: £25 2 days, £55 5 days (1981). Includes tuition and VAT.

SCOTTISH STUDIES

CENTRAL, Stirling

The Heritage of Scotland
University of Stirling

The resurgence of interest in traditional Scottish culture has encouraged Stirling University to offer on-campus summer school courses at picturesque Airthrey Castle. You can study traditional fiddle playing, bagpipes, Scottish dancing, ballad singing, Scottish Gaelic singing and clarsach playing. (The latter is a celtic harp, whose use was first recorded in 54 BC.) Some courses include excursions to historic places linked to the lectures. All tutors are tops in their field; for instance Anne MacDearmid, clarsach teacher, who's given recitals of Scottish music in Europe and America and studied harp with Sanchia Pierlou. This summer school's courses can be combined with a family holiday. If you wish to do so enquire about accommodation details. You can be either a residential or a non-residential student, with or without full board.

The University, Stirling, Central. Telephone: (0786) 3171 ext. 2035. Director of Continuing Education: Robert Innes. Duration: weekly, July and August. Price: £85 per person per week (est). £65 per week 13 to 19 year olds (1981). Includes tuition, lectures, excursions and full board. Residential students under 16 must be accompanied by a parent.

EDINBURGH

Gaelic Summer School
University of Edinburgh

For 1500 years Gaelic has been spoken in Scotland. Now it's mainly confined to around 100,000 people in the highlands and islands. Nonetheless this century has seen a flowering of high quality modern Gaelic literature. In response to demand for a course which provides an authoritative *entrée* to the language and its sources Edinburgh University has introduced a four-week intensive course for the beginner or near-beginner. Course Director Professor Gillies and five tutors will provide an introduction to Gaelic pronunciation, grammar and traditional and modern texts through illustrated lectures and tutorials as well as informal language sessions. If there's enough interest, an optional week-end trip to Skye may be arranged (at an extra charge of approximately £80).

Accommodation is in the Pollock Halls of Residence in modern single study bedrooms.

Departments of Extra Mural Studies, University of Edinburgh, 11 Buccleuch Place, Edinburgh EH8 9JY, Scotland. Telephone: (031) 667 1011, ext. 6506. Duration: 4 weeks, July, August. Price: £336 (est). Includes tuition, bed and breakfast and VAT.

14) 280. Duration: 3 weeks July, 2 weeks August to September. Price: £77 (est) 3 weeks, £60 (est) 2 weeks. Includes tuition only. Membership price £3. Accommodation list available, sample price: £5 per person, per day (est), bed and breakfast.

HIGHLAND, ISLE OF SKYE, Sleat

Summer School for Gaelic Learners
Sabhal Mor Ostaig

Shine up your Gaelic on the Isle of Skye. These summer school courses for Gaelic learners are specifically aimed to help beginners become conversant in Gaelic. Students come from all walks of life – including linguists, journalists, artists and teachers – and lodging is in local homes.

The staff includes such Gaelic luminaries as Dr Sorely MacLean, a Gaelic poet of international renown (regarded by many as one of the great European poets of the 20th century). These courses are run in association with the University of Stirling and many of the teachers are on the University's staff. Courses include lectures, conversation tutorials, ceilidhs (Gaelic musical cultural evenings) and dancing.

Bed and breakfast accommodation is available with local families (many speaking Gaelic – but you'll still get your porridge even if you can't ask for it properly). Light lunches and evening snacks are available at the college.

Sabhal Mor Ostaig, Teangue, Sleat, Isle of Skye IV44 8RQ, Highland. Telephone: (047

WESTERN ISLES, ISLE OF LEWIS, Stornaway

Gaelic Summer Course
An Comunn Gaidhealach

Up and away to Stornaway. These Gaelic summer courses with the accent on conversation, cater for all levels of ability. You'll learn the language in the midst of an area where it still flourishes, as does traditional ancient Gaelic culture. Tuition is from 9 a.m. to 5 p.m. with one and three-quarter hours for lunch. Classes take place in medium sized groups chosen according to ability. In the evening there are poetry readings, ceilidhs (Gaelic musical, cultural evenings) and talks about island life, Gaelic music and literature. All these are designed to put the language in its context.

Accommodation is in modern school hostel premises. These are far from luxurious but contain all modern requirements and meals are provided. Information on recommended books to bring and other optional learning material can be obtained from An Comunn Gaidhealach.

An Comunn Gaidhealach, Abertarff House, Stornaway, Isle of Lewis, Western Isles. Telephone: (0463) 31226. Duration: 6–17 July (provisional). Price: £150 (est).

SCULPTURE

LEICESTERSHIRE, Loughborough

Carved Sculpture
Metal Sculpture
Loughborough University

Carved and metal sculpture are both taught during this combination course at the well-equipped studios of the Loughborough College of Art's Sculpture Department. Under the direction of staff

members David Tarver and John McGill, you'll tackle traditional techniques of carving wood and stone, study the use of applied finishes, adhesives, jointing processes and the maintenance of tools, and learn how to select appropriate tools and equipment so you can carry on sculpting on your own when the course is over. Practical work is supplemented by talks and slides.

The metal sculpture course is centred around the forging, welding and casting processes. Oxyacetylene welding enables you to create marvellous forms from scrapyard salvage, and you'll learn how to shape polystyrene (simply using a hot wire) and also how to make aluminium casting. Sanding and polishing techniques, test-wax casting and simple tool making are also taught. Practical work is backed by illustrated talks on historical and contemporary work in metal sculpture.

You'll be accommodated in the student village (small housing units grouped around communal dining halls), normally in a single study bedroom with washbasin. Families with young children are given units with bedrooms leading off a central sitting room. Older children are given separate rooms.

Centre for Extension Studies (BR), University of Technology, Loughborough, Leicestershire LE11 3TU. Telephone: (0509) 63171 ext. 249/213. Duration: 1 week, August. Price £127 per person per week (est). Includes tuition, full board and VAT. 1981 prices not final at press time, send for brochure.

See also CAR MAINTENANCE, CREATIVE WRITING, NEEDLEWORK.

WILTSHIRE, Marlborough

Sculpture
Marlborough College

In this course you'll explore the relationship of the human form to space through drawing and three dimensional construction. Complete novices and more advanced students alike will examine the problems of composition, scale, balance and rhythm, under the direction of a highly-qualified instructor. Keen artists can also choose from several summer courses on landscape painting in oil or gouache. Every evening you'll have a choice of entertainment including concerts, celebrity lectures, discos, films and a weekly sherry party. Two bars are also available.

For further details of accommodation see ARCHAEOLOGY.

Marlborough College, Summer School, Marlborough College, Marlborough, Wiltshire SN8 1PA. Telephone: (0672) 53888. Secretary: Mrs Glynis Lewis. Duration: 7 days July. Price: £125 (est) per person (dormitory), £155 (est) (single); £104 (est). (child under 14). Includes 7 nights accommodation, all meals and tuition. No VAT.

See also ARCHAEOLOGY, CHINA, FISHING: GAME, FURNITURE RESTORATION, MUSIC.

SENIOR CITIZENS

BORDERS, Melrose

Saga's Dancing Holidays
Waverley Hotel

Come dancing at Waverley Castle in bonnie Scotland. Albert and Ivy Gelder, both expert dance teachers, will teach you new steps and organize old-time and modern sequence dancing. Here's your chance to acquire new skills and brush up on old favourites. There are competitions with plaques and medallions for winning couples in the set dances.

Waverley Castle, in the Scottish Borders, has an excellent ballroom, and its amenities include a comfortable TV lounge, reading and games rooms and bars. There are also excursions (included in the cost) into the beautiful surrounding countryside, and entertainments are laid on at the hotel. Cost includes return rail tickets to your home town, meals and transport across London, if necessary.

Saga Senior Citizens Holidays. 119 Sandgate Road, Folkestone, Kent CT20 2BN. Telephone: (0303) 30000. Duration: 7–14 February, 7–14 March, 28 March–2 April. Price: from £73–£88 per person (1981) (£7 single room supplement). Includes 7 nights accommodation, all meals, transport to hotel (including return rail tickets to your home town – and transport across London if necessary) and tuition. Price includes VAT.

See also SENIOR CITIZENS Bowls, Bridge, 'Only Ones'.

CORNWALL, Bude

Over 50s Activity and Special Interest Week
Shoreline Holidays

Shoreline offer a year-round range of study and sporting holidays specially designed to take full advantage of the coast's many natural assets. Over-fiftys are offered many multi-activity subjects but emphasis is placed on churches, local history and leisurely walks. If you're interested in bingo and/or dancing, just let Nick and Jeannie Cole know and they'll be glad to arrange it for you. Activities offered include coastal path walks along the most interesting sections of the 150 mile North Cornwall footpath; canoeing for both beginners and the experienced on local lakes, canals and rivers; map and compass work with an introductory evening talk and practical work in what can best be described as an orienteering treasure hunt with historical and navigational references and clues: geology, with an introductory evening talk and field work along the Cornwall shores; canal archaeology – you follow the path of the old Holsworthy to Launceston route with its ingenious system of water wheels and pit buckets; shoreline ecology – the study of the plants and animals found from cliff to low water line; horseback riding – a trek along the coast; and geographical fieldwork – based on the town of Bude itself. You can also visit historic churches, the local museum, Bude's oldest house (Ebbingford Manor), tour a Norman castle and a local Civil War Battlefield.

Evening activities include talks, films, table tennis, swimming, laboratory work, beach games, music, beach barbeque and driftwood art. Accommodation is based at the licensed guest house 'Shoreline'.

The 1981 programme includes an 'Over Fifties Special Interest Week' in early June; write for details.

Shoreline Holidays, 'Shoreline', 23 Downs View, Bude, Cornwall EX23 8RG. Telephone: (0288) 3134. Proprietors: Jeannie and Nick Cole. Duration: 6–13 June. Price: £64 per person (est), includes tuition, all meals, transport and VAT. Other activity holidays also available, send for brochure.

COUNTY DURHAM, Durham

Saga's 'Only Ones' Holidays
Collingwood College

Many on their own want companionship – that's what 'Only Ones' holidays are all about. Here's your chance to make new friends in a relaxed atmosphere at one of England's finest universities, set in a historic cathedral town in the heart of some of Britain's most dramatic countryside.

At the start of the holiday there is a special 'getting to know you' reception, and excursions into the countryside and to nearby sights are included in the cost. (There are also optional extra excursions at reduced prices.) You'll stay at Collingwood College at the University of Durham, which is situated in its own beautiful grounds. The bedrooms (all with washbasins) are spacious and well-equipped, with kitchenettes, toilets and bathrooms all near at hand.

Saga Holidays, 119 Sandgate Road, Folkestone, Kent CT20 2BN. Telephone: (0303) 30000. Duration: 7–14 July. Price: £97 per person (1981). Includes 7 nights accommodation, all meals, rail travel (inc. meals) to and from your home town, excursions, entertainments and VAT. (£4 lower floor supplement).

See also SENIOR CITIZENS *Bowls, Bridge, Dancing.*

ENGLAND, SCOTLAND

Theme Tours
Golden Circle's Special Interest Holidays

The Golden Circle organization specializes in holidays for the over fifty-fives. Choose from short breaks and one or two week holidays at a dozen top seaside resorts and inland centres including Paignton and Caister. Accommodation varies from hotels and holiday centres to colleges and university residences. Generally holidays include full board but you can sometimes choose half board or just bed and breakfast. Return rail tickets from your local British Rail station to the resort plus excursions and entertainment are also included. Many holidays offer up to four trips while some feature talks, film shows, bridge and dancing. Special 'Theme Tours' will give you an opportunity to pursue or develop a hobby such as bridge, whist and dancing supervised by qualified instructors.

The 1981 programme includes one and two week holidays based in Exeter, Devon. To acquaint you with this historic city, local experts will brief you on its background and suggest what spots are most worth visiting. You'll be enchanted by Exeter University gardens – they're fine enough to have earned a place in Shell's guide to Britain's top hundred attractions. Golden Circle has an horticultural expert to take you on a conducted tour. Four excursions are included in this holiday: one to the elegant seaside town of Dawlish, one to Dartmoor, another to Torquay and Totness and a final visit to picturesque Budleigh Salterton and the exquisite Bickleigh Gardens.

You'll stay in either St Luke's Hall with single room accommodation plus free leisure facilities such as a bar, library, TV room and indoor pool or Moberly House which is also near the city centre – another modern residence with both twin and single rooms.

Golden Circle Holidays Ltd, Glen House, 200 Tottenham Court Road, London W1P 0JP. Telephone: (01) 580 9872. Duration: 4 and 5 days October to March; 1 and 2 weeks April to September. Price: from £36 per person for 3 nights from £72 per person for 1 week (1981). Includes rail travel, full board (except Edinburgh, London and Stratford-Upon-Avon holidays where half board, room and breakfast arrangements can be made), cancellation insurance, resort transfers and VAT.

KENT, Folkestone

Bridge Holiday
Burlington Hotel

It's never too late to learn to play bridge. These holidays for Senior Citizens cater for beginners as well as accomplished players. And there's no need to worry if you haven't got a partner. The holidays are under the supervision of Frank and Zita Simmonite, and other friendly and fanatic tutors. The emphasis is on a happy 'special-interest' holiday run by genial hosts who pay particular attention to individual guests.

Accommodation is at the Burlington, Folkestone's only four star hotel, on the Leas, a famous promenade which overlooks the sea. Excursions to Rye, Canterbury and Dover are available at special package prices, and there's an all-inclusive day trip to France, with a meal in a Boulogne restaurant. A special £3 supplement covers use of cards, score sheets, clocks, paper and pencils. Progressive and duplicate bridge competitions are organized for which the overall winner will receive holiday vouchers. There are day-to-day prizes too. Similar holidays are available at the Covenanters Inn, Aberfoyle, and Waverley Castle, Melrose. For details send for brochure.

Saga Senior Citizens Holidays, 119 Sandgate Road, Folkestone, Kent CT20 2BN. Telephone: (0303) 30000. Duration: 1 week, 25 April–1 May. Price: £159 per person (1981) (single room supplement £7). Includes 7 nights accommodation, all meals, transport to hotel and tuition. £3 supplement for cards, and scorecards, etc. and VAT.

See also SENIOR CITIZENS Bowls, Dancing, 'Only Ones'.

KENT, Margate

Saga's Bowling Holidays
Cliftonville Bowling Club

Bowl off to Margate for a week. Saga Senior Citizens holidays will organize your whole trip from door to door and the initial cost will include return rail fare to your home town (and transport across London if necessary), full board in a friendly, comfortable guest house or private hotel, a money-back scheme if you have to cancel through unexpected illness and all the bowls you can possibly play. Special competitions and instruction will be organized by expert Bill Crump. Free admissions, or reduced entry fees, for visits to local attractions.

All games are played under the IBB laws (as adopted by the EBA and EWBA) on the excellent greens of the Cliftonville Bowling Club, which overlooks the sea. Ladies should play in white, gentlemen in white shirts and club jackets.

Other bowling weeks are organized at Torquay and Llandrindod Wells.

Saga Senior Citizens Holidays, 119 Sandgate Road, Folkestone, Kent CT20 2BN. Telephone: (0303) 30000. Duration: one week, 5–12 and 12–18 May. Price: from £66–£72 per person (1981). Includes 7 nights accommodation, all meals, transport to and from hotel, bowling and VAT. (Single supplement £7.)

See also SENIOR CITIZENS Bridge, Dancing, 'Only Ones'.

SUSSEX, Fittleworth

Open Door to Craft
The Old Rectory

The Old Rectory is an unusual adult education centre – all courses here are designed for those who are retired or are about to become so. The 16th century main building and its modern extension are set in extensive gardens near the South Downs. Guests can use the swimming pool and croquet lawn free of charge. Four of the twenty-one bedrooms are ground floor single rooms; all baths have hand grips, and some parts of the house and grounds are specially designed for wheelchair users. The Old Rectory is family run. Here's a chance to try your hand at various crafts and see if you're intrigued enough to take up one of them as a hobby at home. One hostess, Brenda Salmon, is a member of the Guild of Craft Enamellers, and Daphne Lee demonstrates crafts on ITV's 'Houseparty'.

The Old Rectory, Fittleworth, Pulborough, Sussex RH20 1HU. Telephone: (079882) 306. Proprietors: Brenda and George Salmon. Duration: 3 and 4 days, June and October. Price: from £50 per person (est) (3 nights twin with bath) £53 (est) (4 nights), all meals, tuition. VAT extra.

See also CASTLES AND HISTORIC HOUSES, CLOCKS, GENEALOGY, MUSIC, ORNITHOLOGY, QUILTING AND PATCHWORK, SENIOR CITIZENS: Wine making.

SUSSEX, Fittleworth

Wine Making
The Old Rectory

This convivial wine making course is geared to beginners, but if you've already discovered the combined pleasure and economy of making your own wine, bring some along for tasting and assessment. The principles of wine making, including construction of your own recipes, are dealt with in a relaxed and easy-to-understand manner.

For details of the Old Rectory see SENIOR CITIZENS: Crafts.

The Old Rectory, Fittleworth, Pulborough, Sussex RH20 1HU. Telephone: (079 882) 306). Proprietors: Brenda and George Salmon. Duration: 3 and 4 days, June and October. Price from £50 per person (est). (3 nights twin with bath) £53 (est) (4 nights), all meals, tuition. VAT extra.

See also CASTLES AND HISTORIC HOUSES, CLOCKS, GENEALOGY, MUSIC, ORNITHOLOGY, QUILTING AND PATCHWORK, SENIOR CITIZENS: Crafts.

YORKSHIRE, Ripon

Making Use of Leisure in Retirement
Grantley Hall

Finances may be tighter after retirement, but life can be richer. This course suggests how to make the best use of your new opportunities and how to lead a life at least as varied, active and satisfying as before. Discussions will include a realistic look at the important considerations of money and health. Various lecturers, some of whom are social workers, will speak on 'Voluntary Work', 'Ageing and Education' and 'Leisure Opportunities'. Yorkshire residents should enquire about reduced rates.

Grantley Hall, Adult Residential College, Ripon, Yorkshire HG4 3ET. Telephone: (076586) 259. Contact: the Warden. Duration: 25–26 May. Price: £15 (£8 for residents of North Yorkshire and parts of surrounding area) per person, per day (1981). Includes accommodation, all meals and tuition. No VAT.

See also LACEMAKING.

SHOOTING

BORDERS, Reston

Shooting
Houndwood House

This 1143 hunting lodge is believed to be Scotland's second oldest inhabited building. One-fifth of the estate's 7000 acres is woodland, while much of the rest is hills and deep valleys. The grounds support a wide range of game including pheasant, duck, geese, snipe, woodcock and hare. Mixed shooting for four to twelve guns involves a varied bag and approximately ten per gun – both walking and driven. Rough shooting is walking only for one to four guns, with a bag of five to ten per gun. Duck flights have a bag of four to five birds and guns are entitled to one brace of game per day. You can also stalk roe deer, with a surcharge for trophies. Fees include transport to the shoot, insurance, keepers and beaters. Accommodation at the lodge includes full board.

Houndwood House, Reston, Borders, Scotland. Telephone: (03904) 232. Proprietor: I. D. Forsyth. Duration: September to January. Price: from £25 per person per day (duck flighting). Pheasant shooting £8.50 per bird. Shooting tailored to individual requirements. Includes 3–12 guns, transport, insurance, keepers and beaters. Keeper's tip £3 extra. Accommodation from £27 per person (1981). Includes 1 night, breakfast, lunch and dinner. £145 per person (est) includes 7 nights all meals. Includes VAT.

COUNTRYWIDE

Shooting

The John Birth Organizations are experts in personally supervised top quality shooting on private estates in East Anglia, Northumbria and other parts of Britain. You can bag partridge from September, then pheasant, duck, woodcock, snipe, pigeon, rabbit or hare – depending on the estate selected. A special grouse shooting programme is also offered. In some cases you're offered one duck flight per day for a supplementary £28 per gun (plus VAT). Two head of game per day is given to each gun.

Accommodation is arranged at personally selected hotels or, for small groups, at private hunting lodges. Transport from the nearest airport or station is included in the cost.

The John Birth Sporting Organization, Greenwalls Lodge, Duddo, Berwick-on-Tweed, Northumberland TD15 2PR. Telephone: (089 082) 261. Duration: from 2 days, all year. Price: from £350 per person (est). Includes 2 days mixed walked-up shooting. Non-shooting guest £145 (est). Accommodation, meals, cartridges, keepers' tips (£5 per gun per day) and VAT extra.

HIGHLAND, Grantown-on-Spey

Shooting
Palace Hotel

The Palace Hotel has been Grantown's premier hostelry for over a century. Its original features have been retained, despite recent modernization with added central heating, private bathrooms, radios, intercoms and TV points. You must book four weeks in advance to arrange for private shooting tuition. Guns can be hired but guests usually bring their own. The price includes the cost of clay pigeons and cartridges, one day's 'real' shooting for rabbits, and a visit to a local game farm. At the end of the day you can enjoy local delicacies such as venison and salmon in the hotel's Egon Ronay recommended Regency Restaurant and choose from a large selection of malt whiskies in the cocktail lounge with its splendid views over the gardens to the Cromdale Hills.

Palace Hotel, Grantown-on-Spey, Highland PH5 3HB. Telephone: (0479) 2706. Manager: Graham Sword. Duration: April, May, September. Price: from £175 per person per week (est). Includes tuition, full board and service. VAT extra. Visitors must possess a shotgun licence.

·

HIGHLAND, Whitebridge

Shooting
Knockie Lodge

Knockie Lodge is delightfully situated on a forested estate of ten square miles overlooking Loch Nan Lann and facing the towering Bienn a' Bhaccaidh which rises from Loch Ness. There are two private lochs and fishing rights on three others. Accommodation is in ten double and two single rooms, or two three-bedroomed self-catering cottages on the estate. The farm and garden provide fresh milk, cream, butter, eggs, fruit and vegetables, supplemented by the results of guests' successful shooting and fishing expeditions. You can shoot grouse, hare, pheasant, black game, rabbit, pigeon, duck and snipe. Game belongs to the estate but you can purchase it at wholesale prices. You've advised to book in advance for shooting.

Knockie Lodge Hotel, Whitebridge, Highland. Telephone: (04563) 276. Duration:
12 August–1 March. Manager: Jon Craig-Tyler. Price: £25 per person per night (est). Includes dinner, bed, breakfast and VAT. Mid-week and weekend rates £42 for 2 nights (est); £100 for 5 nights (est). Includes dinner, bed, breakfast and VAT. Self-catering also available. Shooting: £30 per gun (est), £35 per keeper with dog (est). Equipment can be hired (£5 for 12 bore). VAT extra. Stalking, riding, fishing also available.

See also STALKING.

NORTHUMBERLAND, Rothbury

Shooting Holidays
Whitton Farm House Hotel

Northumberland is fine shooting country with excellent grouse moors and shooting estates and Whitton Farm specializes in organizing such things. A typical five-day holiday might consist of a day's part-walked-up, part-drive grouse shooting over the moors at Harbottle, followed by a day of partridge shooting in mid-Northumberland. Then a day's rest before going after more grouse over different moors at Harbottle. You can also arrange driven pheasant shoots, with an anticipated bag of sixty to eighty head depending on cost. There's a wide variety of game in the region; grouse and snipe (from 12 August – 'The Glorious Twelfth'), black game (from 20 August), pheasant (from 1 October), and duck, partridge and woodcock (from 1 September). Each of the shoots is accompanied by keepers and dogs.

Whitton Farm also arranges fishing, pony trekking, golf and hunting holidays.

Whitton Farm House, Rothbury, Northumberland. Telephone: (0669) 20811. Secretary: Kathy Muckle. Duration: Sunday to Friday, end of September to November. Price: £380 per person (est). Includes 3 days shooting, 5 nights accommodation, full board and VAT. Bring gun; all guns must be insured and a copy of insurance certificate must be produced on booking.

SCOTTISH HIGHLANDS

Sport in Scotland
Selected Estates

Bill Nicholson, former Director of the Scottish Tourist Board, personally arranges these Highland Estate sporting holidays. You stay in carefully selected hotels, or private lodges on the estates selected. Stalking is confined to one or two guns, with only one sportsman at a time shooting. Grouse and mixed shooting parties can be arranged between 12 August and 10 December in most areas of Scotland.

Tourist Promotion (Scotland), 36 Castle Street, Edinburgh EH2 3BN. Telephone: (031) 226 6692. Contact: Bill Nicholson. Duration: 4 days (or longer) by arrangement. 1 July–15 February (red deer), 1 May–30 October (roe deer), 1 August–30 April (sika deer), 12 August–10 December (grouse). Prices: from £750 per person (1981) for 4 days, varies according to number of days stalking and choice of accommodation. Roe deer stalking is usually much cheaper. Grouse and mixed shooting prices vary, but on average 4 days grouse shooting (5 days mixed shooting) for 8 people costs from £1500. This includes keepers, beaters, accommodation, food, shooting and VAT.

See also CRUISING: COASTAL, FESTIVALS.

SUSSEX, Rushlake Green

Rough Shooting
Priory Country House Hotel

What better hunting grounds could a sportsman ask for? The Priory offers a thousand acres of unspoilt countryside on the Kent–Sussex border where you can rough shoot rabbit and pigeon year round or go after woodcock and pheasant in season (1 October–31 January). Upon arrival you'll be shown the most promising areas (no shooting at weekends unless you're staying all week).

In 1412 monks from the Augustinian Priory at Hastings moved inland and began work on The Priory. With the dissolution of the monasteries Henry VIII gave it to his Attorney General Sir John Baker. He sold it to the ancestors of the present owner (who still has Henry's original Deed of Grant). Over three years the house has been lovingly restored by a master craftsman who has used wood from oak trees felled on the estate.

There's central heating throughout. Each bedroom has its own bathroom and telephone with TV if desired. Lunch and dinner can be arranged for an extra charge.

The Priory Country House Hotel, Rushlake Green, Heathfield, Sussex TN21 9RG. Telephone: (043 56) 553. Manager: Peter Duke. Duration: all year. Price: from £25 single, £35 double per day (est). Includes accommodation with bath, breakfast and VAT. 12½% service extra. Shooting £25 (est) per gun, 12% service charge extra.

Skid Control

NORFOLK, Norwich

Barnham Broom Hotel and Golf Club

This new hotel, designed along the lines of a traditional Norfolk farm, offers a weekend package that includes three sessions on a skid pan as well as training at a local racing drivers' school. You arrive on Friday evening and after breakfast on Saturday head for Snetterton, fifteen miles away, where you'll receive an introductory briefing and see a film by professional driver Jim Russell. After a lunch break, you receive practical instruction in the school's cars. By Sunday morning you should be proficient enough to be skidding on your own. If you think you're ready for the big league, enquire about the mid-week opportunity to take the wheel of a Formula 1 racing car.

For details of the Barnham Broom Hotel see GOLF.

Barnham Broom Hotel and Golf Club, Barnham Broom, Norwich, Norfolk NR9 4DD. Telephone: (060 545) 393 or Best Western on (01) 940 9766. Duration: weekends, all year. Price: £68.50 per person (est). Includes 2 nights accommodation, all meals, 1½ days instruction in skid control.

SKIING

HIGHLAND, Aviemore

Ski Packages
Cairngorm Hotel

The Scottish-Norwegian Ski School combines the talents of Director Eilif Moen, who holds the top grade certificate of the Norwegian School of Skiing, with Britain's best skiing territory. The ski season runs from Christmas to late April (sometimes into May) and roads, chairlifts (up to 3500 feet) and tows have put the highest slopes within reach. The Ski School meets daily at 10.15 a.m. and 1.15 p.m. at an assembly point below the bottom station of the chairlift. Your team of instructors, mainly British and Norwegian, make learning to ski fun all the way. The Ski School main office is situated behind the Cairngorm Hotel in Aviemore, and you should address your enquiries there.

The hotel also makes a good holiday base; it offers modern amenities such as a restaurant with dance floor, two attractive bars and a TV lounge. Eight of the twenty-four bedrooms are singles, the rest either double rooms or family size.

Cairngorm Hotel, Aviemore, Highland, Scotland. Telephone: (0479) 810233. Duration: 5 and 7 days, January to May. Price: £95 (4–30 January, 28 April–8 May) per person, Monday to Friday (1981); £110 for 5 days; £147.30 for 7 days (31 January–28 April). Includes accommodation, bed and breakfast, ski hire, tuition and VAT. Supplement of £2 per day 14–28 February, 4–28 April.

HIGHLAND, Kincraig .

Inclusive Ski Package Holiday
Insh Hall

Come ski in the crisp air of bonnie Scotland! The Insh Hall programme gives you five days ski and boot hire, five days of instruction, three hours per day, five days unlimited use of lifts and six nights dinner, bed, breakfast and packed lunch with accommodation in two, four or six bunked rooms.

Insh Hall is fourteen miles from the chairlift, and you'll need to provide your own transport (unless you're booking as a group, in which case it can be arranged). Groups of ten or more can make self-catering arrangements – there are excellent cooking facilities available.

For details of accommodation see SAILING, CANOEING.

Insh Hall, Kincraig, Highland PH21 1NU. Telephone: (05404) 272. Manager: Chris Freshwater. Duration: Sunday to Saturday mid-December to mid-April. Price: from £113.50 per adult (est), £97 per child under 17. Includes 6 nights accommodation (2 bunk room), breakfast, dinner and packed lunch, 5 days ski, stick and boot hire, instruction (3 hours per day), unlimited use of chair lift. Includes VAT.

See also CANOEING, MULTI-ACTIVITY.

TAYSIDE, Blairgowrie

Skiing
Angus Hotel

Blairgowrie is ideally situated for skiing holidays and the Angus Hotel boasts a ski shop which stocks over 300 pairs of skis, sticks and boots for hire. Glenshee (only three-quarters of an hour away) has many runs with tows and lifts. Skiing has been good in this area well into April during the past few years. The hotel boasts eighty-two bedrooms with *en suite* bathroom or shower, colour TV, radio, intercom/telephone and tea-making facilities.

Hotel amenities include indoor heated pool, sauna, solarium and squash court, three bars and a large ballroom. Ski hire and instruction are included in the fee.

Angus Hotel, Blairgowrie, Tayside PH10 6NQ. Telephone: (0250) 2838. General Manager: Robert Wiles-Gill. Duration: Sunday to Friday, Saturday to Saturday, January to April. Price: Sunday to Friday from £54 per person (1981). Saturday to Saturday from £74 per person. Includes instruction, ski hire, room, breakfast and dinner.

TAYSIDE, Glenshee
HIGHLAND, Loch Morlich

Ski Glenisla
Ski Cairngorm
Youth Hostels

The Scottish YHA offers two great week-long ski courses. One is at the Loch Morlich Grade I standard ski school in Glenmore Forest. It overlooks the lake with a panoramic view of the Northern Cairngorms and facilities include central heating, showers and drying room. Glenisla ski school is set in a scenic glen, convenient for the Glenshee ski complex at Cairnwell mountain where you'll find some of Scotland's finest skiing. Your coach at Glenisla is Jim Bryden, a Grade One instructor and BASI coach. Both centres offer a week's accommodation with breakfast, packed lunch and dinner, five days skiing with expert tuition (plus one free day) graded classes limited to ten, latest clip boots, sticks and skis, daily transport to and from slopes, and transport to and from the nearest railway station at the start and finish of courses.

Scottish Youth Hostels Association, National Office, 7 Glebe Crescent, Stirling FK8 2JA, Central. Telephone: (0786) 2821. Duration: weekly 3 January–18 April. Price: Glenisla: £72 Senior, £70 Junior, £69 Juvenile per week (1981). Includes instruction, full board, equipment hire, return transport from Perth station, daily transport to ski slopes, VAT. £5 per week dis-

count if you bring sticks, skis and boots. Cairngorm: £97 Senior, £82 under 18 per week includes instruction, full board, unlimited ski pass for chairlift and ski tow, *equipment, return transport from Aviemore Station, daily transport to slopes.*

See also WALKING.

SPECIALLY FOR KIDS

AVON, Bristol

West Country Weekender
Holiday Inns

Whirl away to the West Country. Your Weekender programme includes admission tickets to Bristol Zoo and the choice of a visit to the Slimbridge Wildfowl Trust (the world's largest and most varied collection of wildfowl) or a two-hour guided tour of the great caves at Wookey Hole.

Bristol's Holiday Inn has a heated indoor swimming pool, sauna, fully equipped gymnasium and its own 'disco', the 'Club Chicago' (free membership for hotel guests). Ten miles from Bristol is historic Bath and within twenty miles you'll find the Cotswolds, the Cheddar Caves, Longleat Safari Park and the Clifton Suspension Bridge.

For full details of Holiday Inn Weekenders, see Grampian Weekender.

Holiday Inn, Lower Castle Street, Bristol, Avon. Telephone: (0272) 294281. Duration: 1 May–31 October. 2 nights (Friday to Sunday or Saturday to Monday). Price: doubles £39 for 2 adults per night with breakfast (1981). Free accommodation to those under 20 sharing room with parent. Meals extra. Price includes excursions, varied activities for children and adults, and VAT. Send for colour brochure.

GRAMPIAN, Bucksburn

Grampian Weekender
Holiday Inns

The Holiday Inns Weekender programme is designed especially for families. Each Inn provides a Weekend Hostess to help you organize your activities, look after your children (free) for a total of five hours on Friday or Saturday evening and arrange an hour's free swimming tuition for each child. The programme also gives you a free magic or film show for kids, a Weekender T-shirt in each room, entrance tickets to local attractions (as described in the individual programmes) and a welcome drink on arrival. All Holiday Inns have large family rooms with two double beds. Children up to nineteen stay free if sharing their parents' room and pay for meals as taken; cots are supplied free. Rooms have private bathrooms, radio, telephone and a colour television on which free full-length feature films are shown daily.

The Grampian Weekend at Bucksburn offers accommodation in an unusual inn partly converted from an old mill. Special features include free car parking, use of the gym's keep fit equipment, a heated indoor pool and a choice of two bars. You're given a tour of Aberdeen or, if you prefer, Royal Deeside. For the latter, your hostess will not only arrange your tour but also supply an explanatory cassette tape for your car player or portable. And she'll be glad to arrange entry tickets to any National Trust property and supply you with guide maps. On arrival, each child will be given a 'Scotland for Children' book full of information, games and quizzes. On Sunday morning, parents can enjoy a 'lie-in' while your hostess organizes swimming lessons and children's film shows.

Holiday Inn, Bucksburn, Old Meldrum Road, Aberdeen, Grampian, Scotland. Telephone: (0223 71) 3911. Duration: weekends May to October. Price: £42 for 2 adults per night (1981). Includes double room and breakfast. Children under 19 free if sharing parents' room. Meals extra. 'Scotland for Children' book free, loan of car cassette road-routing tape, a tour of Aberdeen and (by prior arrangement) the Speyside whisky trail tour, free swimming lessons for children, use of keep fit equipment, free in-room movies.

KENT, Dover

Kentish Weekender
Holiday Inns

The Dover Holiday Inn is a large, modern hotel in the town centre, just a few minutes from the station, the seafront and the international hover-port and ferry terminals. Dinghy sailing is a special feature of this holiday. The hotel will supply the dinghys for a reasonable charge, and if you want to learn how to sail, tuition will be arranged with Royal Yachting Association instructors in three classes of boat at approximately £3.50 per hour. Your weekend includes free entrance to the grounds of famous Leeds Castle (packed lunches provided). Guests have the use of the hotel gymnasium's keep fit equipment and heated indoor pool.

For full details of Holiday Inn Weekenders, see Grampian Weekender.

Holiday Inn, Townwall Street, Dover, Kent. Telephone: (0304) 2032170. Duration: Weekends, May to October. Price: £39 for 2 adults per night (1981). Includes double room and breakfast. Accommodation free to 12 year olds and under, sharing room with parent. Meals extra. Price includes excursions and varied activities for children and adults. Price of holiday includes service and VAT.

LONDON, Chelsea

Chelsea Weekender
Holiday Inns

The Chelsea Weekender puts you in the heart of one of London's most fashionable areas. With the help of free maps and guides, take yourself to all the major London stores and fashionable shopping areas – Kensington High Street, Oxford Street, Regent Street, Knightsbridge and King's Road. And you're only two minutes away from Harrods. On the house and as part of the programme, you can take the children to afternoon tea at Harrods. Alternatively, entertain them with a free visit to Pollock's Toy Museum. On Sunday, take a two-hour guided sight-seeing tour of London by coach (choose from three departure points).

The hotel's amenities include the Bohemian Bar and the elegant Papillon Restaurant beside the tropical-style indoor pool. At lunch on Sunday, a Dixieland band will entertain you here during 'Memphis Brunch'. The hotel porter will be happy to make theatre reservations and you're only a short walk from some of London's finest free attractions. Visit the Tate Gallery, Chelsea Antique Market and the Natural History and Science Museums with their special children's sections. A fifteen minute walk will take you to Buckingham Palace to see the Changing of the Guard.

For full details of Holiday Inn Weekenders, see Grampian Weekender.

Holiday Inn, Sloane Street, London SW1. Telephone: (01) 235 4377. Duration: weekends May to October. Price: £58 for 2 adults per night (1981). Includes double room and breakfast. Free accommodation for 12 year olds and under sharing room with parent. Meals extra. Price includes excursions and varied activities for children and adults, and VAT.

LONDON, Marble Arch

West End Weekender
Holiday Inns

This summer weekend break is based at the 'world's most famous street corner', Marble Arch. You'll find flowers and a bottle of champagne waiting in your room. Enjoy them while the children are entertained at a special welcome party and cartoon film show. If available, tickets for any London show can be booked by the hostess, who'll look after your children while you enjoy yourselves. Choose between a free river trip to Hampton Court Palace, or a visit to Madame Tussaud's, the London Planetarium and Laserium. Take a free tour of HMS Belfast, moored on the Thames by the Tower, then on to the London Dungeon. Special features of the hotel include heated indoor pool, sauna and excellent French cuisine in La Bibliothèque restaurant.

For full details of Holiday Inn Weekenders, see Grampian Weekender.

Holiday Inn, George Street, London W1. Telephone: (01) 723 1277. Duration: weekends May to October. Price: £58 for 2 adults per night (1981). Includes double room and breakfast. Accommodation free to 12 year olds and under sharing room with parent. Meals extra. Price includes excursions and varied activities for children and adults and VAT.

NORTH YORKSHIRE, Whitby

Adventure and Activity Holidays
Larpool Hall, Redhouse, Newton House

Here's a chance for the youngsters to get out and about where they know what young people like to do, and how to help them enjoy themselves. Run by Geoffrey Watson, these Adventure and Activity Holidays have been popular for over twenty years.

Each course is limited to a small group (ten, fifteen, twenty-five) within a certain age range (nine to twelve, twelve to fourteen, for example), and courses range from fossil hunting to sailing, sea fishing to football coaching, with instructors specially selected for their particular experience and ability to encourage young people. Accommodation is at one of the Adventure Centres – large homes, set in their own grounds in the Yorkshire countryside, each specifically adapted for young people. Holidaymakers assist with washing up, making beds and other light duties to help develop confidence, responsibility and a communal spirit. Equipment is provided, but youngsters must be sure to bring their own clothing, rucksacks, suitable personal equipment, etc. (see brochure for details). In most cases, no previous experience is required – only the interest of the participant.

Northern Field and Activity Centres, Larpool Hall, Whitby, North Yorkshire. Telephone: (0947) 4073. Director: Geoffrey Watson. Duration: 1 week July to September. Price: from £52 per person per week (est). Includes tuition and full board, VAT extra. Bring linen, notebook and pencils, small haversack, suitable clothing and equipment.

SOMERSET, Wellington

Summer School
Wellington School

The Elite Summer School for Jewish Children is internationally famous. Eager participants come from Britain, Europe and Israel to spend the summer at Wellington School, where superb sporting facilities include twenty-four acres of playing fields, grass and hard tennis courts, a squash court, a large heated open-air pool and excellent gymnasium facilities too. These are supplemented by visits to the sports centre in town, with its Olympic size indoor pool, badminton courts, trampolines and ski slopes.

Other activities include arts and crafts, bingo, camp fire evenings, debates, discos, dramatics, fancy dress competitions, horse riding, judo, rambles, treasure hunts and video games. One hour courses in trampoline, tennis, art, etc., are held five mornings a week, with other classes such as judo, squash and swimming at the Wellington Sports Centre. Most of the instructors, coaches and youth leaders have been at Elite for years. Together with the resident matron, they get kids off to a relaxed start. Under twelves are escorted everywhere; older children can leave the school premises in small unescorted groups during the day. Accommodation is in three dormitories, each with common room, of four to six beds.

Elite Summer School, Wellington School, Wellington, Nr. Taunton, Somerset. Enquiries: 14 Oman Avenue, London NW2 6BG. Telephone: (01) 452 3930. Secretary: Sandra Grossman. Duration: 15 days July to August. Price: £190 (est) + VAT. Includes course, accommodation, all meals and excursions. 30 day course, £370 (est) + VAT.

TYNE AND WEAR,
Newcastle-upon-Tyne

Northumbrian Weekender
Holiday Inns

Your programme at the Newcastle Holiday Inn, set amid Northumbria's scenic beauties and close to unspoilt beaches, includes tickets to Durham's magnificent Castle and to the Beamish Open Air Museum, where reminders of the North East's history include a row of furnished pit cottages, a farm, a steam engine and even a colliery complete with pit cages. You can also take a nostalgic ride on a tram car. Tickets to visit the Craster Kipper Factory are included too, as well as a boat trip to the Farne Islands, where grey seals cavort on the rocky shores, and a visit to Bamburgh Castle. On Saturday and Sunday mornings, parents can relax while the kids are treated to swimming lessons, film shows, games and a professional magic show. Treat yourself on Saturday evening to a candlelit medieval banquet at Seaton Delaval Hall. This costs extra but Holiday Inns will provide free transport.

For full details of Holiday Inn Weekenders see Grampian Weekender.

Holiday Inn, Great North Road, Seaton Burn, Newcastle-upon-Tyne. Telephone: (089 426) 5432. Duration: weekends May to October. Price: £39 for 2 adults (1981). Includes double room and breakfast. Accommodation free to 12 year olds and under sharing room with parent. Meals extra. Price includes excursions and varied activities for children and adults, and VAT.

WALES, GWYNEDD, Beaumaris

Multi-Activity Holidays
Carnelyn Manor

Mum and Dad can do their own thing here while kids get expert tuition in a programme of activities which includes climbing, sailing, canoeing, archery, pony trekking, trampolining, fishing and mountain walking. They'll spend part of the week on the sloop *Sea Feather*, and parents can join in if they like, or just relax in the residents' lounge, games and TV rooms, or wander through eight acres of glorious gardens. Unaccompanied children from eight to sixteen are also welcome.

Built in 1861, the manor has been modernized to a high standard – each bedroom is fully carpeted, centrally heated, has hot and cold water and a thermostatic shower; beds have continental duvets. Children sleep in bunk beds in small dormitories of four to eight. The elegant Victorian dining room with licensed bar has great views over the Menai Straits and Snowdonia.

Carnelyn Manor, Llangoed, Beaumaris, Isle of Anglesey, Gwynedd, Wales. Telephone: (0248 78) 255. Duration: 1 week, 23 May–5 September. Price: from £85–£130 per person (1981). Includes double or single room, bath or shower, full board, all activities. From £75–£115 for children 8–16 years. VAT extra. Rates approximately £10 less for the balance of the season November–April; 10% reduction for families.

WEST MIDLANDS, Birmingham

Shakespearian Weekender
Holiday Inns

Shake a leg through the Shakespeare country. These Shakespearian Weekenders are just the thing to get you away from it all to the heart of England. Birmingham's Holiday Inn is handy for the multi-level traffic-free Bull Ring Shopping Centre, yet within minutes you can be speeding through the beautiful Warwickshire or Worcestershire countryside.

Historic Stratford-upon-Avon is twenty miles down the road. Visit Anne Hathaway's cottage and Shakespeare's birthplace, and, 100 yards away, the Stratford Motor Museum (free tickets supplied as part of your weekend).

Back at the Inn, take a dip in the heated indoor pool or make use of the fully equipped gym, or the sauna. Let your weekend hostess take the children to Birmingham's Art and Science Museums or the Botanical Gardens. Other attractions are boat trips on the canal, an 18th century water mill, Sarehole Mill and Blakesley Hall, a notable timber-framed yeoman's house of the 17th century.

For full details of Holiday Inn Weekenders see Grampian Weekender.

Holiday Inn, ATV Centre, Holliday Street, Birmingham. Telephone: (021) 643 2766. Duration: weekends May to October. Price: doubles £39 for 2 adults per night with breakfast (1980). Accommodation free to under 20s sharing room with parent. Meals as taken. Price includes excursions, varied activities for children and adults and VAT.

$\mathcal{S}$PINNING

STRATHCLYDE, ISLE OF ARRAN, Whiting Bay

Basic Spinning Course

Silverbirch Workshop

Come spinning on the Isle of Arran in the Firth of Clyde. This basic spinning course is designed to give guests a thorough knowledge of spinning wheel use and maintenance, experience in different thicknesses of twist and plying and how to work the wool from various sheep. You can learn to make everything from 'wedding ring' shawls to quickspun children's sweaters. Spinning wheels are provided free. The Isle of Arran, with its spectacular peaks, glens and crystal pools, is renowned for its scenery, historic sights and hospitable inhabitants: it's the perfect location to learn a traditional craft.

Silverbirch Workshop, Whiting Bay, Isle of Arran, Strathclyde, Scotland. Telephone: (077 07) 232. Director: Lynn Ross. Duration: 1 week. Price: £40 per person per week (1981). Includes tuition and use of spinning wheel. Accommodation at Sandford Guest House, Whiting Bay. Price: £8.50 per person (est). Includes room, breakfast, dinner and VAT.

See also TAPESTRY, WEAVING.

WALES, GWENT, Tintern

Spinning, Natural Dyeing and Weaving
The Nurtons Field Centre

Run by Adrian and Elsa Wood, the beginners' holiday course teaches you how to make useful textiles from natural raw materials. Lectures, demonstrations and introduction tell you in detail about all stages of manufacture. Courses are conducted in a part-Elizabethan, part-Victorian house which overlooks the river in a picturesque part of the Wye Valley. There are single, double and family rooms, with reduced rates for children under twelve who share their parents' room.

The Nurtons Field Centre, Tintern, Nr Chepstow, Gwent, Wales NP6 7NX. Telephone: (029 18) 253. Proprietors: Elsa and Adrian Wood. Duration: 7 days April, July and October. Price: £85 per person (est) (single room supplement 15% extra). Includes 6 nights accommodation and all meals. Materials and VAT extra.

See also YOGA.

SQUASH

GLOUCESTERSHIRE, Westonbirt

Squash Players Special Breaks
Hare and Hounds Hotel

The original Hare and Hounds Inn dates from the early 19th Century and was originally a farm house; the present main building was added in 1928. The hotel's grounds include ten acres of well-tended lawns and flower beds with two all-weather tennis courts and a well-maintained squash court. This special squash player's break includes free use of the hotel court, free loan of a racket and ball and a daily snack bar lunch. You're advised to book one three-quarter hour squash session per day when you make your room reservation.

Hare and Hounds Hotel, Westonbirt, Tetbury, Gloucestershire, GL8 8QL. Telephone: (06666) 233. Managers: Jeremy and Martin Price. Duration: all year. Price: from £33 per person (1981). Includes 2 nights accommodation, (double occupancy), dinner, bed, breakfast, bar lunch and use of squash court, service and VAT. 3 night breaks also available. Other breaks available, send for brochure.

TAYSIDE, Edzell

Squash Weekends
Panmure Arms Hotel

The Panmure Arms Hotel (in the lovely village of Edzell) is a mini-sporting complex which boasts two glass-backed squash courts, a large heated indoor pool, a sauna and a plunge pool. The emphasis is on modern comfort; all seventeen rooms have colour TV and telephone, and fourteen doubles have an *en suite* bathroom. There's a large cheerful pub, a nautical style lounge bar and (in summer) a Sunday cold buffet. You can choose a one night weekend squash holiday, a two night weekend or a three day full board break.

Panmure Arms Hotel, High Street, Edzell, Tayside DD9 7TA. Telephone: (035 64) 420/427. Director: A. L. Broadley. Duration: 1–3 days all year. Price: £20 (1 night) £42 (2 nights), £58 (3 nights) per person (until Easter 1981, afterwards slightly higher). Includes accommodation, all meals, service and VAT. Squash 65p per 45 minutes extra. Squash courts must be booked two weeks in advance.

STAINED GLASS

OXFORDSHIRE, Oxford

Association of British Craftsmen

Paul San Casciani conducts these courses for intermediate and advanced students. Since making and painting stained glass involves many crafts Paul stipulates that students must have previous art or design experience and suggests that your course should be a minimum of two weeks. Paul and his wife provide a high standard of accommodation in their modern home in the centre of Oxford. You'll stay in a ground floor bedsitting room with *en suite* toilet and shower. If you like your host/tutor will conduct excursions to the University Colleges with their magnificent examples of the ancient craft you're studying.

Avocations (Bristol Crafts) Ltd, 57 Coombe Bridge Avenue, Stoke Bishop, Bristol, Avon BS9 2LT. Telephone: (0272) 686417. Duration: 1 week. Price: £117 per person double, £135 per person single (1981). Includes tuition and accommodation. Transport and materials not included.

See also BATIK, DRESSMAKING, ENAMELLING, NEEDLEWORK, TAPESTRY, WOODWORKING.

SOMERSET, Butleigh

1 Stained Glass A
2 Stained Glass B
Dove Workshops

Tutor Janet Banks introduces beginners to traditional methods of making stained glass windows. You can make small items which you can hang in a window, as well as larger panels, mirrors with decorative borders, and three-dimensional pieces. An illustrated outline of the historical development of the art will be given. Materials are charged for as used (glass at 7p per square inch, lead at 25p per foot, solder at 35p per stick) (in all around £15 to £20).

The second course is for those who've mastered the basics. You'll examine the question of design in relation to the medium's limitations and to variations in light and colour. You'll also explore how to create special effects while keeping these limitations in mind. Colour slides will be used to illustrate how these problems have been approached in the past and by contemporary artists.

'Dove Workshops Course', Dove Workshops, Barton Road, Butleigh, Nr Glastonbury, Somerset. Telephone: (0458 50) 682. Proprietor: Barbara Stubbs. Duration: weekly, August. Price: £40 per person for 5 day course (est). Materials from £3 extra. Bed and breakfast accommodation £4 per person per night (est).

See also POTTERY.

STALKING

HIGHLAND, Whitebridge

Knockie Lodge

This ten square mile lochside Highland estate offers stalking for roebuck, sika stag, red stag, red hind and wild highland goat. The basic charge includes exclusive use of proven deer moor or forest and the services of a keeper, pony and ponyman. The objective is a deer (or goat) stalk in

traditional Highland style, culminating with a shot within reasonable range. A stalk isn't guaranteed but if deer or goats aren't seen (or the keeper doesn't think a stalk is possible) you'll be given a fifty per cent rebate on the basic charge. Note: venison belongs to the estate but you can purchase it at wholesale prices.

For details of Knockie Lodge, see SHOOTING.

Knockie Lodge Hotel, Whitebridge, Highland. Telephone: (04563) 276. Manager: Jon Craig-Tyler. Duration: 1 roebuck, 1 May–16 June; 2 sika stag, 25 August–20 October; 3 red stag, 13 August–20 October; 4 red hind, winter, dates on request; 5 wild highland goat, 1 September–15 February. Price: 1 £80 (est); 2 £130 (est); 3 £130 (est); 4 £65 (est); 5 £65 (est). Trophy fees from £20 (est). Deer rifle can be hired for £10 per day. Prices include services of keeper, pony and ponyman. VAT extra. Accommodation: £25 per person per day (est). Includes dinner, bed, breakfast and VAT. Midweek and weekend rates £42 (est) for 2 nights, £100 (est) for 5 nights includes dinner, bed, breakfast and VAT.

Stone Polishing

SHETLAND, Lerwick

Shetland Summer School

Your instructor on this course is Mr L. B. Smith, who studied with Scottish practitioners of the art. He's conducted popular evening classes in stone polishing in Unst and instructed at successive summer schools.

You'll stay in the comfortable, well-appointed school hostel, overlooking the entrance to Lerwick Harbour. It's dormitory accommodation in two, three and four bedded rooms.

Shetland Islands Council, Education Department, 1 Harbour Street, Lerwick, Shetland ZE1 0LS, Scotland. Telephone: (0595) 3535. Director: R. A. B. Barnes. Duration: 2 weeks, August. Price: £125 per person (est). Includes tuition, dormitory accommodation, all meals, excursions, visits, use of tools and equipment. Daily air service from Edinburgh, Glasgow, Inverness and Aberdeen. Ferry service from Aberdeen.

See also TAPESTRY.

SUB-AQUA

DEVON, Plymouth

Diving Courses
Fort Bovisand Underwater Centre

This centre (Britain's largest diver training school) is housed in a converted 19th
century fort whose grounds cover several
acres and has its own L-shaped jetty and
harbour which provides a sheltered training area in the sea. The harbour area incorporates a four-metre wide slip, a boat
park and a trailer park which allows you
to launch your boat with a minimum of
effort. The National Diving Centre of the
British Sub-Aqua Club is here as well as
the clubrooms of two major independent
clubs. Thus it's easy to organize your own
underwater activities. Complex facilities
include a well-stocked diving shop, an
equipment hire centre, a photographic
darkroom, an operational recompression
chamber, class and lecture rooms with
slide and cine projectors, specialist teaching rooms such as a rigging room, equipment servicing and repair workshops, two
training tanks, use of a pool, numerous
inflatables and outboard engines and converted diving launches with full navigational equipment. In total there's accommodation for one hundred. This ranges
from two-berth rooms with attached
bathroom and shower facilities to dormitory accommodation in the historic
fort gunrooms. The centre's café provides
a daily meal service and a bar. The wide
range of diving courses and holidays and
many social and landbased activities available are detailed in the centre's brochure.
One example of what's on offer is the
five-and-a-half day BSAC Elementary
Training Course. All practical instruction
(with the exception of one aqualung session) takes place in the sea. Here are
some do's and don't's: practise swimming
as much as possible before starting the
course because you'll have to pass a
rather strenuous test first of all. Don't
buy your equipment before starting a
course (after a few days you'll be better

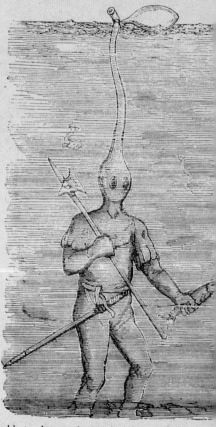

able to choose what's best suited to your
needs). Discounts are available to students at the Centre Dive Shop.

*Fort Bovisand Underwater Centre, Ply-
mouth, Devon, PL9 0AB. Telephone:
(0752) 42570/45641. Duration: weeks and
weekends, April to November. Price: varies
according to course taken. Sample price:
£145 per person (est) for 5½ days elementary training course. Includes tuition,
dormitory accommodation, all meals,
equipment and VAT. Bring sleeping bag.
Minimum age 15 years. For details of
other courses, send for brochure.*

DORSET, Swanage

Swanage Diving School
Swanage Youth Hostel

YHA Adventure Holidays are run from suitable hostels in the countryside. This sub-aqua course is set in Swanage in one of the best and most attractive diving areas on the Dorset coast. Choose from courses for beginners, or those which lead to the Third Class Diver Award, both available through this BSAC (British Sub-Aqua Club) school.

Youth Hostels Association Adventure Holidays, Trevelyan House, St Albans, Hertfordshire AL1 2DY. Telephone: (56) 55215. Duration: 1 week starting Sunday, April to October. Price: £140 (est) per person per week (est). Includes tuition, 6 nights youth hostel accommodation, breakfast, dinner and VAT. Equipment available free for those taking courses. A wide variety of other holidays; send for brochure.

See also WALKING.

ISLES OF SCILLY, Warleggan

Sub-Aqua
Warleggan Guest House

Dive for doubloons off the Isles of Scilly. The local Isles of Scilly Underwater Centre, started by Jim Heslin and Terry Heran in 1971, has opened up to the amateur the possibilities of sub-aqua diving in the crystal clear water of the Scillies. They have diving sites near such famous wrecks as the *Association*, *Hollandia*, and *Schiller*. Air and equipment is transported to the quay each morning at 9.30. Your diving boat, a forty-foot, twin diesel powered launch is skippered by an experienced local boatman, and there's a dive leader on hand to offer help and advice. You'll dive twice each day, and your two dives will include at least one wreck, as well as some spectacular underwater scenery at depths of up to 150 feet. The geography of the Scilly Isles enables you to make every day a diving day in all but the very worst weather conditions.

Accommodation, just a few hundred yards from St Mary's Quay, is in the centre's headquarters at Warleggan. This is no spartan hostel but a first-class well-appointed modern guest house, with home cooking (hot soup on each diving day), a separate colour TV lounge, and family accommodation. Visitors must bring their own wet suits, equipment and one air bottle. (Full bottles for further dives in any one day are supplied at extra cost.) Experience is essential, and you will be required to state your qualifications on the booking form.

Isles of Scilly Underwater Centre, Warleggan, St Mary's, Isles of Scilly. Telephone: (0720) 22563. Director: Jim Heslin. Duration: weekly all year. Price: from £120 per person per week (1981). Includes tuition, 2 daily dives, room, breakfast, dinner and VAT. Bring wet suit, equipment and 1 air bottle.

SURFING

CORNWALL, Bude

Activity and Adventure Holiday
Efford Down Hotel

Take your life in your hands on an ocean roller. These surfing holidays are organized by experienced physical training instructors Keith Marshall and Paddy Foist and designed for action and adventurous spirits. Besides surfing, there's also horse riding, wind-surfing and surf-skiing. One day is set aside for each activity, and there's a day at a modern health studio too, where you can work out on the most up-to-date equipment. For the less energetic, there's a solarium and sauna. Friday is Expedition Day where you'll go off to explore the countryside, ending up with a beach barbecue.

Accommodation is at the Efford Down Hotel in Bude, set in twelve acres of its own gardens. All activity equipment is included in the cost, together with wetsuits for surfing. However, the organizers say you need to bring your own tracksuit, swimsuit, training shoes or plimsolls and a good waterproof jacket. Children must be accompanied and over ten. Unaccompanied children should be sixteen plus. Packed lunches are provided each day.

Galleon World Travel Association Ltd, Galleon House, King Street, Maidstone, Kent ME14 1EG. Telephone: (0662) 63411 or (01) 859 0171. Duration: 1 week, April to June, and September. Price: from £178 per person (est) (single room supplement £4.90 (est)). Includes full board, tuition, equipment, wet suit and VAT. Insurance £1.60 per person (est). Minimum age 10 years, unaccompanied 16 years. Bring tracksuit, swimwear, plimsolls and a waterproof.

See also ANTIQUES, CRUISING: INLAND WATERWAYS, GARDENS, HISTORY, PONY TREKKING.

CORNWALL, Porthcurno

Surfing
Skewjack Surf Village

Cornwall's surf is unrivalled in Britain and you'll find some of the most challenging waves at Sennen Cove. Skewjack Surf Village provides self-contained cabins. These range from those large enough for a party of eight, to two-berth studio units. All have fully-equipped kitchens and everything including linen is provided – all you must bring are towels. If you don't feel like cooking the Bistro serves simple farmhouse-style food. Other amenities include the Sunset Bar (a disco which features a resident DJ, 'Doctor

Fun' and light shows), a small swimming pool, free transport to and from the beach, free wetsuits and surfboards and a shop where you can buy everything from a can of beans to a super surfboard. Instructor Chris Tyler will give you free tuition, assisted by Life Guard Surf Instructors. There's plenty to do when you're not surfing. This includes beach football matches, volleyball, softball, skateboarding, table tennis, darts tournaments, fishing, sightseeing boat trips from Penzance, barbecues, midnight movies and fancy dress competitions.

Skewjack Surf Village, Sennen, Porthcurno, Cornwall. Telephone: (073 687) 287. Manager: Chris Tyler. Duration: May to September. Price: from £30 per person per week (est). Includes tuition, surf boards, wetsuits, self-catering accommodation. VAT extra. Bring towels.

CORNWALL, St Agnes

Surfing Safari

At St Agnes where the Atlantic breakers provide plentiful all-year-round surf, go on a surfing safari. This, the first company to organize surfing holidays in the UK, has instructors who are all professional surfers as well as being members of the British Surfing Association.

Your choice of accommodation is either in local guest house or (at a campsite only two kilometres from the beach) camping in continental frame tents with camp beds and sleeping bags. Upon arrival – if you come by train you'll be met at Truro station – you'll choose your Malibu board then learn how to wax it for a better grip. Your days are spent in the surf or, if your instructor decides conditions aren't good for surfing, you'll go on an underwater safari (no extra cost). At 6.30 p.m. you return to your accommodation for supper.

After supper the evening is free. You might like to catch one of the surf films usually showing in St Agnes or discuss 'tubes', 'wipeouts' and 'hot-dogging' with fellow surfers in the local pubs.

You should bring 1 or 2 swim suits, T-shirts, a couple of big bath towels and a warm jumper for the evenings. You'll also need a wetsuit (these can be hired).

Surfing Safari, Wheal Pye, Trevaunance Road, St Agnes, Cornwall. Telephone: (087 255) 2892. Proprietor: C. A. Adcock.

Duration: 1 week May to September. Price: £64–£74 per person (1981) for tent accommodation (tents provided) £74–£84 per person for guest house accommodation. Includes use of surfboard, tuition, dinner, bed and breakfast. Deposit of £8 required. Insurance £2. Wet suit hire £3.

SURVIVAL TRAINING

SUSSEX, Chichester

Safety Afloat
The Earnley Concourse

All yachtsmen need to know how to come out on top when the sea turns cruel. This course will give you expert advice and practical experience in emergency procedures, including inflating a raft (in the heated swimming pool) and the use of flares. The most dramatic part of the course is putting out a simulated shipboard fire. First aid, man overboard drill and weather forecasts will also be dealt with.

For details of the Concourse see ANTIQUES.

The Earnley Concourse, Nr Chichester, Sussex PO20 7JL. Telephone: (0243) 670392. Duration: Friday to Sunday, March. Price: £36.10 per person (up to April 1981, add approx. 10% thereafter). Includes 2 nights accommodation (double with bath), all meals. VAT extra. Minimum age 16. Transport from Chichester Station 90p each way.

See also ANTIQUES, CREATIVE WRITING, FLOWER ARRANGING, FOLK AND JAZZ, LANGUAGES, MUSIC, PUPPETRY, WINE TASTING.

TABLE TENNIS

COUNTY DURHAM, Durham

Table Tennis Summer School
Tees Sport

Here's a table tennis holiday with a difference – you'll dine and socialize in the magnificent Great Hall of Maiden Castle, alongside Durham Cathedral. Play takes place nearby at the spacious Castle Sports Hall. This is set in beautiful grounds surrounded by rolling hills and woodlands. Players (all standards welcome) receive an average of five hours of coaching a day from a staff composed of England's lead-

ing players such as course director Alan Ransome, ex-English international player and captain, ETTA three star coach and team manager to Britain's leading club, Ormesby. There'll be stroke demonstrations and exhibitions, daily personal tuition sessions, and personal bat advice if required); after an assessment the recommended bat will be made up overnight. Evening seminars include talks by coaches on their specialist subjects, the opportunity to question the experts in the Open Forum session and the chance to watch international players in action on video. Optional physical conditioning periods are held daily. Everyone enjoys the final night disco and an informal prize giving ceremony in the Undercroft.

Accommodation is in single or twin rooms in a modern section of Durham University's residences. Tees Sport staff members will meet course members who arrive in Durham by bus or train and return you to Durham at course's end.

Tees Sport, Zetland Place, Middlesborough, Cleveland TS1 1HJ. Telephone: (0642) 249000/217844/5. Duration: 7 and 9 day courses 20 July–30 August. Price: £150 for 7 days (1981). £230 for 9 days. Includes tuition, accommodation, all meals. Bring your own table tennis bat.

TACTICAL ESCAPES

HAMPSHIRE, Weyhill

Adventure Training School

There's never been a holiday like this. For £30 you can join the ranks of forty paying prisoners of war at a chillingly realistic Colditz-style concentration camp complete with barbed wire, searchlights, watchtowers and fifty guards in SS uniforms. 'Prisoners' arrive in railway cattle trucks late Friday evening, have serial numbers stamped on their foreheads and spend the rest of the weekend enjoying forced labour, punishing army drills, dowsing with hoses and sleep deprivation. Inmates who try to escape (a not unnatural reaction) and are captured are fiercely interrogated and thrown into solitary confinement. The camp's commandant and originator, former paratroop sergeant Bob Acraman, promises 'no jolly times' at Butlitz.

Adventure Training School, Nightingale Park, Sarsons Lane, Weyhill, Nr Andover, Hampshire. Telephone: (026) 477 3377. Commandant: Robert Acraman. Duration: Friday to Sunday. Price: £30 per person. Includes accommodation in barracks, meals of gruel and stale bread. Bring a sharpened spoon.

TAPESTRY

SHETLAND, Lerwick

Tapestry Weaving
Shetland Summer School

This course is offered under the tutelage of Mrs Twatt, who took a post-graduate diploma in tapestry after obtaining a Diploma in Art from Edinburgh College of Art.

For details of accommodation see STONE POLISHING.

Shetland Islands Council, Education Department, 1 Harbour Street, Lerwick, Shetland ZE1 0LS, Scotland. Telephone: (0595) 3535. Director: R. A. B. Barnes. Duration: 2 weeks August. Price: £125 per person (est). Includes tuition, dormitory accommodation, all meals, excursion visits. Use of tools and equipment. Daily air service from Edinburgh, Glasgow, Inverness and Aberdeen. Ferry service from Aberdeen.

STRATHCLYDE, ISLE OF ARRAN, Whiting Bay

Holiday Tapestry Course
Silverbirch Workshop

Here's your chance to try your hand at the ancient craft of tapestry weaving in a traditional location. The spectacular

Arran landscape and the rustic environment of the workshop are guaranteed to inspire your efforts to relate colour and weave structure to visual impressions – the origin of so many of Scotland's finest craft patterns. The course includes instruction in basic interlocking and Gobelin techniques, and you're encouraged to interpret your own designs in weave. Accommodation (not included in the cost of the course) is in a nearby guesthouse.

Silverbirch Workshop, Whiting Bay, Isle of Arran, Strathclyde, Scotland. Telephone: (077 07) 232. Director: Lynn Ross. Duration: 1 week. Price: £40 per person per week (1981). Includes tuition only. Accommodation at Sandford Guest House, Whiting Bay. Price: £8.50 per person (est). Includes room, breakfast, dinner and VAT.

See also SPINNING, WEAVING.

WALES, GWYNEDD, Snowdonia

Tapestry and Ethnic Design

Granville Marshall and his wife Sheila are both noted craftsmen. He offers instruction in all areas of weaving but specializes in rug, tapestry and three-dimensional techniques. Sheila specializes in the design and making of ethnic garments, embroidery, smocking and traditional hand techniques. Both welcome students at all levels of experience. (There's a £26 supplement for Granville's instruction.)

You'll stay with them for a week in their farmhouse on a Welsh hillside just south of Snowdonia National Park. The scenery is inspiring and the house has been lovingly renovated – the old world kitchen and living rooms are especially charming. It's good walking and riding countryside, with rivers, lakes and mountains all around. Once you've booked your week's course, you'll receive full details of how and where to get there.

Avocations (Bristol Crafts) Ltd, 37 Coombe Bridge Avenue, Bristol, Avon BS9 2LT. Telephone (0272) 686417. Contact: Gerald Richardson. Price: £117 per person per week (1981). Includes tuition, use of equipment, full board (twin), single room supplement 15% extra. No VAT.

See also BATIK, DRESSMAKING, ENAMELLING, NEEDLEWORK, STAINED GLASS, WOODWORKING.

TENNIS

BEDFORDSHIRE, Milton Ernest

Tennis Coaching International
Woodlands Craft Centre

Head instructor Peter Smith has coached in six countries and operated joint courses in the United States with a former Wimbledon and US champion. He's one of forty British professional tennis coaches selected (out of about three hundred) by the Lawn Tennis Association for their specialized knowledge to serve as panel coaches. He's assisted by a highly qualified staff, many of whom have won championships. Over a four-year period with Peter Smith more pupils have passed the Professional Tennis Coaches Association Performance Award Scheme than with any other coach in the British Isles. Facilities include instant-replay video tape, ball machines and stroke developer apparatus. Your racquet can be repaired or restrung here on an Oliver machine, and you'll receive individual advice on racquet grips and sizes. Coaching for any age or standard is available. Course mem-

bers have the exclusive use of six grass courts, eleven all-weather courts and two new indoor courts as well as a practice wall and a gymnasium. There are four students per court and a maximum of eight students to one coach (maximum sixty players in the camp). Added amenities include a cinema, badminton court, table tennis, indoor and outdoor heated pools, television and squash courts. Gold, silver and bronze awards are given to players at all levels for achievement.

In 1981 accommodation will be in Peter Smith's new home, the converted Woodlands Craft Centre, former stables of a local vicarage and built in 1694.

Woodlands Craft Centre, Thurleigh Road, Milton Ernest, Bedfordshire MK44 1RF. Telephone: (02302) 2914. Principal: Peter G. Smith. Duration: weekends, weekly, June to September. Price: weekends from £70 (est), 1 week courses from £175 (est). Includes coaching, room and full board, excursions, activities and insurance.

BUCKINGHAMSHIRE, Beaconsfield

Beaconsfield School of Lawn Tennis

The Beaconsfield School of Lawn Tennis is the only school in Europe which provides a complete coaching and training programme for players at all levels. Founded in 1961 by Sue Livingston, this school has coached many a player who has won a national title, in addition to many county and club championships.

There are a wide range of courses. These range from private tuition (especially geared to the individual's needs) to group coaching courses for juniors and adults. All are at beginners', intermediate and advanced levels. Intensive five day courses are designed for those who wish to make exceptional progress over a short period. Specially designed programmes from 10 a.m. to 1 p.m. and 2 to 6 p.m. include individual and group coaching, tactics, fitness training exercises and practice.

Accommodation is at nearby hotels or guest houses. In the case of unaccompanied children accommodation can be arranged with a local family (cost approximately £6–£7 per night).

Beaconsfield School of Lawn Tennis, The Oval, Beaconsfield, Buckinghamshire. Telephone: (04946) 4744. Principal: Sue Livingston. Duration: all year. Price: from £2.25 per hour (est), £10.00 per week (5 lessons), £40.00 per week intensive course. Accommodation list provides sample price £15 per person per day (1981) hotel accommodation, includes bed and breakfast.

Many courses available, write for brochure.

CORNWALL, Bodmin

Tennisville Holidays
Tennisville

Who's for tennis at Tennisville? Four times Cornwall County singles champion and a finalist in the British Professional Coaches Championship, James Webster and his wife Hilary, a qualified Assistant Coach, aim to provide a tennis-oriented holiday that will not only be enjoyable but also help to improve your game.

Tennisville is a large town residence, centrally situated in Bodmin, close to the famous Moor and within a half-hour drive of most of Cornwall's best known holiday resorts. There are two hours of group training each morning and at least two hours of play each afternoon. Guests also have the use of a tennis ball machine. Accommodation is in shared rooms, with no mixed accommodation available. Guests should bring their own racquet and suitable clothing (together with sensible shoes for walking or riding), although these may be purchased at the Tennisville shop. The house also has a smoke 'Coke' bar – the 'Van Inn'. Weekly membership of the local tennis club (with floodlit courts) can also be arranged.

'Tennisville Holidays', 55 St Nicholas Street, Bodmin, Cornwall PL31 1AF. Telephone (0208) 2723. Director: James Webster. Duration: 1 week April to September. Price £71.50 per person per weekend (est), £180 per week (est). Includes accommodation, full board, laundry and VAT. Bring tennis racquet and clothing.

THEATRE GOING

BERKSHIRE, Elcot Park

Watermill Theatre
Country House Hotel

This elegant hotel offers you the chance to combine a night in the country with a relaxed evening at the theatre and fine dining. The Watermill Theatre near Newbury was once a working watermill, and has now been lovingly restored and converted into a delightful showcase for plays ranging from G. B. Shaw to Michael Frayn. Performances begin at 7.30 p.m. and dinner is served afterwards in the theatre's fully licensed restaurant where the menu changes with each play.

Country House Hotel, Elcot Park, Nr Newbury, Berkshire RG16 8NJ. Telephone: (048 85) 276. Duration: nightly May to October. Price: from £22 per person (est). Includes dinner, 1 night accommodation, breakfast, theatre seat, service and VAT.

See also HOT AIR BALLOONING, NEEDLEWORK.

LEICESTERSHIRE, Leicester

Theatre Weekend
Belmont Hotel

This charming period building is a few minutes walk from the town centre, but right beside a quiet woodland walk. The weekend includes a candlelit dinner on Friday night and theatre tickets for a Saturday evening performance followed by a buffet supper at the hotel.

Belmont Hotel, Belmont, Leicestershire LE1 7GR. Telephone: (0533) 544773. Duration: Friday to Sunday all year. Price: from £38 per person (1981). Includes 2 nights accommodation, breakfast, dinner, tickets, service and VAT.

LOTHIAN, Musselburgh

Edinburgh International Festival Course
Carberry Tower

The annual Edinburgh International Festival attracts many regulars, which gives it the festive air of a reunion of arts lovers. If this is your first visit, you're sure to have a lively time. Morning lectures by experts introduce the evening performances, and your pre-booked tickets to five main concerts and plays include the opening concert, daily transport to and from Edinburgh, and a full day, mid-week coach outing to places of historic and scenic interest.

You'll be based at Carberry Tower, a splendid ancient mansion house set in thirty-five acres of parkland eight miles from Edinburgh. The original Tower House dates from 1480, and the present extended building was the home of the Queen Mother's sister from 1901 to 1961. Subsequently redecorated by the Church of Scotland (the present owners), it now accommodates seventy people in two- and three-bedded rooms, and an additional seventeen in a single bedroom annexe. An indoor recreation hall is equipped for badminton, netball, snooker, etc., all free.

Carberry Tower, Church of Scotland Residential Training Centre, Musselburgh, Lothian EH21 8PY. Telephone: (031) 665 3135/3488. Warden: Rev. Colin Day. Duration: 1 week 15–22 August (1981). Price: £62.50 per person (est). Includes lectures, transport, bed, breakfast and lunch. Ticket prices are extra and not yet available; 1980 price was £33.50. Write for brochure. Includes VAT.

LONDON
WARWICKSHIRE, Stratford-upon-Avon

1 London Theatre
2 Theatre in the Midlands
Astor College London

Course Director Roger Jerome is Senior Lecturer in English and Drama at the Polytechnic of the South Bank. He'll lead this one-week overall survey of London's theatre scene which includes theatre visits, lectures and seminar discussions. You'll see and analyse five plays and hear talks by both creative and administrative theatre workers. Lecture topics include: the Arts Council and public subsidy; the National Theatre; writing and directing and design in the theatre; critics; and acting today. Accommodation is in single rooms at Astor College, Charlotte Street, near the theatre district.

The six-day theatre in the Midlands course is also directed by Roger Jerome. You'll examine the work of Stratford-upon-Avon's Royal Shakespeare Company, and some important provincial Midland repertory companies such as Birmingham, Coventry, Nottingham or Leicester. Five nights will be spent in Stratford guest houses, so you can make visits to the town, including at least one theatre performance.

Association for Cultural Exchange, 9 Emmanuel Road, Cambridge CB1 1JW. Telephone: (0223) 65030. Duration: 1 1

week; 2 6 days. Price: 1 £127 per person (est). Includes lectures, 5 theatre tickets, room and breakfast; 2 £92 per person (est). Includes lectures, visits, 3 theatre tickets, twin room and breakfast.

See also ARCHITECTURE, CHURCHES AND CATHEDRALS.

SOMERSET, Taunton

Theatre Weekend
Castle Hotel

Once part of a Norman fortress (the original garden remains) the Castle has been welcoming travellers to Taunton since the 12th century. Less than welcoming Judge Jeffreys held his infamous Bloody Assizes here. Forty-five sumptuously appointed rooms, each completely different, provide luxurious accommodation. One double boasts a magnificent four-poster and the Bow Suite offers you a master bedroom, two bathrooms and an elegant Georgian-panelled sitting room. There are two bars, a well-stocked cellar (220 wines, including some of the best post-1924 vintages) and a fine restaurant – whortleberry pie with clotted cream has been a house speciality since the 1930s.

This year's theatre weekend begins at 6.30 p.m. with a welcoming cocktail party. The performance starts at 7.15 p.m. with dinner at 9.00 p.m. You'll see four 'entertainments' based on the public and private lives of the Tudors and Stuarts. These have been devised by Jill Nott-Bower and Robert Spencer (who also provide the music) and star Judi Dench, Michael Williams and Gabriel Woolf of the famous Royal Shakespeare Company. There's a lavish farewell luncheon on Sunday at 1.00 p.m.

The Castle Hotel, Castle Green, Taunton, Somerset TA1 1NF. Telephone: (0823) 72671. Managing Director: Christopher Chapman. Duration: Friday p.m. to Sunday p.m., 20–22 February. Price: £88 per person (1981). Includes accommodation, private bath, all meals, entertainment and service. VAT extra. Other weekends also available. Send for brochure.

See also MUSIC.

SUSSEX, Chichester

Chichester Festival Theatre
West Dean College

This residential weekend holiday has been arranged by Maureen Davis-Poynter for theatre-goers, and those involved in dramatic productions of all kinds. You'll hear talks by the Liaison Officer, Artistic Director and Designer of the Chichester Festival Theatre, which cover the origins of theatre, past plays and players, and the director and designer's viewpoint. You'll visit the Festival theatre itself on Saturday night for a performance, and you'll stay in a fine old country mansion, now used as a college, in the Sussex Downs.

For details of West Dean College see ART APPRECIATION.

West Dean College, West Dean, Chichester, West Sussex PO18 0Q2. Telephone: (024 363) 301. Duration: weekends August. Price: £39.50 per person (1981). Includes lectures, full board and VAT. Single room supplement £3. Theatre tickets extra.

See also ART APPRECIATION, CALLIGRAPHY, CANEWORK, COLLECTING, UPHOLSTERY.

SUSSEX, Eastbourne

A Theatre Weekend
Lansdowne Hotel

If you're looking for a family holiday, this one has something for everyone – an evening at an Eastbourne theatre for the adults, and a Saturday afternoon visit to Drusilla's, in Alfriston, where there's a children's zoo. Be sure to visit the antique shop and craft shop while you're there and buy a bottle of delicious English wine at the vineyard. Then have afternoon tea in the thatched barn in Alfriston. All the theatres in Eastbourne are within easy walking distance of your hotel, but you need your own transport to get to the children's zoo.

The Lansdowne is an elegant Victorian seafront hotel on the promenade. All bedrooms have radio, telephone and tea and coffee making facilities; there are three colour TV lounges.

Lansdowne Hotel, King Edwards Parade, Eastbourne, Sussex BN21 4EE. Telephone: (0323) 25174. Duration: mid-January to April, October to December. Price: from £31.50 per person (until March 1981). Includes 2 nights accommodation (Friday to Sunday), breakfast, dinner, theatre tickets, entrance and tea at Drusilla's, service and VAT. Supplement of £2 from April 1981.

WARWICKSHIRE, Stratford-upon-Avon

Drama and Theatre
The Fold

Shakespeare's home town is the perfect setting for this theatre buff's special. An experienced lecturer will show you places of theatrical and historical interest, organize talks and arrange play readings. Cost of the holiday includes four theatre visits – to the Royal Shakespeare Theatre, The Other Place and sometimes the Belgrade Theatre in Coventry. During your stay you'll be put up in a town house of historical interest in itself; it's tucked away in a charming, quiet street with its own garden and car park.

For details of Holiday Fellowship see WALKING, *Loch Awe.*

Holiday Fellowship, 142/144 Great North Way, London NW4 1EG. Telephone: (01) 203 3381, Booking Department. Duration: 1 week, May. Price: from £76 per person (est). Includes full board, course and theatre tickets. Service and VAT extra. New members £10 subscription.

See also BOWLS, BRASS RUBBING, CREATIVE WRITING, ECOLOGY, FOLK MUSIC, GENEALOGY, JEWELLERY, ORIENTEERING, WALKING, YOGA.

WARWICKSHIRE, Stratford-upon-Avon

Theatre Holiday
Stratford House Hotel

Have a break with the Bard. These all-inclusive Stratford-upon-Avon holidays give you a chance to relax away from it all, and enjoy the cultural delights of the world's greatest plays performed by the world's greatest Shakespearian acting company. Best seats are reserved for you for the evening performances at the Royal Shakespeare Company's two Stratford theatres. A minimum of forty-eight hours notice is required for booking, as tickets are often scarce on Friday and Saturday nights (no performance Sunday).

Accommodation is at Stratford House, one hundred yards from the theatre, a fine Georgian house which has been completely refurbished by its resident proprietors, Pamela and Peter Wade. The interior, decorated with the owner's own furniture, china and pictures, is cheerful and welcoming. All rooms have colour TV, most have private bathrooms.

Stratford House Hotel, Sheep Street, Stratford-upon-Avon, Warwickshire CV37 6EF. Telephone: (0789) 68288. Proprietors: Pamela and Peter Wade. Duration: 2 days. Price: £49 per person (1981). Includes 2 theatre tickets, dinner at the Box Tree restaurant, 2 nights accommodation, double with bath, breakfast and VAT.

UPHOLSTERY

WEST SUSSEX, West Dean

Soft Furnishing, Loose Covers for Chairs
West Dean College

This course is given in two parts; a weekend and, three weeks later, a five day stint. (If you're interested you must book both courses.) Jose O'Brien leads the first part, a weekend which deals with the preliminary stages of making loose covers for a chair. You'll get advice on selecting fabrics, measuring chairs, cutting plans, estimates of required material, and making piping and a cushion. Students will then have a three week interval in which to buy the material and make the piping before coming back to complete the cover. Tutor Raymond O'Brien takes the second course.

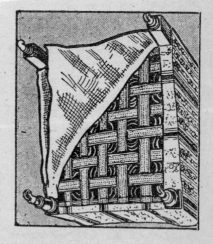

For details of West Dean College see ART APPRECIATION.

West Dean College, West Dean, Chichester, West Sussex PO18 0Q2. Telephone: (024 363) 301. Duration: 30 January–1

February and 22–27 February. Price: £112 per person (1981). Includes tuition, full board and VAT. Single supplement £10.50.

See also ART APPRECIATION, CALLIGRAPHY, CANEWORK, COLLECTING, THEATRE GOING.

WALKING

COUNTRYWIDE

Youth Hostels Association

Choose from over twenty different, carefully graded walking holidays, according to your level of fitness and age group. A good pair of boots and a rucksack are the only special equipment you'll need. Almost every one of these holidays involves walking from hostel to hostel, so if you've never done it before you're advised to choose a grade C tour, such as the New Forest and Isle of Wight walk. Distances in this category average between ten and twelve miles daily. Grade B tours, such as the 167-mile long Pembrokeshire Coastal Footpath, take you through more rugged country, while Grade A tours involve a week or more of strenuous mountain walking with a loaded rucksack. You might be among the marvellous landscapes of the Lake District, or along Offa's Dyke, a 170-mile route which runs the entire length of Wales, from Chepstow to Prestatyn. Some holidays include a self-cooking night when your party will prepare food in the YHA kitchen.

Youth Hostels Association Adventure Holidays, Trevelyan House, St Albans, Hertfordshire AL1 2DY. Telephone: (56) 55215. Duration: 7 or 14 nights, June to October (1981). Price: from £65 per person per walk (est). Includes Youth Hostel accommodation, bed, breakfast, dinner and VAT. Bring broken-in, waterproof boots. For details of these and other holidays, send for brochure.

See also SUB-AQUA.

CUMBRIA, Grange-over-Sands, NORTH YORKSHIRE, Pickering

Hill and Fell Walking Holiday
Crossways Hotel and Grange Hotel

This is really two holidays in one. During the first week you're based in North Yorkshire in the ancient market town of Pickering. From here you can cover miles of interesting, scenic terrain – heather-covered moors, deep vales, wildlife filled forests, rocky shores and coastal paths along towering cliffs. Moorsrail, a railway operated by the North York Moors Historical Railway Trust, will take you to stations at Levisham, Goathland and Grosmont by steam or diesel engined train. From each of these stations there are walks in all directions.

Week two is based in Grange-over-Sands. The surrounding Lakeland Fells are a mellow contrast to the Yorkshire terrain. To the north you have Lake Windermere with its tranquil lakeside walks and (if you're after high peaks and panoramic views) you can easily reach the high fells by public transport.

Freedom of Ryedale Holidays, 23a Market Place, North Helmsley, York YO6 5BT. Telephone: (0439) 70775. Duration: 2 weeks, dates by arrangement. Price: £235 per person (est) includes accommodation, dinner, bed and breakfast, maps, route suggestions and VAT. Transport between Pickering and Grange-over-Sands not included. Other activity holidays also available, send for brochure.

See also CYCLING, RAILWAYS.

CUMBRIA, Keswick or Windermere

Mountain Walking
Mountain Goat Holidays

Some of the most spectacular scenery in the Lake District is best reached on foot. If you're reasonably fit and want to scale those tempting but lofty mountain tops

Mountain Goat will arrange transport (in twelve-seater minibuses) to a starting point on each of four mornings thus saving you up to one thousand feet of leg work. As a result you can spend the maximum amount of time on the high ground. The walks are led by trained guides whose main concerns are your safety and enjoyment of the holiday – there's no 'whip cracking' or urging on of laggards. These are walking, not climbing, holidays and frequent stops are made. As groups are restricted to ten it's easy to adjust the pace. These holidays, beginning on Saturdays at either Windermere or Keswick, are available for one week or for a two week combination. Four walks are included at each centre. All culminate on the final day with the ascent of either Helvellyn (3118 ft) from Windermere or Scafell Pike (3206 ft) from Keswick.

Accommodation is in carefully selected hotels and guest houses (seven in Windermere, three in Keswick).

Mountain Goat Holidays, Victoria Street, Windermere, Cumbria, LA23 1AD. Telephone: (09662) 5166. Duration: 1 or 2 weeks, May to September. Price: from £139.50 per person per week (1981). Includes hotel accommodation, dinner, bed and breakfast. From £110.50 (Windermere), £111 (Keswick), for guest house accommodation. Price includes VAT. Minimum age 12. Bring waterproof jacket, ankle supporting boots, over-trousers, rucksack. Equipment packs can be hired for £18 per week. Other walking holidays and explore Lakeland by minibus holidays also available, send for brochure.

CUMBRIA, Sedbergh

Fell Walking Weeks
Whernside Cave and Fell Centre

Here's a chance for both experienced and inexperienced walkers to enjoy the Dales with like-minded companions. All tastes are catered for – walks differ in length and severity every day, from an initial relaxed ramble to a final hard day on the

tops. Every evening your guide rounds off the day with a lecture on some aspect of walking or Dales life. You and your fellow walkers decide the course of the walks after an initial pre-programme discussion. (Note: these weeks are geared for adults rather than younger people.) Courses start on Saturday at 5.00 p.m. and end at 9.00 a.m. on the following Saturday.

For details of Whernside see CAVING AND POTHOLING.

Yorkshire Dales National Park, Whernside Cave and Fell Centre, Dent, Sedbergh, Cumbria LA10 5RE. Telephone: (058 75) 213. Warden: M. K. Lyon. Duration: 30 May–6 June; 15–22 August; 19–26 September. Price: £81 per person (1981). Includes tuition, full board, dormitory and VAT. Transport from Oxenholme Station £2.50 each way, requires 7 days notice.

See also CAVING AND POTHOLING, ECOLOGY.

DERBYSHIRE TO SCOTLAND

Walking Tour
Pennine Way

Here's a challenge for the hardiest hikers – seventeen miles of rough, tough walking and wonderful views every day for three weeks. You and your group of twelve will be led along the 250 mile route, Britain's premier long-distance footpath which links Edale in Derbyshire with Kirk Yetholm over the Scottish border. At several points, such as Kinder Scout and Windy Gyle, you'll reach as high as 2,900 feet as you follow old packhorse trails, shepherds' tracks and ancient Roman roads. The path crosses the rivers Calder, Ure, Tees and Tyne, even Hadrian's Wall.

Holiday Fellowship, 142/144 Great North Way, London NW4 1EG. Telephone: (01) 203 3381, Booking Department. Duration: 3 weeks June, July, August. Price: £245 per person (est). Includes full board and guide. VAT extra. New members £10 subscription.

See also GARDENING, THEATRE, YOGA.

DORSET

English Wanderer

On English Wanderer holidays small guided groups of five to fifteen walk through areas of outstanding natural beauty. You stay overnight in a guesthouse, farmhouse or inn in shared rooms so there's no need to carry a tent or sleeping bag. All meals from dinner on the first night to breakfast on the last day plus packed lunches are included as well as transport between centres for scheduled excursions plus entry fees for historic houses and castles.

The springtime Dorset walk (about forty miles in all) starts off from Dorchester and heads west. You'll visit the Iron Age earthwork fortifications at Maiden Castle on the way. You reach the sea by the Swannery on the Chesil Beach, tour the sub-tropical gardens at Abbotsbury then walk along the edge of Lyme Bay to Lyme Regis, whose six-hundred-foot long Cobb Harbour has stood for seven hundred years.

English Wanderer, 13 Wellington Court, Spencers Wood, Reading, Berkshire RG7 1BN. Telephone: (0734) 882515. Organizer: Tom Harrison. Duration: 1 week mid-May. Price: £110 per person per week (est). Includes transport between centres, excursions, entry fees, full board. Children accompanied by an adult 20% discount. VAT extra.

EIRE, COUNTY WICKLOW, Ashford

Wicklow Walking Tour
Tiglin Adventure Centre

These tours, based at Tiglin, take you through some of Ireland's most spectacular mountain scenery. At the end of each day's hike, a minibus will return you to Tiglin and bring you back next morning to the spot where you finished the previous day. You and your group will walk over Sugarloaf, through the valleys Glencree, Powerscourt and Glenmalure; each walk lasts four or five hours. A daily

packed lunch is provided. A climax of the tour is the last day's scaling of Lynaquilla.

For details of accommodation see CANOEING.

Tiglin Adventure Centre, Ashford, County Wicklow, Eire. Telephone: (0404) 4169. Director: Paddy O'Leary. Duration: (Saturday to Saturday) June to September. Price: £80 (est). Includes accommodation (dormitory), breakfast, dinner, packed lunch, guide and transport. Boot hire 25p per day. Includes VAT.

See also CANOEING, ORIENTEERING.

HIGHLAND, Onich

Highland Walking

Superbly situated in the rugged beauty of the Scottish Highlands, this mountain centre is perched on the north slope of Loch Aber with sweeping views of the mountains of Glencoe. Conducted walks take full advantage of the mountain setting and there are lots to suit all degrees of skill and enthusiasm, whether you want to scale the heights or just stroll through the scenery. Sailing can be arranged and there's clock golf, croquet and putting. Accommodation is in the main house or new chalets. Each room has its own shower and WC; nine singles are available.

For details of Holiday Fellowship see WALKING, *Loch Awe.*

Holiday Fellowship, 142/144 Great North Way, London NW4 1EG. Telephone: (01) 203 3381, Booking Department. Duration: 1, 2, 3 or 4 weeks May to October. Price: from £59 per person (est). Includes 1 week full board, excursions. Service and VAT extra. New members £10 subscription.

NORTHUMBERLAND, Wooler

Walking Week
Cheviot Field Centre

The Border Hills are one of the few great 'wilderness' areas left in Britain. Your guide, Colin Burgess, will lead you from the wild heights of the Cheviots to the windswept North Sea coast, past remote hill forts and settlements abandoned 2000 years ago, the strongholds of warring Border lords, tumbling waterfalls and a wealth of wildlife. If you're in luck you may even catch sight of a wild Cheviot goat. Along the way, Mr Burgess, a University tutor in archaeology, will fill you in on points of archaeological, historical and environmental interest.

For details of accommodation see ARCHAEOLOGY.

Cheviot Field Centre, Padgepool Place, Wooler, Northumberland NE71 6BL. Telephone: (06682) 711. Warden: Kevin Danforth. Duration: 22–29 August. Price: £85 per person (est). Includes 7 nights accommodation (single), all meals, tuition and transport. VAT extra. Bring soap, towels, waterproof clothing, strong footwear and thermos.

See also ARCHAEOLOGY, BATTLEFIELDS, CASTLES AND HISTORIC HOUSES.

SCOTLAND

1 West Highland Line
2 Trossachs Tour
3 Cairngorm Encounter
Scottish Youth Hostels

These walking tours are offered under the auspices of the Scottish YHA. For the West Highland Line, meet your leader at Ardgarten to walk through the Arrochar Alps via Abyssinia and Loch Stoy to the head of Loch Lomond and Crianlarich. Then your party will catch a train to Corrour for the Loch Ossian Youth Hostel. When you've explored the wildness of Rannoch Moor, you'll move on through the Mamores to Glen Nevis and Fort William.

For the Trossachs tour you'll meet at Stirling and bus to Callander, travelling by Loch Venacher, Ben Ledi, Ben Venue and Ben Lomond to Loch Lomond. During the week you'll stay at Youth Hostels at Trossachs, Loch Ard and Rowardennan, while the Cairngorm Encounter starts from Aberdeen Youth Hostel. For this you'll travel by bus along Deeside, on to Braemar via Jock's Road, then across the famous hill pass Lairig Ghru, which brings you to the rugged splendour of the Cairngorms, Ben Macdin, Braeriach and Cairn Toul. It's a spectacular journey, at the end of which you can relax at Loch Morlich Youth Hostel.

Scottish Youth Hostels Association, National Office, 7 Glebe Crescent, Stirling FK8 2JA, Central. Telephone: (0786) 2821. Duration: 1 *7 days starting 11 July and 1 August;* 2 *7 days starting 4 and 25 July;* 3 *7 days starting 18 July and 8 August. Price:* 1 *£57 per person (1981);* 2 *£63 per person (1981);* 3 *£60 per person (1981). Includes leader, any necessary transport, Youth Hostel accommodation and all meals, some self-cooked.*

See also SKIING.

STRATHCLYDE, Loch Awe

Hill Walking
Loch Awe House

The non-profit-making organization Holiday Fellowship runs forty UK centres (all unlicensed) where you're received with the kind of hospitality you'd expect as a house guest. The main feature of an HF holiday is walking excursions organized and led by a competent guide. They're graded to all levels of ability and energy; you'll be walking with a small group in about the same shape as you are. During the day you'll walk and talk outdoors, while in the evening you can dance, sing, play table tennis or just relax with new friends. It's easy to see why the organization claims 'You just cannot be lonely on an HF holiday.'

Loch Awe House is set right on the edge of the water in four acres of pine forest. There are eight grades of walks from leisurely five-mile hikes to a six-hour, 2000 foot climb – for which you need to be fairly fit! There's plenty of variety in the terrain – one week's programme features Ben More and Horseshoe, Beann Ime and The Cobbler, Rest and Be Thankful, Ben Cruachan, Glen Nant Forest Walk and a boat trip on Loch Etive. If you're feeling lazy, the chair lift used for winter skiing operates year-round. You can rent a bicycle from the centre, and you can fish in the loch. The house will accommodate 117, and there are sixteen single rooms.

Holiday Fellowship, 142/144 Great North Way, London NW4 1EG. Telephone: (01) 203 3381, Booking Department. Duration: 1, 2, 3 and 4 weeks May to October. Price: from £58 per person (est). Includes 1 week full board, excursions. Service and VAT extra. New members £10 subscription.

See also BOWLS, BRASS RUBBING, CREATIVE WRITING, ECOLOGY, FOLK MUSIC, GENEALOGY, JEWELLERY, ORIENTEERING, THEATRE GOING, YOGA.

WALES, GWYNEDD, Maentwrog

Walking Week Holiday
Plas Tan y Bwich

The HF organization (see Walking at Loch Awe) has joined forces with the Snowdonia National Park to create a fascinating holiday based on the Park's study centre. You'll be led on a series of walks, some fairly strenuous, to visit the park's rich variety of archaeological remains, including Neolithic burial chambers and medieval settlements. Accommodation is in a modernized mansion set in fine grounds, and includes the use of three lounges, a bar and a lecture room. There are only twenty places available, so book early.

For details of Holiday Fellowship see WALKING, *Loch Awe.*

Holiday Fellowship, 142/144 Great North Way, London NW4 1EG. Telephone: (01)

203 3381, Booking Department. Duration: 1 week, July and August. Price: £73 (per person (est). Includes full board and course. Service and VAT extra. New members £10 subscription.

See also GARDENING, THEATRE, YOGA.

WELSH BORDER

Walking Tour
Offa's Dyke

Between AD 750 and 800, King Offa, of Mercia built a 170-mile system of mounds and ditches to keep out the fierce Welsh tribes. His line of defence makes a magnificent present-day walk that will take you, in a party of twelve, from Chepstow to Prestatyn; from the estuary of the River Severn, across the spectacular Wye Valley, and through the Black Mountains and the Shropshire Hills.

For details of Holiday Fellowship see WALKING, *Loch Awe.*

Holiday Fellowship, 142/144 Great North Way, London NW4 1EG. Telephone: (01) 203 3381, Booking Department. Duration: 2 weeks June and August. Price: £235 per person (est). Includes full board, guide. Service and VAT extra. New members £10 subscription.

See also GARDENING, THEATRE, YOGA.

WAR GAMES

CUMBRIA, Bassenthwaite Lake

Campaigns of Marlborough
Higham Hall

Your tutor David Chandler is eminently qualified: he's Head of Department of War Studies at the Royal Military Academy Sandhust, and President of the British Commission for Military History. Marlborough's standing as a military commander of great merit has withstood the test of time. You'll examine his generalship in the context of the military conditions of his day. Special attention will be given to the campaign leading up to Blenheim and the one which surrounded the Siege of Lille. There'll also be an opportunity to participate in a war game, guaranteed to give you a deeper insight into the brilliant strategy behind one of these historic battles.

For details of Higham Hall see ART APPRECIATION.

Higham Hall, Bassenthwaite Lake, Cockermouth, Cumbria CA13 9SH. Telephone: (059 681) 276. Warden: Peter Hadkins. Duration: 13–15 February. Price: £24 per person (est). Includes tuition, 2 nights accommodation, all meals. Cumbrian residents £2 reduction. Minimum age 18.

See also ART APPRECIATION, DRESSMAKING, MUSIC.

WATER SPORTS

CENTRAL, Lochearnhead

Canoeing, Sailing, Waterskiing, Windsurfing
Lochearnhead Watersports Centre

Tuition includes all four watersports available at the centre – sailing, waterskiing, windsurfing and canoeing – so you'll develop a variety of skills during the week.

All this under the capable guidance of Jon Stuart, a qualified Senior Instructor to Royal Yachting Association standards and his crew of instructors. The day's activities start after a substantial breakfast at 9.30 a.m., and then you're on the go till 5.30 p.m. All required equipment is included in the course fee.

For details of accommodation see SAILING.

Lochearnhead Water Sports Centre, Lochearnhead, Central. Telephone: (056 73) 330. Principal: Jon Stuart. Duration: March to October. Price: from £135 to £165 per *person (1981) (according to season). Includes accommodation, all meals, tuition, equipment and VAT.*

WEAVING

STRATHCLYDE, ISLE OF ARRAN, Whiting Bay

Holiday Weaving Course
Silverbirch Workshop

Weave your way through a holiday on the Isle of Arran and have something to show for it at the end. This basic cloth and rug weaving course at the Silverbirch Workshop aims to equip the student with a working knowledge of weaving natural fibres in all thicknesses. With the expertise gained here, you'll be able to plan any weaving project and achieve the correct cloth effect. You'll use an old Swedish loom capable of producing twill and plain weave without changing thread. Courses also discuss the most economical ways of using homespun fibres for particular projects.

Accommodation (not included in course fees) is at the Sandford Guest House nearby.

Silverbirch Workshop, Whiting Bay, Isle of Arran, Strathclyde, Scotland. Telephone: (077 07) 232. Director: Lynn Ross. Duration: 1 week, May to October (1981). Accommodation at the Sandford Guest House. Telephone: (077 07) 232. Price: course: £40 (1981), bed and breakfast £5.50, with dinner £8.50 per person (est). VAT extra.

See also SPINNING, TAPESTRY.

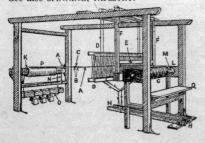

SUFFOLK, Thornham Magna

Beginners and Advanced Weaving Courses
Thornham Magna Weavers' Training Centre

All students at this centre, no matter how inexperienced, will have started weaving by the end of the day. You'll work at a fully-equipped self-contained weaving unit, so there's no queuing for shared apparatus. Each unit consists of a new twenty-four inch wide, eight-shaft table loom, a weaver's bench, a set of warping stakes, a doubling/spinning wheel, all necessary tools and accessories. There's a well-stocked yarn store (course fee includes all yarn used).

The beginner's course is the most popular. At the end of your stay you'll take away two samplers, one made on a thick woollen warp, the other on a more complex fine worsted one, together with written and diagrammatic instructions as to how they were made. Thus, after one week of around thirty hours' tuition, you'll have advanced to the point where you'll be able to continue the craft unsupervised. More advanced courses are available after April 1981, using the centre's new eight-shaft countermarch fly shuttle loom, or a sixteen-shaft dobby loom. There's also a thirty-six inch wide vertical rug loom and several tapestry frames, an inkle loom and a tablet loom. Course Director Gordon Cant was staff, then chief director of the Scottish Tweed Trade for fifteen years. He also holds two Design Council awards. The centre is situated on an estate twenty-five miles from Norwich in some of East Anglia's prettiest countryside.

Thornham Magna Weaver's Training Centre, 1 Red House Yard, Gislingham

Road, Thornham Magna, Nr Eye, Suffolk IP23 8HH. Telephone: (037 983) 670. Proprietor: Gordon Cant. Duration: 5 days, all year, Monday to Friday, or Wednesday to Wednesday (excluding weekend). Price: £50 per person (1981). Includes tuition, equipment and all materials.

Accommodation can be arranged in family homes nearby. Price £8 per person per night for bed, breakfast and dinner. There are also certified Caravan Club sites a few hundred yards from the centre. Transport to and from lodgings, and pubs and restaurants at lunchtime, is free.

WELSH STUDIES

WALES, GWYNEDD, Bangor

Welsh Studies
1 Introducing Wales – Past and Present
2 Learning Welsh
University College of North Wales

Both these summer school courses are primarily intended for foreign and overseas students who want to know more about Wales. The first is led by Course Director Dr John Williams who will introduce the country's history, culture and people from earliest times to present day. Lectures and informal discussion are supplemented with half and full day visits to some of the area's most impressive historic sites, such as the megalithic tomb of Bry Celli Ddu, the concentric castle of Beaumaris and the Roman fort of Segontium.

Headed by Course Director Dr Geraint Jones, the language course offers a fortnight of intensive (six hours daily) tuition.

You'll be grouped according to oral fluency with a tutor to every ten to twelve students. There's a minimum of seventy-two hours with a teacher, plus free use of the language laboratories. Advanced learners are encouraged to go into the local community to use the language in different contexts. Most evenings feature informal activities such as folk singing and dancing, language games and there'll also be some evening lectures.

Summer School Secretary, Department of Extra-Mural Studies, University College of North Wales, Bangor, Gwynedd, Wales LL57 2DG. Telephone: (0248) 51151, ext. 404. Secretary: Mrs M. Jones. Duration: 1 2 weeks, 11–25 July; 2 2 weeks, 4–18 July. Price: £95 per person per week (1981). Includes tuition and full board. Excursions extra. 1981 dates and prices provisional at press time. No VAT.

See also HISTORY.

WILDLIFE

COUNTRYWIDE

Field Studies Courses
Field Studies Council

The Council operates nine residential centres in England and Wales where outdoor enthusiasts can study a wide range of subjects in over 300 courses: natural history, ecology, birds and animals, flowers and other plants, weather, marine life, local history and archaeology, landscape, geology, art, photography and various crafts.

Courses are planned and led by centre staff or by visiting experts; most are suitable for beginners. Your fee covers board and lodging, use of facilities such as library and laboratory and tuition. Send for the brochure for full details. A good example of the wide variety of holidays available is the study of 'South Devon and Dartmoor through the Ages' course given in 1980 at Slapton Ley Field Centre, Kingsbridge, Devon. This beginner's archaeology course explored the area's unparalleled wealth of field monuments, including chambered tombs, barrows, cairns, stone circles, hill forts and Iron Age settlements all set against Dartmoor's scenic background. While in Yorkshire Dr Henry Disney led students on an exploration of the Malham Moor area (designated a site of special scientific interest). Course members studied the collection and identification of the diversity of insects, molluscs, crustacea and other small creatures found here. At Preston Montford there was an introductory course on British mammals in the field which included badger and deer watching.

Field Studies Council, Preston, Montford, Montford Bridge, Shrewsbury, Salop SY4 1HW. Telephone: (0743 71) 674. Duration: 1 week, programme on application. Price: £84 per person per week (est). Includes tuition, accommodation, all meals. Membership of the Field Studies Council required, subscription £2.00 per year.

CUMBRIA, Sedbergh

Natural History of the Dales Week
Whernside Cave and Fell Centre

This is a fascinating insight into the development of the Dales' marvellous scenery. With a guide you'll examine the area's flora and fauna in daily walks, examining the ecology and discovering the reasons for varieties in the scenery, vegetation and agricultural uses. Evening lectures by qualified instructors provide a valuable back-up to the daytime field trips. The course is geared to students over sixteen who can walk five to six miles a day.

Yorkshire Dales National Park, Whernside Cave and Fell Centre, Dent, Sedbergh, Cumbria LA10 5RE. Telephone: (058 75) 213/286. Warden: M. K. Lyon. Duration: 22–29 August. Price: £81 per person (1981). Includes tuition, dormitory accommodation (2–9 per room), all meals, use of equipment and VAT. Campsite available. Transport from Oxenholme Station £2.50 (7 days notice required).

See also CAVING AND POTHOLING, ECOLOGY, WALKING.

HIGHLAND, Beauly

Wildlife
1 Natural History at Aigas
2 Orkney Birds, Flowers and Archaeology
3 Shetland Birds
Aigas Field Centre

This elegant centre, a Victorian Gothic castle in thirty wooded acres, is the permanent home of your hosts John and Sorrel Lister-Kaye and warden Peter Wortham. You can enjoy the baronial comforts of dining on homegrown produce with fine wines by a log fire in the Great Hall. Other grand, spacious rooms include the lounge and library. After dinner, staff and local experts present lectures and slide shows, or you may be entertained by an exhibition of piping. Sleeping accommodation is in five specially designed timber cabins beside the castle. Each has two twin-bedded rooms, carpeting, central heating, double shower room, separate WC and a kitchenette.

The Field Centre is modelled along the lines of a safari base. Each day, you'll set out in a small group with an expert guide to explore the magical scenery of the Central Highland glens and watch for the area's shy wildlife. You'll leave the castle around 9.30 a.m. and, according to location, spend from three to seven hours walking quietly through the wilderness where casual visitors would never venture. There are over 150 bird species including golden eagles and peregrine falcons; herds of red and roe deer; grey seals; pine-martens and wildcats. In 1981, the centre will again offer its successful two week ornithological expedition (twelve people plus guide) to Shetland, and a similar tour of Orkney.

Aigas Field Centre, Beauly, Highland 1V4 7AD. Telephone: (046371) 2443. Directors: Sorrel and John Lister-Kaye. 1 Natural History at Aigas. Duration: weekly from 11 April to 4 July, 22 August to 17 October. Price: £175 per person per week (1981). Includes course, full board and VAT. 2 Orkney Birds, Flowers and Archaeology. Duration: 27 June–4 July, 4–11 July. Price: £190 (1981) per person per week. Includes tuition, return ferry, transport from Inverness, full board and VAT. 3 Shetland Birds. Duration: 15–20 June, 22–27 June. Price: £365 per person per week. Includes tuition, return air fare Inverness to Shetland, full board and VAT. Minimum age 12 years. Bring walking shoes, waterproof clothes, thermos. Binoculars may be hired.

HIGHLAND, Inverness

Highland Holidays
Caledonian Wildlife Services

The Scottish Highlands are home to an astonishing variety of wildlife – deer, eagles, ospreys, grouse, badgers, seals and more. Caledonian Wildlife Services arrange these holidays to let you observe and enjoy the area's wild creatures under the expert guidance of Sinclair Dunnett who has worked as a game warden in Tanzania, and Baxter Cooper, a qualified botanist and ecology lecturer at the University of Edinburgh; both hold Master's degrees in wildlife management. Each party of ten is transported by minibus into mountain and forest country. Then you're free to accompany the guide on a foray, set off on your own or stay near the bus. (It's assumed you're fit enough to walk about five miles at an easy pace.) Each week is carefully planned in relation to the tides, sunrises and sunsets, but the schedule is flexible enough to allow for other variables. For example you'll visit bird migration points in late summer and autumn if the winds are favourable.

Most clients stay at Tigh a'Mhuilian (Gaelic for 'House of the Kill'), a modern guest house that overlooks a golf course. Caledonian Wildlife Service will also recommend hotels in the area.

Caledonian Wildlife Services, 2 Kingsmills Gardens, Inverness IV2 3LU. Telephone: (0463) 38257. Manager: Sinclair C. Dunnett. Duration: 1 week, early April to end October. Price: from £150 per person per week (est). Includes accommodation (twin shared), all meals, excursions and VAT.

Bring walking shoes and wellingtons. Some binoculars available but bring your own if you have them. For full details of this and other programmes send for brochure.

STRATHCLYDE, ISLE OF ARRAN, Glen Sannox

A Closer Look at Arran
Isle of Arran Field Studies

This organization offers a variety of nature holidays on Arran, the southernmost isle of the Inner Hebrides. Its vast, unspoilt open spaces and sixty miles of varied coastline make it a rich focal point for a study of Britain's northern natural history. Led by a knowledgeable naturalist, small groups will explore the dramatic landscape by boat, car, foot and bicycle, easy-going rambles with frequent stops. There are holidays devoted entirely to special interests such as birds, mushrooms and herbal lore, but this all-round introductory week takes a general look at the island's wildlife, folklore and ancient history. In a series of daily outings you'll discover first-hand why Arran has been dubbed 'Scotland in miniature'.

The programme includes a drive around the entire island, including a visit to the famed Bronze Age standing stones on Machrie Moor; cycling along the coastal faults; a trip to the small offshore Holy Isle, a nature reserve; and a field trip by boat around the isolated northeast coast. Your guide is John Williams, long-time Ranger for the Arran Nature Centre and present editor of the journal the *Arran Naturalist*.

Accommodation is at the AA listed, centrally heated Blackcrock Guesthouse in the quaint seaside village of Corrie. Or, for an additional £1.50 per day, you can stay at the two star, AA listed Corrie Hotel.

Isle of Arran Field Studies, Woodside Cottage, Glen Sannox, Isle of Arran, Strathclyde KA27 8JD. Telephone: (0770 81) 207/282. Chief Naturalist: John Williams. Duration: Saturday to Saturday,

April to September. Price: from £15 per person per day (est). Includes tuition, full board, equipment and VAT. Bring binoculars and pocket lens. Reduced rates for groups, hostel accommodation available.

See also BOTANY, GARDENS.

STRATHCLYDE, Isle of Colonsay

Naturalist Breaks
Isle of Colonsay Hotel

Study the wildlife of the Islands. This naturalist break on Colonsay and Oronsay enables you to study some of the rarest birds in the British Isles. (The Iceland gull and rose-coloured starling have both been spotted here.) Colonsay is one of the most remote islands of Argyll. Northwards it looks across fifteen miles of sea to Mull, and south to Donegal. To the east twenty-five miles away, the mainland of Argyll lies beyond the spectacular skyline of the islands of Jura and Islay. Westwards, only Du Histead lighthouse stands between Colonsay and Canada, yet Colonsay is not a bleak and monotonous island – far from it. In a day's walk you can see cliffs and moorlands, sandy beaches and lily-filled lakes, rhododendron woods and cultivated farmland. In summer, this is one of Scotland's sunniest spots – and in late September come hundreds of grey Atlantic seal pups to the surrounding rocks and islets.

Included in your hotel cost is a special bird list (prepared by D. Alexander, the island's resident expert) and a map. The hotel is deliberately unpretentious, serving a table d'hote based on fresh local produce. They also have an excellent cellar with inexpensive wines.

Isle of Colonsay Hotel, Strathclyde, PA61 7YP. Telephone: (09512) 316. Proprietor: Kevin Byrne. Duration: open all year. Price: £12–£13.50 (singles); £11–£12.50 per person per day (double or twin room) (1981). Includes bird list, map folder, bed, breakfast and VAT. Dinner extra, £6.30 per person per day. Ask specially for 'Natural-

ist Breaks' when booking. There is a car ferry from Oban to Colonsay 3 times a week. Journey takes 2½ hours, single fare £3.50; book through Caledonian MacBrayne, Telephone: (0475) 33755.

TAYSIDE, Enochdhu

Wildlife
1 Insects
2 Natural History of the Highlands
3 Autumn in the Highlands
Kindrogan Field Centre

Study the natural life in the wilds of Tayside. The Kindrogan Field Centre runs a variety of related courses for naturalists, suitable for beginners, undergraduates, interested amateurs and teachers alike. P. A. Page conducts the 'Autumn in the Highlands' Course, and A. Sommerville runs a course on the identification and ecology of insects. The 'Autumn Birds' Course, run by J. N. Mutch, gives you an ideal opportunity to see large numbers of wild winter visitors to the Highlands, with others of Britain's rarest fauna in their natural habitat.

The Kindrogan Field Centre is set amidst woodlands near the River Ardle, where there are numerous lochs, dry and wet moorlands and several mountains over 3,000 feet. The courses include expeditions into the local countryside. Accommodation is of the hostel type, and you may be expected to help with meals. The centre has fully equipped laboratories and classrooms which are used on the courses.

The Scottish Field Studies Association, Kindrogan Field Centre, Enochdhu, Blairgowrie, Tayside PH10 7PG. Telephone: (0250 81) 286. Warden: Brian Brookes. Duration: 1 22–29 July, 12–19 August; 2 29 July–5 August; 3 14–21 October. Price: £84 per person per week (est). Includes tuition, full board and VAT.

See also BOTANY, GEOLOGY.

WINDSURFING

HAMPSHIRE, Barton-on-Sea

Windsurfing Bargain Break
Red House Hotel

Perched on the cliffs overlooking the Isle of Wight, the Red House offers one-and-a-half days of expert windsurfing tuition on land and water supplemented by video instruction, plus half a day's free windsurfing. (Yes, you *can* learn this exhilarating new sport that quickly!)

Red House Hotel, Barton-on-Sea, Hampshire BH25 7HJ. Telephone: (0425) 610119. Duration: 2 days, 20 March–31 May. Price: from £61 (1981). Includes 2 nights accommodation, breakfast, dinner, tuition. Includes VAT and service.

HIGHLAND, Aviemore

Windsurfing
The Post House

Try this exciting new water sport amid the grandeur of the Scottish highlands. The fee allows you five nights at Trust-House Forte's Post House Hotel with dinner, full Scottish breakfast, four half days hire of board and wet suit, plus instruction on the first two days.

Children under fourteen years sharing parents' room have the above without meals which are charged as taken.

The Post House (THF), Aviemore Centre, Highland PH22 1PJ, Scotland. Telephone: (0479) 810771. Duration: May to October. Price: £144 per person (est). Includes 5 nights accommodation, breakfast, dinner, instruction, board, wet suit hire and VAT. Children under 14, £33.75 sharing parents' room. Meals extra.

See also FISHING: GAME, GOLF, SAILING.

WINE TASTING

DEVON, Moretonhampstead

Wine Appreciation Weekends
Manor House Hotel

This hotel is a huge Jacobean-style mansion with sweeping views across fine parkland. You'll stay in kingly splendour – the imposing décor includes a huge pillared hall with its impressive staircase as well as a luxurious classical bar. The vast elegantly furnished rooms boast colour TV and radio. Guests have use of the gardens and the golf course or can fill their time in no end of ways: including game fishing, billiards, tennis and squash. Wine lovers can spend an enjoyable weekend in these sumptuous surroundings with Master of Wine Clive Coates, who selects the wines for BTH Hotels. He'll oversee tasting sessions and you'll also be treated

to films, talks and a cookery class which demonstrates the use of wines in *haute cuisine*. The manor also holds 'Extra Special Weekends'. A typical programme starts off with a Friday evening welcoming cocktail party. This is followed by a relaxed informal dinner and an introductory talk. For an unusual nightcap you'll be served a delicious Scrumpie Punch. Saturday includes a full English breakfast, late morning coffee and biscuits, a buffet lunch and a Devonshire cream tea, then there's a pre-dinner champagne reception followed by a super four course dinner with wines and liqueur. The programme continues after breakfast on Sunday with a pause for mid-morning coffee. You round off the weekend with a traditional Sunday lunch accompanied by appropriate wines.

Manor House Hotel, Moretonhampstead, Newton Abbot, Devon. Telephone: (06474) 355. Duration: 13–15 March, 20–22 November. Price: £130 per person (1981). Includes accommodation, all meals (wine included) service and VAT. Other special weekends also available, send for brochure.

HEREFORD AND WORCESTER, Hoarwithy

Wine Weekends
Upper Orchard

Jon Hurley claims to have 'invented' the wine tasting weekend. He lives in a nice old rambling house (around 300 years old) and grows nearly all his own vegetables, keeps hens for eggs and stocks a large range of fine wines. Jon prefers to 'make up' his weekends according to the preference and convenience of his guests – so be sure to state whether your preference is for a Beginners', Fine Wine or Classic Wine weekend. Each weekend has its own specific character, though the excellence of the menu remains unaltered.

Upper Orchard is in the quiet Herefordshire village of Hoarwithy near the banks of the River Wye. Take one of the many fine walks to work up an appetite for the next meal, or a thirst for the next tasting. You'll find that Jon is excellent company and a fund of vinous information.

Upper Orchard, Hoarwithy, Hereford and Worcester. Telephone: (043270) 649. Proprietor: Jon Hurley. Duration: weekends October to May. Price: £35 per person (until May 1981), £38 (from October 1981) 'Beginners' Weekend'; £45 per person (until May 1981), £48 (from October 1981) 'Fine Wine Weekend'; £65 per person (until May 1981), £68 (from October 1981) 'Classic Wine Weekend'. Includes tuition, full board and VAT.

LANCASHIRE, Chorley

Wines and Spirits Trust
Lancashire College

Lancashire College is Britain's first purpose-built adult residential college. It occupies a pleasant twenty-acre campus at the edge of Chorley, a bustling market town, and has single-room accommodation for fifty-one students. The Wine and Spirits weekend lets you study the noble grape, what's more it's designed for professionals and amateurs. The course covers the origin and spread of wine making, general factors which affect wine production, an introduction to wine tasting and European wine regions, what's meant by sparkling wines and how they and other wines should be stored and served, what liqueurs are and how they differ from spirits, how beer is made, and much more. It leads to an examination and certificate if you wish.

Lancashire College for Adult Education, Southport Road, Chorley, Lancashire PR7 1NB. Telephone: (025 72) 76719. Duration: weekend, September. Price: £32 per person (est). £30 (est) Lancashire residents. Includes tuition, full board. Wine extra. No VAT.

See also DANCE, LANGUAGES.

NORFOLK, Great Yarmouth

Wine Weekend
Carlton Hotel

Wine and dine at the Carlton on the seafront at Great Yarmouth. Their popular Wine Weekends begin with a champagne reception and special banquet, where fine wines are carefully selected to go with the special menu. There's an illustrated talk on Saturday morning followed by a wine tasting which features vintages from the region you've been hearing about. Enjoy yourself at the gala dinner dance and cabaret on Saturday night, and, after a leisurely breakfast on Sunday morning, there's another talk about wines from different regions, followed by a wine tasting and question time.

These weekends are supervised by Grahame Tinnion, Director of the Carlton Hotel. Their location opposite the Wellington Pier on the Marine Parade, makes this an ideal setting for a special interest weekend 'away from it all'.

Carlton Hotel, Great Yarmouth, Norfolk. Telephone: (0493) 55234. Director: Grahame Tinnion. Duration: weekend, dates not confirmed, phone hotel. Price: from £47.50 per person (1981). Includes all meals and wine, 2 nights accommodation, bath, TV, telephone and VAT.

SUSSEX, Chichester

Wonderful Wine
The Earnley Concourse

'Wonderful Wine' takes a lively two-day look at the noble grape. You'll cover its production, quality, differentiation, storage, serving and tasting. Highlights are a visit to a vineyard and the Saturday evening wine tasting. There's a follow-up 'Wine Tasting Weekend' which deals with the subject in more detail.

For details of the Concourse see ANTIQUES.

The Earnley Concourse, near Chichester, Sussex PO20 7JL. Telephone: (0243) 670392, Booking Department. Duration: weekends November to December. Price: £40 per person (est). Includes double room with bath. VAT extra. Course supplement £10 (est). Minimum age 16. Minibus transport from Chichester Station 90p each way.

See also ANTIQUES, CREATIVE WRITING, FLOWER ARRANGING, FOLK AND JAZZ, LANGUAGES, MUSIC, PUPPETRY, SURVIVAL TRAINING.

WEST MIDLANDS, Coventry

Fine Wine Weekends
Hotel Leofric

Your palate could win you a prize from Grants of St James's. Each of these weekends ends with a wine tasting competi-

tion. You can't really lose on this holiday. Michael Hooley, former training officer of Grants has set up a series of talks, films and tastings, plus a visit to the famous Harvey's of Bristol wine museum, which includes a guided tour and buffet lunch accompanied by wine, sherry and port.

Each weekend specializes in a different wine-growing region. In March 1981 you can sample fine French wines and in September 1981, Northern European vintages, starting with Champagne and ending with the Rhine Valley, Moselle and Alsace. Write for further details.

Leisure Learning Weekends, Embassy Hotels Ltd, Station Street, Burton-upon-Trent, Staffordshire DE14 1BZ. Telephone: (0283) 66587. Organizer: Gordon Hopper. Duration: 13–15 March, 11–13 September. Price: £63 per person (1981), March; £68 per person, September. Includes 2 nights full board with bath, lectures, tasting, service and VAT.

See also CASTLES AND HISTORIC HOUSES, CHURCHES AND CATHEDRALS, LITERATURE, PHOTOGRAPHY, POTTERY.

WEST MIDLANDS, Wolverhampton

Wine Appreciation
Pendrell Hall

Explore wine tasting with Mr R. Beal, who's worked in some of the world's best hotels. You'll concentrate on French wines during tasting and assessment sessions and on Saturday evening your group will get together with the students taking a French language course to enjoy a French meal – accompanied, of course, by appropriate vintages.

For details of Pendrell Hall see LANGUAGES.

Pendrell Hall, College of Residential Adult Education, Codsall Wood, near Wolverhampton, West Midlands, WV8 1QP. Telephone: (090 74) 2398. Secretary: Mrs W. Whitehead. Duration: weekend April. Price: £30 per person (est), lower rates for West Midlands residents. Includes course and 2 nights full board.

See also FLOWER ARRANGING, LANGUAGES, YOGA.

WOODWORKING

CHESHIRE VILLAGE

Woodworking

This is the ideal holiday for a capable couple. Leslie and Mary Syson are professional teachers in their respective fields of woodwork and cookery. He specializes in small handmade items of furniture, particularly dovetailed boxes for presentation and jewellery, and wood turning. His well-equipped workshops are located in farm buildings in the three-quarter acre grounds. Mary is a highly qualified domestic science teacher who's speciality is traditional English cooking, and she'll be glad to give lessons to a spouse whose better half is wielding a chisel in the workshop.

Their 16th century timber-framed farm-house, in a small Cheshire village fifteen minutes from the Peak District National Park, has been beautifully restored. One double room is available for guests, and Mary provides high-quality traditional

English fare during your stay. Full details of how to find them will be sent to you when the booking is made (through ABC).

Avocations (Bristol Crafts) Ltd, 37 Coombe Bridge Avenue, Bristol, Avon BS9 2LT. Telephone: (0272) 686417. Director: Mr Gerald Richardson. Duration: 1 week all year. Price: £117 per person per week (1981). Includes tuition, use of equipment, full board (twin), single supplement 15% extra. No VAT.

See also BATIK, DRESSMAKING, ENAMELLING, NEEDLEWORK, STAINED GLASS, TAPESTRY.

BUCKINGHAMSHIRE,
Great Missenden

Traditional and Contemporary Wood Sculpture
Missenden Abbey

Complete beginners are guaranteed to be amazed at the progress they'll make on this weekend course. Even if you're an experienced carver you're sure to benefit from the excellent tuition in the company of fellow enthusiasts. While you can bring your own tools, they're supplied for beginners. A fifty pence supplement covers wood for practice and fully seasoned timber can be bought here at cost price.

The school fee includes the cost of bed, breakfast and dinner at Missenden Abbey, plus lunch, coffee and tea at Misbourne School, whose workshops you'll use. These stay open in the evening, but you may be tempted by the many other events such as wine tasting, jazz, poetry and folk evenings. For an optional extra charge you can attend a National Theatre performance.

Missenden Abbey, Great Missenden, Buckinghamshire HP16 0BD. Telephone: (02 406) 2328. Duration: weekend 16–18 January. Price: £30 per person (1981). Includes 2 nights full board and tuition. Reduction for Buckinghamshire residents. Course supplement for wood 50p.

See also HISTORY, LACEMAKING, LITERATURE, PARANORMAL, YOGA.

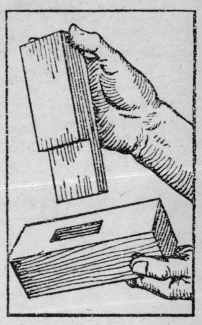

WEST YORKSHIRE, Micklethwaite

Woodturning
Micklethwaite Studio Workshops

Robert and Jan Ellwood are your hosts and course directors at their early 19th century textile mill in the pretty conservation village of Micklethwaite on the edge of the Yorkshire Dales. The Mill has been restored to provide space for a small group of enthusiastic specialists who combine making high quality craftwork with teaching crafts and design to residential groups. Most participants are beginners although an increasing number of

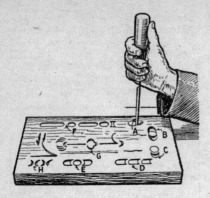

woodworking course which accepts a maximum of three students. It covers spindle turning, faceplate turning, long-hole boring, laminated work, box and lid making, finishing techniques, selection and seasoning of timbers, design and marketing. Emphasis throughout is on the production of high quality work with cutting tools. The course starts with Wednesday dinner at 7.30 p.m. and finishes after Friday tea. Accommodation, in the former mill owner's modernized house, is in single, double or twin bedded rooms. Jan, a professional caterer, prepares delicious meals.

guests return to develop their skills further.

Robert Ellwood, qualified as a woodwork teacher at Loughborough College, studied at Sheffield College of Design and was awarded the Final City and Guilds Certificate in Silversmiths and Goldsmiths work. He leads this two-day

Micklethwaite Studio Workshops, Micklethwaite, Holroyd Mill, Beck Road, Micklethwaite, near Bingley, West Yorkshire. Telephone: (0274) 562464. Duration: 3 days May to October. Price: £92 per person (est). Includes tuition, all materials and full board.

See also CLOCKS.

WORKING HOLIDAYS

COUNTRYWIDE

Working Weekends on Organic Farms

If you're a frustrated city dweller longing for the country life become a 'Wwoofer'. WWOOF (Working Weekends on Organic Farms) is a modest mutual aid society which puts hard-pressed smallholders in touch with volunteer helpers. In return for your labour (full time and quite hard) you're given meals, somewhere to sleep and (if necessary) transport to and from the local station. As a new member you'll receive bimonthly newsletters for one year which give you details of places where help is needed and includes instructions on how to arrange your weekends. When you've satisfactorily completed two weekends you can apply for a list of farms where you can make your own arrangements. Always bring a sleeping bag, towel, waterproof clothing, boots, work gloves and a torch.

Working Weekends on Organic Farms, 19 Bradford Road, Lewes, Sussex BN7 1RB. Price: membership fee £4 per year (1981).

COUNTRYWIDE

British Trust for Conservation Volunteers

Who wants to work for a holiday? Many do – and find it great fun too. The British Trust for Conservation Volunteers organize their holidays with the aim of preserving our national heritage. You can do everything from cleaning a river to constructing steps along a nature trail. The work often involves clearing habitat for wild life – heathland for the rare sand lizard or excavating lagoons for wading birds or sometimes, even doing protective replanting of exotic rare flora.

These holidays are normally limited to

volunteers between the ages of 16 and 70 (some local volunteer camps take children of 12 and over). All tools for the work are provided as well as food and accommodation but you'll need to provide your own rough clothes and a sleeping bag. Accommodation varies from camping to cottages and all volunteers are insured while working. (For some jobs, tetanus injections are recommended.)

These projects can last from a day to a week or more. Besides having an energetic time amongst lively (mainly young) people you'll also have the satisfaction of a worthwhile job well done.

British Trust for Conservation Volunteers. 10–12 Duke Street, Reading, Berkshire RG1 4RU. Telephone: (0734) 596171. Duration: varies, but generally a few days to a week. Price: annual membership £3 (1981) and £1 to cover accommodation costs. Bring work clothes, waterproofs, boots and sleeping bag.

CUMBRIA, Ulverston

Summer Working Holiday
Manjushri Institute

During this 'open month' you're invited to participate in the following programmes: martial arts, organic gardening, bread making, painting classes, massage, meditation and yoga. The seventy-strong resident community are students of Tibetan Buddhism under the spiritual direction of Lama Thubten Yoshe and Lama Thubten Zopa Rinpoche.

For details of the Priory, see RELIGIOUS RETREATS.

Manjushri Institute, College of Tibetan Buddhist Studies, Conishead Priory, Ulverston, Cumbria LA12 9QQ. Telephone: (0229) 54019. Secretary: Emily Strang. Duration: 4 weeks July to August. Price: £4 (1981). Includes dormitory accommodation and all meals. Camping also available. Visitors welcome at other times (not January to March).

See also RELIGIOUS RETREATS.

NOTTINGHAMSHIRE, SURREY, ESSEX

Working Holidays
Skylarks, Crabhill House, Jubilee Lodge

If you're over sixteen and have a strong back, Winged Fellowship needs you. It's a charity organization which provides fortnight-long holidays for the severely disabled at three attractive centres in Nottingham, Surrey and Essex. There's a small permanent staff at each, including nurses who are available twenty-four hours a day to help you with any situation with which you can't cope. The work includes getting guests up, washed and dressed, sometimes helping to feed them and some domestic chores. But mainly you're there to enjoy yourself as much as the guests, and to offer your companionship in the relaxed, informal atmosphere and share in the fun. Your food and lodging is free.

The Fellowship arranges different types of holidays. Some are for specific age groups (all guests are over sixteen), some for special interests such as music or theatre, and some are activity fortnights which involve riding, fishing and canoeing. Daily outings, shopping expeditions and visits to the pub are also part of these holidays. All the centres are open from March to mid-December; each takes up to thirty-six guests and needs from nineteen to twenty-seven helpers. It's often hard work but so rewarding that many volunteers return year after year.

Volunteer Recruitment, The Winged Fellowship Trust, 2nd Floor, 64/66 Oxford Street, London W1 9FF. Telephone: (01) 636 5886. Duration: March to mid-December. Free board and lodging, minimum age 16 years. Volunteers should be strong as work involves lifting.

WALES, GWYNEDD, Porthmadog

The Festiniog Railway

Come and help keep a tradition alive. The Festiniog Railway, opened in 1836 and closed in 1946, was rescued and rehabilitated by dedicated railway buffs in 1954. Keen volunteers pitched in to overhaul original steam and diesel locomotives, purchase and adapt new ones, restore old coaches and build new ones, install new signalling and, amazingly, to run this venerable railway as a commercial undertaking. It's hugely successful as a tourist attraction; trains run in all but six winter weeks and daily more than half the year. Your help is still necessary if the resuscitated railway is to have a secure future. Volunteers are needed to replace worn out equipment, maintain and operate the line, reopen more track, rebuild several locomotives and work on the signalling and communications systems. You're usually started off cleaning locomotives, with the possibility of promotion to driver. If you have a professional manual skill such as engineering, carpentry or metalwork your talents will certainly be put to good use; unskilled volunteers are equally welcome, especially in the summer season when you'll be useful in booking offices, guards' vans, signal boxes, buffet cars, shops, cafés and for station duties.

The Festiniog Railway Society, Harbour Station, Porthmadog, Gwynedd, Wales LL49 9NF. Telephone: (0766) 2384. Contact: General Manager. Duration: all year. Price: hostel accommodation arranged 40p per night (1981) (bring linen) or make your own arrangements. Accommodation list available.

Yoga

BUCKINGHAMSHIRE,
Great Missenden

Yoga and the Advent of Rebirth
Missenden Abbey

A setting that's taken eight centuries to create makes the perfect backdrop for two tranquil days of yoga. This midsummer weekend offers lots of practical work in accordance with the teachings of I. S. Ixengar, the India-based inspiration for all Inner London Education Authority courses. You'll find it equally valuable whether you're a beginner or an advanced student. Sessions are arranged in appropriate groups according to prior experience and ability.

The winter weekend aims to use concentrated yoga practice to put you in touch with the essential meaning of the Christmas Spirit.

Both courses are led by Resident Course Director, Penelope Nield-Smith and her two assistants. A vegetarian menu is served on both weekends. Apply early, resident places are in great demand. Bring suitable attire (leotard, loose trousers, elasticated shorts) and a floor mat.

Missenden Abbey, Great Missenden, Buckinghamshire HP16 0BD. Telephone: (02406) 2328. Duration: weekends, July and December. Price: £30 per person (est). Includes 2 nights full board, tuition. Reduction for Buckinghamshire residents. Bring floor mat and suitable clothes.

See also HISTORY, LACEMAKING, LITERATURE, PARANORMAL, WOODWORKING.

LONDON

Annual International Yoga Festival
Caxton Hall

This highly successful festival, organized in cooperation with the British Wheel of Yoga, offers a full programme of classes, workshops and lectures and catering by one of London's best-known vegetarian restaurants, 'Food for Thought'. Last year's distinguished participants included the famous yoga teacher and author, Swami Janakananda, Ian Carstairs of Canada's Kundalini Research Institute, renowned Yogi Siddhapurush Nityananda and Joy Burling, chairman of the British Wheel of Yoga. The festival is presented in connection with Grand Metropolitan Hotels, who provide accommodation in Central London.

Fourth Annual Festival of Yoga, 7 Stratford Place, London W1A 4YU. Telephone: (01) 629 6618 ext. 221. Director: Antonia Boyle. Duration: 2 nights, November. Price: £46 per person (est), double with bath; £54 (est) single with bath. Includes seminar fee, accommodation, English breakfast, one supper, 2 lunches, hotel charge, VAT.

STRATHCLYDE, ISLE OF ARRAN, Lochranza

Yoga
Kincardine Lodge

The idyllic, inspirational setting for this yoga course is Lochranza, gem of Arran's coastal villlages. Your hostess (and hotel proprietor) Yorkshire-born Mrs Margaret Finch has been practising Hatha yoga for fifteen years and teaching it for seven. She organized North Yorkshire's teacher training programme for the British Wheel of Yoga. Group numbers are limited to fifteen so you're assured of individual tuition. A typical day begins at 7.45 a.m. with half an hour's pranayama (breathing exercises) and meditation followed by 8.30 a.m. breakfast and practising asanas (postures) from 10.00 a.m. to 12.00 a.m. Afternoons are left free so you can walk, climb, pony trek or just relax. Dinner at 6.30 p.m. is followed by an 8.00 p.m. talk. One example: The Philosophy of Yoga. (A vegetarian menu will be provided if requested.)

Eight bedroomed Kincardine Lodge is ideally situated with panoramic views of a 16th century castle and magnificent mountain scenery and faces a sea loch.

Kincardine Lodge, Lochranza, Isle of Arran, Strathclyde. Telephone: (077083) 267. Organizer: Margaret Finch. Duration: 1 week spring and autumn. Price: from £70 per person (est). Includes tuition, *accommodation, dinner, bed, breakfast and packed lunch. VAT extra.*

WARWICKSHIRE,
Stratford-upon-Avon

Yoga
The Fold

Go to Stratford to relax and learn the time-honoured yoga techniques of relaxation of mind and body. The sessions, which combine gentle stretching exercises for muscle control and deep breathing techniques, are held in the morning and late afternoon. Women should bring leotards and footless tights, or normal tights and narrow stretch sweaters. Men need stretch trousers, shorts or track suits, with vest or sweater. Be sure to bring a mat or rug to work on.

For details of Holiday Fellowship see WALKING, *Loch Awe.*

Holiday Fellowship, 142/144 Great North Way, London NW14 1EG. Telephone: (01) 203 3381, Booking Department. Duration: 1 week April, September. Price: from £33.50 per person (est). Includes full board and course. VAT extra. New members £10 subscription.

See also BOWLS, BRASS RUBBING, CREATIVE WRITING, ECOLOGY, FOLK MUSIC, GENEALOGY, JEWELLERY, ORIENTEERING, THEATRE GOING, WALKING.

WEST MIDLANDS, Wolverhampton

Yoga
Pendrell Hall

The course is led by Mrs M. Elshaw, proprietor of the Woodcote School of Yoga and a tutor with the British Wheel of Yoga. It's designed for recent beginners who want to extend their knowledge of Hatha Yoga. Each session starts with a warm-up, then breathing exercises and postures, with explanations of the benefits of each asana (posture). You'll also attend talks and discussions on diet, exercise, weight control and the help yoga can offer in stress situations. Ladies should wear tights, loose trousers or leotards; men loose trousers or shorts with an elasticated waist. Bring a mat or rug to work on.

For a description of Pendrell Hall see LANGUAGES.

Pendrell Hall, College of Residential Adult Education, Codsall Wood, near Wolver-hampton, West Midlands WV8 1QP. Telephone: (090 74) 2398. Secretary: Mrs Sally Whitehead. Duration: 3 days November. Price: £30 per person single (est). £25 (est) shared; reductions for West Midlands residents. Includes course and full board. Bring yoga mat or rug and loose clothing. No VAT.

See also FLOWER ARRANGING, LANGUAGES, WINE TASTING.

ZEN

NORTHUMBERLAND, Hexham

Buddhist Retreats
Throssel Hole Priory

These Buddhist retreats are only for sincere seekers. The best introduction to the training offered is a weekend retreat, where novices are given basic instruction in formal meditation, and all activities are led by fully qualified priests. More advanced meditators are also encouraged to come to these weekend retreats where they can benefit from the opportunity to concentrate undisturbed for two days. The priory holds longer intensive meditation retreats, or sesshins, several times a year. Sesshin, meaning 'to search the heart', is open to applicants who have had prior experience of formal Soto Zen meditation, and whom the Prior thinks are ready for such an intensive retreat. Private retreats can be arranged if you don't feel able to participate fully in the regular daily schedule. (Priests are always available for counselling during private retreats.) The priory has no facilities for accommodating married couples or chil-dren. A typical daily retreat schedule would begin at 6.15 a.m. with meditation, followed by 8.30 breakfast, morning scripture study, a lecture/discussion, work (such as farm chores), 1.00 p.m. dinner followed by more work, evening service and meditation, lecture/discussion, supper, zazon, Kinhin (walking meditation), vespers, 9.00 p.m. tea and 9.40 lights out.

Throssel Hole Priory is located in eighteen acres of a beautiful Northumberland valley. Most daily activities are centred around the renovated 19th century farm buildings which priory members are still modernizing. It was founded in 1972 by the Spiritual Director of Shasta Abbey, California headquarters of the Order of Buddhist Contemplatives of the Soto Zen Church.

Throssel Hole Priory, Carrshield, Hexham, Northumberland NE47 8AL. Telephone: (049 85) 204. Duration: weekends and weekly all year. Price: £14 per person per weekend (981): £20 per person per week (1981). Includes instruction, full board. Bring sleeping bag and warm cloth-ing.

The End

AS WE WENT TO PRESS

Bell ringing course on all aspects of bell ringing. Duration: 1–3 May. Price: £15 per day (£8 for residents of North Yorkshire and parts of surrounding areas) (est). Grantley Hall, Ripon, Yorkshire HG4 3ET. Telephone: (076 586) 259.

The art of biography led by Brian Wilkes, a lecturer at Leeds University and himself a biographer – a study of classic biographies e.g. Jane Austen, the Brontës. Duration: 30 January–1 February. Price: £15 per day (est). Grantley Hall, Ripon, Yorkshire HG4 3ET. Telephone: (076 586) 259.

Crossword compilation a study of difficult crosswords – *The Times*, *Daily Telegraph* and the theory behind crossword compilation. Duration: July. Details not finalized. Marlborough College Summer School, Marlborough, Wiltshire SN8 1PA. Telephone: (0672) 53888.

Driving courses 1) for those who want to improve their driving skills; 2) for novices; 3) for those with some experience. Duration: 1) 13–15 February; 2) 2–6 March; 3) 9–13 March. Price: 1) £39; 2) and 3) £87. Includes tuition. Accommodation: from £9.20 per person per day full board (1981). The Earnley Concourse, near Chichester, Sussex PO20 7JL. Telephone: (0243) 670392/670326.

Homestays an enterprising agency which liaises between you and over 250 British families who will welcome you into their homes as they would good friends. Self-catering holidays also available in South East England. All year. Price: from £35 to £500 per week. Home from Home in England, 30a High Street, Haslemere, Surrey GU27 2HJ. Telephone: (0428) 53133/53155.

Knitting Shetland hand knitting with instruction in Shetland knitting and in particular Fair Isle patterns. Home produced wool will be available. Duration: 2 weeks, August. Price: £125 (est). Includes accommodation. Shetland Islands Council Education Department, 1 Harbour Street, Shetland ZE1 0LS, Scotland. Telephone: (0595) 3535.

Life planning courses aimed at helping women clarify values and goals in order to accomplish long term objectives. Courses include Career Planning and Stress Management. Small groups are led by a professional psychologist. Duration: 1–3 days. Price: £25 for 1 day course, £75 for 3 days (est). Cairn Corporation Conferences, 32 Launceston Place, London W8. Telephone: (01) 937 2938. Contact: Ms Ginger Irvine.

Macramé all the techniques of this popular craft. Duration: weekends, dates on application. Price: £32 (est). Lancashire College, Southport Road, Chorley, Lancashire PR7 1NB. Telephone: (025 72) 76719.

Picture framing how to mount and frame pictures. Duration: weekend 6–8 March; 5 days, 8–13 March. Price: £39.50 (weekend), £93 for 5 days (1981). West Dean College, Chichester, West Sussex, PO18 0QZ. Telephone: (0243 63) 301.

Public speaking how to conquer the problems and nerves we face when we have to speak in public – this course deals with the techniques through informal study sessions. There is also a follow-up session for those who wish to improve their skills. Duration: 20–22 March, 6–10 April (follow-up course). May also be available in the autumn. Price: £9 (follow-up £14.50) (1981). Includes tuition. Accommodation from £9.20 per day (1981). Includes all meals.

The Earnley Concourse, near Chichester, Sussex PO20 7JL. Telephone: (0243) 670392/670326.

Typewriting tuition for complete beginners in mastering the keyboard. There will be opportunities for practice on electric and manual typewriters. Duration: 26 July–1 August. Price: £97 per person (est). Includes tuition, accommodation and all meals.
The Centre for Extension Studies, (BR) University of Technology, Loughborough, Leicestershire LE11 3TU. Telephone: (0509) 63171 ext. 249/213.

The ultimate sportsmen's holiday an exceptional, modernized, fully staffed sporting lodge on the Isle of Jura, Strathclyde, with six double and four single bedrooms is available for fishing, shooting and stalking from August through January. Duration: 1 week Sunday to Sunday. Price: details on request. Fishing holidays are also available notably on the world famed Hampshire chalk streams, the Test and the Itchen. Fishing can be arranged for both the experienced angler and the novice with tuition, ghillies and all necessary gear if desired.
The Rod Box Superservice, Barn Cottage, Church Lane, Twyford, near Winchester, Hampshire SO21 1NT. Telephone: (0962) 713458. Chairman: Colonel 'Scrappy' Hay, DSO.

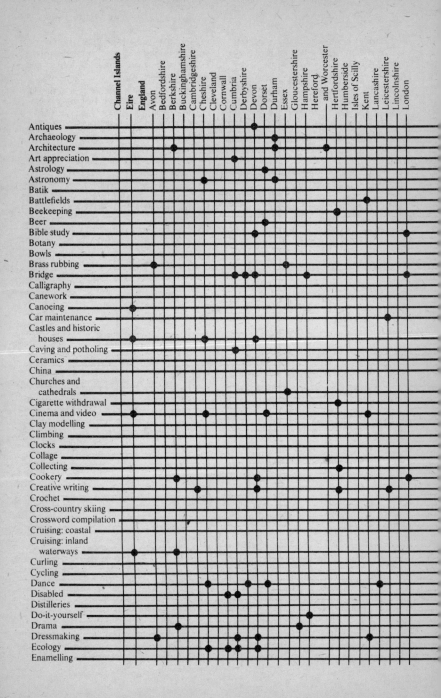

	Channel Islands	Eire	England	Avon	Bedfordshire	Berkshire	Buckinghamshire	Cambridgeshire	Cheshire	Cleveland	Cornwall	Cumbria	Derbyshire	Devon	Dorset	Durham	Essex	Gloucestershire	Hampshire	Hereford and Worcester	Hertfordshire	Humberside	Isles of Scilly	Kent	Lancashire	Leicestershire	Lincolnshire	London
Antiques														●														
Archaeology															●													
Architecture						●									●						●							
Art appreciation								●																				
Astrology															●													
Astronomy								●								●												
Batik																												
Battlefields																								●				
Beekeeping																						●						
Beer															●													
Bible study														●														●
Botany																												
Bowls																												
Brass rubbing					●																							
Bridge													●	●	●				●									●
Calligraphy																												
Canework																												
Canoeing		●																										
Car maintenance																										●		
Castles and historic houses		●							●																			
Caving and potholing											●																	
Ceramics																												
China																												
Churches and cathedrals																		●										
Cigarette withdrawal																					●							
Cinema and video		●							●																●			
Clay modelling																												
Climbing																												
Clocks																												
Collage																												
Collecting																						●						
Cookery					●										●													●
Creative writing						●									●						●						●	
Crochet																												
Cross-country skiing																												
Crossword compilation																												
Cruising: coastal																												
Cruising: inland waterways		●					●																					
Curling																												
Cycling																												
Dance								●						●	●											●		
Disabled										●	●																	
Distilleries																												
Do-it-yourself																				●								
Drama						●												●										
Dressmaking				●									●	●													●	
Ecology								●		●	●			●														
Enamelling																												

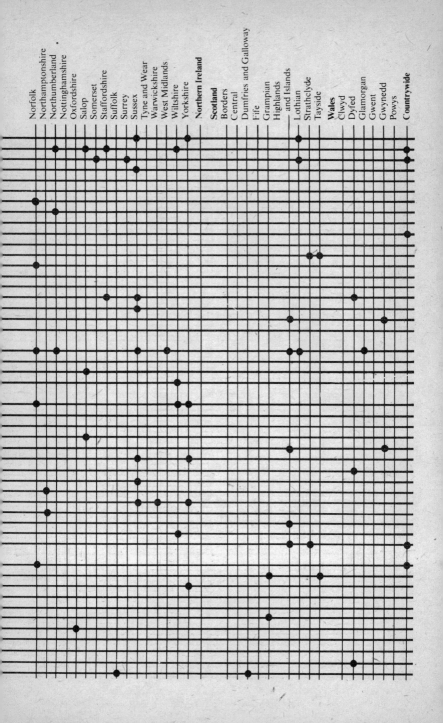

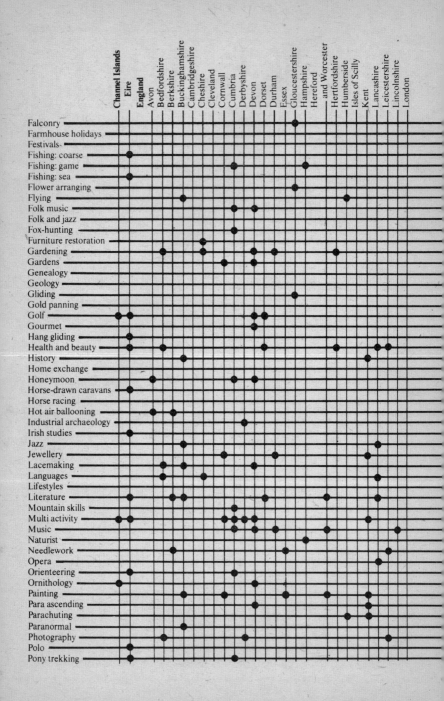

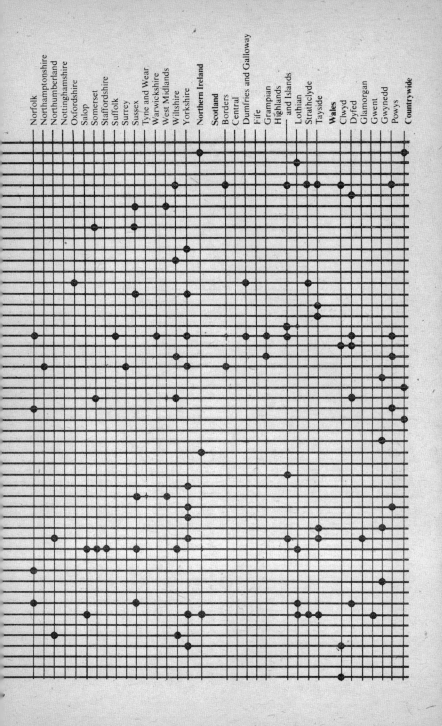

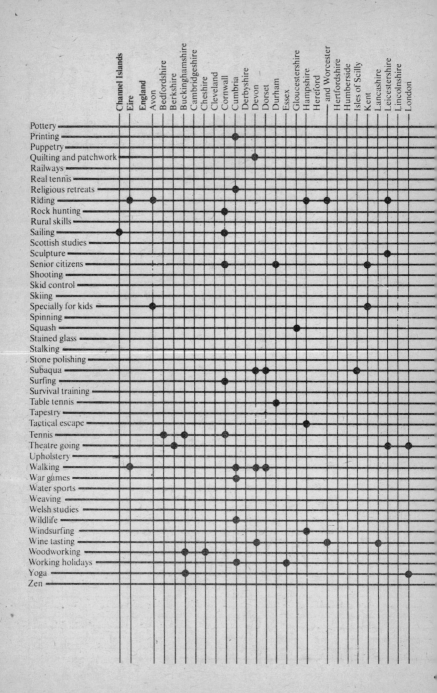

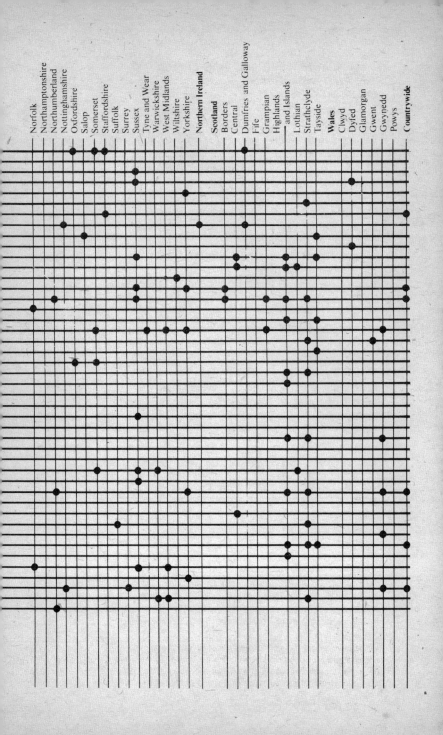

Bestselling Fiction and Non-Fiction

☐ **The Amityville Horror**	Jay Anson	80p
☐ **Shadow of the Wolf**	James Barwick	95p
☐ **The Island**	Peter Benchley	£1.25p
☐ **Castle Raven**	Laura Black	£1.25p
☐ **Smart-Aleck Kill**	Raymond Chandler	95p
☐ **Sphinx**	Robin Cook	£1.25p
☐ **The Entity**	Frank De Felitta	£1.25p
☐ **Trial Run**	Dick Francis	95p
☐ **The Rich are Different**	Susan Howatch	£1.95p
☐ **Moviola**	Garson Kanin	£1.50p
☐ **Tinker Tailor Soldier Spy**	John le Carré	£1.50p
☐ **The Empty Copper Sea**	John D. MacDonald	90p
☐ **Where There's Smoke**	Ed McBain	80p
☐ **The Master Mariner** Book 1: Running Proud	Nicholas Monsarrat	£1.50p
☐ **Bad Blood**	Richard Neville and Julie Clarke	£1.50p
☐ **Victoria in the Wings**	Jean Plaidy	£1.25p
☐ **Fools Die**	Mario Puzo	£1.50p
☐ **Sunflower**	Marilyn Sharp	95p
☐ **The Throwback**	Tom Sharpe	95p
☐ **Wild Justice**	Wilbur Smith	£1.50p
☐ **That Old Gang of Mine**	Leslie Thomas	£1.25p
☐ **Caldo Largo**	Earl Thompson	£1.50p
☐ **Harvest of the Sun**	E. V. Thompson	£1.25p
☐ **Future Shock**	Alvin Toffler	£1.95p

All these books are available at your local bookshop or newsagent, or can be ordered direct from the publisher. Indicate the number of copies required and fill in the form below

Name_____
(block letters please)

Address_____

_____

Send to Pan Books (CS Department), Cavaye Place, London SW10 9PG
Please enclose remittance to the value of the cover price plus:

25p for the first book plus 10p per copy for each additional book ordered
to a maximum charge of £1.05 to cover postage and packing
Applicable only in the UK

While every effort is made to keep prices low, it is sometimes
necessary to increase prices at short notice. Pan Books reserve
the right to show on covers and charge new retail prices which
may differ from those advertised in the text or elsewhere